MAN OBSERVED

BY ASHLEY MONTAGU

The Human Revolution
The Humanization of Man
Man In Process
Human Heredity
The Cultured Man
Man: His First Million Years
Coming Into Being Among the
Australian Aborigines
Edward Tyson, M.D., F.R.S. (1650–
1708): and the Rise of Human and
Comparative Anatomy in England
Man's Most Dangerous Myth: The
Fallacy of Race
Statement on Race
The Direction of Human Development
The Natural Superiority of Women
The Reproductive Development of the
Female
On Being Human
The Biosocial Nature of Man
Darwin, Competition and Cooperation
On Being Intelligent
Immortality
Education and Human Relations
Anthropology and Human Nature
Introduction to Physical Anthropology
Handbook of Anthropometry
Prenatal Influences
Life Before Birth

Race, Science, and Humanity
Up the Ivy
The Science of Man
The American Way of Life
The Idea of Race
The Anatomy of Swearing
Man's Evolution (with C. L. Brace)
The Dolphin in History
(with John Lilly)
The Prevalence of Nonsense
(with Edward Darling)
Anatomy and Physiology, 2 vols.
(with E. Steen)

Editor

Studies and Essays in the History of
Science and Learning
Toynbee and History
The Meaning of Love
Genetic Mechanisms in Human Disease
International Pictorial Treasury of
Knowledge
Atlas of Human Anatomy
Culture and the Evolution of Man
Culture: Man's Adaptive Dimension
The Concept of Race
The Concept of the Primitive
The Human Dialogue
(with Floyd Matson)

MAN
OBSERVED

by Ashley Montagu

G. P. PUTNAM'S SONS
NEW YORK

Seven of the chapters in this book have appeared in slightly different form in
other places. For permission to reprint I am grateful to the following: "Wilder-
ness and Humanity," the Sierra Club, San Francisco, from *Wilderness in a
Changing World*, 1966, pp. 220–227; "The Long Search for Euphoria: Drug
Addiction," Time, Inc., from *The Drug Takers*, 1965, pp. 30–33, 120; "Has
Chastity a Chance at College?" *McCall's*, September 1963, pp. 107sq.; "The New
Litany of Innate Depravity," *Vista*, vol. 2–9, 47–48, 1967; "Quest For Self," *Child-
hood Education*, September 1964, pp. 3–8; "Culture and the Evolution of Man,"
Oxford University Press, New York, from *Culture and The Evolution of Man*,
1964, pp. vii + xiii; "Current Values and Changing Needs of Youth," The
Connecticut State Department of Education, from *The Current Values and
Changing Needs of Youth*, 1966, pp. 21–28.

Library of Congress Catalog Card Number: 68-15517

To Elaine and Kenneth

Contents

CONTENTS

[8

Introduction

The essays in this volume have a single unifying theme: the understanding of human nature. The hope is that such understanding may render it easier for man to achieve fulfillment and to avoid the disasters into which ignorance of his own nature frequently leads him. Man is a unique creature by virtue of a combination of extraordinary traits which he alone possesses in such bountiful measure. These traits are his educability, his problem-solving ability or intelligence, his imagination, and his capacity for the creation of novelty, as well as his ability to love. In previous works I have discussed something of the manner in which these traits have evolved. In the present volume I am more concerned with the consideration of the serious consequences which have followed from man's failure to understand the structure of his own nature and the limits which his unique traits impose upon him.

Function is but another aspect of structure. When a structure is abused, its functions are likely to become deranged. So it is with the structure of human behavior. Human behavior is itself a function of the complex variables of physical and cultural history, genetic constitution, environmental experience from conception to birth and afterward, social heredity, and numerous other factors. Scientists are learning about these things at an increasingly accelerating rate. It is important that such knowledge be as widely diffused and clearly understood as possible, for it is the informed citizen who will ultimately make the difference between man's survival and his extinction.

Our past ignorance of man's nature and needs has already led civilized man into so many self-destructive errors that he has endangered not only his own world but also the whole of animate nature. When our ancestors, not so long ago, lived as food-gathering hunters in the tiny populations which such a way of life could support, in addition to the natural controls that were operative everyone, by his awareness of the fact that the society could not sustain more than a limited number, contributed to the control of population size. Our fellow men, the Bushmen of the Kalahari Desert, constitute a living contemporary example of such a population. Loving children and each other as they do, their sense of responsibility to the child and the future adult causes them to abstain from sexual intercourse until there is a comfortable place for another member of the society. Civilized man has, in large numbers, lost his sense of responsibility to his fellow man and especially to children. He multiplies irresponsibly, degenerates into slums and overcrowding with all their attendant evils, complains about the traffic and builds additional roads in unreflecting expectation that the congestion will thus be relieved. But, somehow, the more roads he builds the more congested they become. This seems to mystify the roadbuilders. But there is no mystery. Roads render people more accessible to one another, and accessibility tends to breed children. Hence, there is really only one effective solution to the traffic problem, and that is birth control. Indeed, unless man learns to control his own reduplication, no matter what other problems he may solve the human enterprise is bound to fail. I have, therefore, considered it desirable to discuss the problem of population and its control at some length. I have also considered some of the consequences which man has suffered and which the natural environment has suffered as a result of uncontrolled population growth. Also considered is the new litany of "innate depravity" associated with the names of Konrad Lorenz and Robert Ardrey, whose writings have unfortunately served to shift the focus of attention from the real causes of human aggression to utterly spurious ones. But the Table of Contents speaks for itself, and I need detain the reader here no further.

A. M.

Princeton, New Jersey

MAN OBSERVED

1. *The population problem*

Introduction

The world has all of a sudden, as it were, discovered itself in the midst of a population explosion. Dire effects of disasters to come are, virtually on all sides, predicted, without most people realizing that mankind is already suffering the early effects of those disasters. As a consequence of the unthinking and irresponsible proliferation of human beings, the rate of multiplication of people has inexorably produced the most awful devastation of the human and natural landscape. One would have to be very unrealistic indeed not to foresee that worse is yet to come.

Whatever the land in which one lives, it is not necessary to travel far to observe the human and natural desolation that is everywhere about us, the debasement of the human spirit, the disinheritance from their birthright of millions of human beings, the disengagement from humanity, the progression from cruelty to callousness to indifference to unawareness. This is the condition of modern man, the product of overpopulation, of what inevitably occurs when human beings uncontrolledly, thoughtlessly, unfeelingly, and irresponsibly do as they please.

If the human landscape has been devastated, what shall one say of the rapine and spoliation of the natural landscape, the congenial environment in which man once lived? Here there has been not only destruction of the natural beauties of the land but an unspeakable uglification of it. The living creatures

13]

that once inhabited the land are everywhere threatened with extinction. Numberless animals, virtually every day, birds and butterflies, beautiful and enhancing, cease to be before the onrushing masses of reduplicating human beings and the poisons they produce.[1] The air, the land, rivers, lakes, and streams are unconscionably polluted, as the silent spring bears poignant testimony to the degradation of the human spirit. As Aldous Huxley remarked after reading Rachel Carson's book,[2] we are exterminating half the basis of English poetry.[3] And as the editor of the *Architectural Forum* put it in the title of a significant book, we are turning God's Own Country into *God's Own Junkyard*,[4] as anyone who travels along our highways and even our byways may see for himself—*if* he any longer has any human vision left with which to see. For perhaps the greatest havoc wrought by the pressures of overpopulation has been the damage it has done to the human spirit, disabling millions of individuals from the ability to perceive and feel as human beings. Conditioned in a world which places an exaggerated value upon things, for them the world becomes a world of things, seeing what they perceive only as things, not in the least in the context of the human situation, in the context of the necessity of beauty, and scarcely ever being humanly affronted by them. On the other hand, they rejoice in the great highways and freeways which have brought about the destruction of thousands of trees, the annihilation of meadows, parklands, farms, and orchards. And to what end? So that the slums of the immediate future may replace them in order to house the millions who will require the sewers, gasoline stations, shopping centers, hot-dog stands, drive-ins, and other public utilities which, like a cancerous growth, spread over the length and breadth of the land destroying everything beautiful or potentially beautiful in its path.

It is a cancer from which a great part of the inhabited world is increasingly suffering. Unless we quickly learn to understand the causes of this deadly disorder, we shall be overcome by our own misguided thrust toward survival. This is no empty jeremiad, for man's survival depends on his ability to care for and use his natural resources.

Even more effectively than the lemmings in their overpowering drive to continue to be, we are as inexorably and as blindly driving ourselves toward destruction as they. If we continue as we have been, thoughtlessly and irresponsibly indulging in the behavior that results in an accelerating birthrate, we shall destroy ourselves. But this need not be. The trend is not irreversible, nor is the damage thus far done, serious as it is, irreparable. The trend *is reversible,* and the damage done can be repaired. However, if the problem of population is to be solved it will take the conscientious understanding and interest and work of the educated classes in every society to do what requires to be done. To provide, as succinctly as possible, some measure of understanding of the problem of population and of some of the steps that need to be taken if that problem is to be solved is the purpose of this chapter.

Population Control in Nonliterate Societies

Among the astonishments to which I am not infrequently subject, the one I find most difficult to assimilate is the profound and pervasive unawareness of the meaning of the population problem or even that a population problem exists. The really astonishing thing about this is that it was not always so; that, indeed, for almost the whole of man's history, men everywhere were aware of the disadvantages of overpopulation and whenever necessary, with foresight and understanding, took the necessary preventive measures. We have no direct evidence of what prehistoric man did about controlling his numbers, but we do know that his community populations were small, varying in number from several score to several hundred individuals. It is, for example, estimated from the number and distribution of prehistoric hearths in England, that some 10,000 years before Caesar landed on the shores of England, the land that today has some 50,000,000 inhabitants then had a winter population of about 200 and a summer population of about 2,000. Among nonliterate peoples of the present day, particularly the food-gathering hunting peoples—a way of life that was characteristic of prehistoric man right up to the first major industrial revolution, the discovery of food production, some 12,000 or so years ago—the communities are always small. Food-gathering hunting peoples are always small in number because such a way of life can support only a limited number of people.[5]

The number of individuals that can be maintained in a food-gathering hunting society is determined by the number it can support during the seasons of scarcity, and not the number it can maintain during the seasons of plenty. The spontaneous productivity of nature varies with the seasons, and during the lean seasons only so many individuals can be sustained within a given territory. Even where seasonal migration is possible to regions in which the food supply is more abundant, the rule stands that it is the factor of seasonal scarcity that determines the size of the group. For the greater part of the year, under such conditions life is hard and often precarious. One lives at a subsistence level, constantly in search of food and eating when one can. If they are to survive, the size of the group must be maintained at equilibrium. It must not fall below or rise above a certain optimum number of individuals of certain age groups. If there is a catastrophe that kills off many of the adult males, the women and children may not be able to shift for themselves and the whole group may die out. Experience has taught food-gathering hunting peoples that only a certain number of individuals of certain age groups can be supported by the group, especially during the seasons of scarcity, and that to increase that number even by a few individuals is to endanger the survival of the whole group. Hence, nonliterate peoples at this level of economy practice, as undoubtedly our prehistoric ancestors practiced, population control.

Natural Equilibrium Mechanisms

There are also certain self-regulating natural population controls which under certain conditions become operative and serve to control the size of natural populations. These are important, and it is only in recent years that we have come to acquire some measure of understanding of such natural population controls. We shall discuss these shortly. It is important for us clearly to understand both the social and natural population controls that have been at work during the greater part of man's history.

Natural regulatory population processes are of much the same kind for all living creatures. Most animals have elaborate means of matching their rates of breeding, and hence the sizes of their populations, to the available food resources. These means assume a variety of different forms. There are adjustments by territory: the food resources limit the number of individuals a territory can contain, and the greater the scarcity the larger will be the territory and the fewer the number of individuals that can be maintained on it. Here, then, is the mechanism which adjusts the population to the food supply. A principal function of social life among animals is, indeed, a means of sensing the size of the population and by various responses limiting, where necessary, the extent of reproduction. Toward this end, when the interests of the individual endanger the welfare of the group, they are either submerged or subordinated to those of the community or group. Social organization among animals represents the homeostatic-feedback mechanism whereby, as Wynne-Edwards has put it, "population density is constantly adjusted to match the optimum level of exploitation of food resources." [6]

What is it by way of feedback that will measure or reflect the demand for food and thus the number of individuals that can be supported in terms of present and future supplies? Competition within the conventional limits provided by the society is such an indicator. The greater the density, the keener the competition and the greater the premium placed upon cooperation. The competition is not competitive in the sense of conflict, not a ruthless selfish contest for food, which in the end inevitably leads to overexploitation, but a cooperative competition, a competition with socially sanctioned goals. It is Wynne-Edward's view that "social organisation and the primitive seeds of all social behavior" have their origin in these processes.[7] From this standpoint the most primitive function of a society is the provision of the organization through which conventional competition becomes possible. In other words, competition brings the competitors into association with one another, and if the rewards are socially sanctioned, then the association of competitors automatically constitutes a society.

These are important ideas. They throw much light on the origin and evolution of social life and on the nature of population processes. But there is evidence that the origins of social life are to be sought for at much earlier levels of differentiation than those indicated by Wynne-Edwards. There appears to be an innate tendency in all living organisms, even at the unicellular level, to react with one another. This reaction has been called by Wallin *prototaxis* [8] and has been fully described by Jennings in a classic work, *The Behavior of Lower Organisms.*[9] I have elsewhere argued that the origin of social life is to be found in the very process of reproduction itself, in the origin of one organism from another, in their interdependence and dependence upon one another in the process of reduplication; that association, "togetherness," is a biologically determined trait that originates in the maternal-reproductive relationship.[10]

However all this may be, as Wynne-Edwards has pointed out, social organization at every level provides the feedback-homeostatic mechanism that under natural conditions controls the densities of populations. Such controls, whatever forms they have taken, have been of high selective value, since by maintaining the population in equilibrium they have served to ensure its survival. When, as in the case of man, culture, the man-made part of the environment, becomes the creature's principal means of adaptation to the environment, cultural practices often replace or supplement natural mechanisms in the control of population densities. Thus, while in human societies, fecundity—the capacity to reproduce—has always been highly valued, fertility—fecundity expressed in performance—valued as it is, has usually been subject to some measure of control. And, as Clellan Ford says, reporting on a cross-cultural study of the data on some 200 societies from all over the world, the impression emerges of "a delicate balance between pressures toward bearing children and the tendencies to avoid birth." [11] Summarizing his findings, Ford writes:

Viewed in cross-cultural perspective, both abortion and infanticide are universally known. In nearly every society, they are practiced at least occasionally. At the same time, it is also clear that strong social pressures are brought to bear against any excessive indulgence in abortion and infanticide. . . . Contraceptive attempts are not . . . viewed as sinful or criminal in most societies, and some sort of device to prevent conception is available to the members of practically all the societies in our sample. These techniques designed to prevent conception vary markedly in their probable effectiveness. Some are so clearly magical that they may be dismissed at once as having no practical effect. Others, just as clearly, are relatively effective.[12]

In passing it should be understood that in nonliterate societies infanticide is generally not considered cruel since the newborn is believed to be not yet properly a human being, and in any event, as among the Australian aborigines, it is believed that its spirit will return to the spirit center from whence it came and enter either the same or another woman of the proper totemic membership at another time.[13] Infanticide is practiced only indirectly in relation to the general food supply, by way of the mother's breast-feeding. When the mother feels that she will be unable to rear the child because she has a small child whom she is still feeding, the newborn is buried in the sand or simply allowed to die. The husband approves because, apart from the trouble of caring for two small children, he does not want anything to interfere with his wife's work so far as his own camp is concerned.[14] It is also felt that when children are too closely spaced, proper justice cannot be done to each one, so it is better to send a burdensome newborn back to the spirit center whence he came, with an invitation to return at some more welcome time. Thus, the average number of live children in the aboriginal Australian family is between two and three.

Abortion is in all societies practiced for much the same reasons.[15]

In most nonliterate societies twins and other multiple-birth children are killed at birth, as are all children showing abnormalities of any sort, even those exhibiting such slight abnormalities as a prematurely erupted tooth. Among the Netsilik

Eskimos, the killing of female children is so common that a girl who is not betrothed at birth is usually doomed. And among Eskimos generally, when starvation threatens, the aged members of the group will beg to be killed or abandoned so that the group as a whole may survive.[16]

In 1922 Carr-Saunders, reviewing the information on infanticide, abortion, and abandonment of the infirm and aged under stress of necessity, wrote,

> It is now clear how these factors originate. Among more or less nomadic peoples abortion and infanticide are practised because of the difficulty of transporting and suckling more than one child at a time. Abstention from intercourse arises as a taboo. The problem we have to face is how these factors could come to be of the necessary intensity. Now men and groups of men are naturally selected on account of the customs they practise. . . . Few customs could be more advantageous than those which limit the number of a group to the desirable number, and . . . once any of these three customs had originated, it would by a process of natural selection come to be so practised that it would produce an approximation to the desirable number. . . . To all members of such a group, confined as they are within the knowledge of them all to a limited area, the disadvantage of too many mouths must be obvious. Therefore even among the more primitive races there may be some semiconscious adjustment of numbers by means of one of these methods. However . . . even if there is no semiconscious deliberation among the lower groups, there is to some extent an automatic adjustment to the needs of the moment.[17]

These views have been thoroughly corroborated by subsequent studies among nonliterate peoples. In addition to such cultural practices in limiting the numbers of a population in man, and omitting any reference to the effect of taboos on intercourse at certain times, the effects of lactation and the like, there are certain natural inbuilt mechanisms that are operative in man as in other animals, directed toward the same end.

For example, it has long been known that under conditions of famine or emotional stress the first functional casualty is the sexual libido. Sexual interest appears to vanish altogether. This, indeed, is perhaps the most striking example of an innate adaptive reaction showing how under conditions of stress the members of a group are literally protected against themselves and against the possibility of endangering both themselves and the survival of the group by the production of conception and birth. Under conditions of stress, conception endangers not only the conceptus but also the mother. Hence, the physiological changes that occur within her body tend to produce anovulatory cycles,[18] and there is also good evidence that in the male spermatogenesis is seriously affected.[19] When pregnancy occurs during preriods of stress, the products of conception are characterized by high frequencies of abortions, stillbirths, malformations, and perinatal mortality.[20, 21] Such inbuilt population-limiting mechanisms will also come into play where population density exceeds the optimum. Observation in the field and experiment in the laboratory have shown that among animals generally, where the population pressure increases so does the social pressure, and the resulting social strife or competitive competition leads to neurohumoral reactions that constitute the regulatory feedback system operative in controlling the size of the population. This feedback system has evolved as a safeguard against overutilization of the environment and the threat of extinction. And, as Christian has said, "However, a high price is exacted from an increasing proportion of the population for this regulation of population growth as population increases." [22]

Briefly summarized, the neurohumoral changes that occur among population-pressured animals are increased aggressiveness, anxiety, behavioral disturbances, hyperactivity of the hypothalamus, hyperactivity of the anterior portion of the pituitary gland, with increased secretion of ACTH (adrenocorticotrophic hormone), which in turn activates the cortex of the adrenal gland to secrete cortin, with suppression of ovarian development and maturation of ova, increased intrauterine mortality, and progressively lowered birthrates. Associated with these changes goes a decreased general resistance to disease and suppression of defense mechanisms; there is also inhibition of antibody production and all healing processes, with increased mortality following infection and decreased resistance to parasitism.[23]

Under natural conditions the effect of these regulatory population mechanisms is to prevent populations from suicidal destruction of the habitat.[24] Much evidence now exists which indicates that such density-dependent regulatory mechanisms have evolved in animals as a means of regulating population numbers under the appropriate environmental pressures. Milne has stated the principle simply: "The *ultimate* capacity of a place for a species is the maximum number of individuals that the place could carry without being rendered totally uninhabitable by utter exhaustion or destruction of resources. . . . The environmental capacity cannot be greater than ultimate capacity; it could, conceivably be equal to ultimate capacity but . . . is usually somewhat smaller." [25] The "somewhat," it is generally agreed, should be modified to read "considerably."

Another mechanism by means of which the numbers of a population are regulated is disease. Malthus and others even before him pointed this out, and perhaps no one has ever stated the fact more clearly than the anthropologist the late W. H. R. Rivers when in 1922 he wrote, "Disease is the name we give to a group of processes by which the size of a population is adjusted so as to enable it best to utilize the available means of subsistence. . . ." [26] With his usual acumen Rivers refers to disease as "a group of processes." And that, of course, is precisely what all diseases are: groups of processes. A disease is seldom if ever a matter of a single causative condition but is usually the consequence of a number of conditions which together constitute the cause. Such conditions are individually the necessary conditions which together comprise the sufficient conditions which constitute the cause. An infective agent under certain conditions may be rapidly overcome by the body defenses. Under unfavorable conditions the same infective agent may affect the same individual lethally. The unfavorable conditions may be either physical or physiological or simply psychological. It is fairly obvious that a person suffering from malnutrition is much more likely to succumb to the effects of invasion by an infective agent than a person in a good state of nutrition. What, however, did not become clear until the first half of the twentieth century had run the greater part of its course was that the psychological state of the person was alone sufficient to make the difference between life and death, without any intervention by any physical infective agent. The psychological state of the individual had long been suspected to play a significant role in his ability to resist disease, but what had not been understood was that the individual's psychological condition could kill him quite as dead as the most virulent of infective agents.

Again, among the earliest students of the subject—if not *the* earliest—to understand this was Rivers, who in a book which he edited, *Essays on the Depopulation of Melanesia,* from which I have already quoted him, pointed out that "such a factor as loss of interest in life could . . . produce the dying out of a people.[27] . . . The special point I wish to make is that interest in life is the primary factor in the welfare of a people." Rivers was able to show that, as a consequence of the changes introduced by Europeans and the resulting breakdown of the traditional ways of life, there had been a catastrophic fall in the birthrate among the natives of the two islands he studied, Eddystone Island and Vella Lavella, in the Solomons. On Eddystone Island childless marriages increased from 19.4 to 46.1 percent and on Vella Lavella from 12.1 to 71.9 percent. In the last generation of which Rivers wrote, less than one child was being born per marriage.

In order to understand how an apparently slight social change introduced by a foreign element may affect a population, I shall quote Rivers' classic observation in full.

No one could be long in Eddystone without recognising how great is the people's lack of interest in life and to what an extent the zest has gone out of their lives. This lack of interest is largely due to the abolition of head-hunting by the British Government. This practice formed the centre of a social and religious institution which took an all-pervading part in the lives of people. The heads sought in the head-hunting expeditions were needed in order to propitiate the ancestral ghosts on such occasions as building a new house for a chief or making a new canoe, while they were also offered in sacrifice at the funeral of a chief. Moreover, head-hunting was not only necessary for the due performance of the religious rites of the people, but it stood in the closest relation to pursuits of an economic kind. The actual head-hunting expedition only lasted a few weeks, and the actual fighting only a few hours, but this was only the culminating point of a process lasting over years. It was the rule that new canoes should be made for an expedition to obtain heads, and the manufacture of these meant work of an interesting kind lasting certainly for many months, probably for years. The process of canoe-building was accompanied throughout by rites and feasts which not only excited the liveliest interest but also acted as stimuli to various activities of horticulture and pig-breeding. As the date fixed for the expedition approached other rites and feasts were held, and these were still more frequent and on a larger scale after the return of a successful expedition. In stopping the practice of head-hunting the rulers from an alien culture were abolishing an institution which had its roots in the religion of the people and spread its branches throughout nearly every aspect of their culture, and by this action they deprived the people of the greater part of their interest in life, while at the same time they undermined the religion of the people without any attempt to put another in its place.[28]

Since Rivers, who was a considerable psychologist as well as a pioneering ethnologist, correctly made this diagnosis, there have been many independent confirmations of it in connection with other aboriginal peoples. I shall refer to one other striking example. Lommel, reporting on the Wunambal tribe of north-western Australia, states that the aborigines themselves claim that "their falling birthrate in recent times is due to the mental disturbance which is caused by the news of the approaching civilization. According to their opinion they 'cannot find the proper dreams' any more which are necessary for fertility, and they explain that they either have too much heavy work at the missions and stations and sleep too deeply to dream properly, or that they 'think too much about white man' in their dreams. Possibly the aborigines in this way correctly point out the cause of the falling birth-rate: the disturbance of their whole psychic life and their peace of mind by the facts and news of the approaching civilization." [29]

The striking thing here is that these Australian aborigines have themselves arrived at the correct explanation of the decline in their birthrate. There *is* a psychic factor in certain forms of sterility. It is now well established that unfavorable life experiences, apathy, anxiety or stress may produce marked disturbances of the sexual function.[30]

Culture is man's adaptive device for increasing the ease and rendering more gratifying the means of satisfying his basic and derived needs. In his adjustive adaptation to his total environment, it is his principal instrument. When, for any reason, this gratification is threatened and the adjustive arrangements of the group are disrupted, the members of the group may be seriously shocked, in the physiological sense, and may suffer what for all practical purposes may be described as a profound depression of vital energy. Physiologically this takes the form of the exhaustion of the sympathetico-adrenal axis or the general alarm reaction system, so well described by Cannon, Selye, Wolff and others.[31]

As Selye, most notably, has shown, scores of thousands of human beings die every year from exhaustion of the (sympathetico-adrenal) alarm reaction system, exhibiting every one of the evidences of physiological breakdown which have been described by many investigators in other mammals. It is evident, then, that the inbuilt homeostatic-feedback mechanisms regulating population numbers are still at work in man; that the crowding, the stress, and the anxieties associated with modern civilized life still exact their toll. However, the important point to grasp is that man, while maximizing the conditions of crowding, anxiety, and stress, has also maximized the conditions by which these regulatory mechanisms are, if not overcome, deferred in their action and prevented from becoming as immediately lethal as they would otherwise be. But a society that does this does not ameliorate the conditions of life; it simply prolongs and worsens them. The Age of Anxiety is not the better for being anxious, but worse. And it is no mitigation of the misery in which so many millions exist that they

25]

have been enabled to be miserable in it longer than they would otherwise have been.

There are certain laws of nature and of man that cannot be outraged with impunity. It was Bacon who remarked that nature to be commanded must be obeyed. Man learns by trial and error. Today he has acquired the necessary knowledge of the conditions of his nature and of those natural laws that affect his own wellbeing. The message of those laws is clear and unequivocal: man must learn to limit his own numbers, at the family, community, national, and international levels, so that the pressures to which excessive numbers give rise are removed and with them the strife and destructiveness, the malfunctioning and the debasement of the humanity which they engender, so that man may once more enter into the realization of his inheritance: development in health and fulfillment of his potentialities.

REFERENCES

1. Rachel Carson, *Silent Spring*. Houghton Mifflin Co., Boston, 1962.
2. Donald E. Carr, *The Breath of Life*. W. W. Norton, New York, 1965.
3. Julian Huxley, "The Future of Man—Evolutionary Aspects." In Gordon Wolstenholme, ed., *Man and His Future*. Little, Brown & Co., Boston, 1963, pp. 1–22.
4. Peter Blake, *God's Own Junkyard: The Planned Deterioration of America's Landscape*. Holt, Rinehart & Winston, New York, 1964.
5. Ludwik Krzywicki, *Primitive Society and its Vital Statistics*. Macmillan, London, 1934; A. M. Carr-Saunders, *The Population Problem*, The Clarendon Press, Oxford, 1922; Norman E. Himes, *Medical History of Contraception*, Williams & Wilkins, Baltimore, 1936; *The Determinants and Consequences of Population Trends*, The United Nations, Department of Social Affairs, Population Division, New York, 1953; Annabelle Desmond, "How Many People Have Ever Lived on Earth?" In Stuart Mudd, ed., *The Population Crisis and the Use of World Resources*, Junk, The Hague, 1964, pp. 27–46; James M. Beshers, *Population Processes in Social Systems*, Free Press, New York, 1967.
6. V. C. Wynne-Edwards, *Animal Dispersion in Relation to Social Behaviour*. Hafner, New York, 1962, p. 14.
7. *Ibid.*, p. 14.
8. I. E. Wallin, *Symbionticism and the Origin of Species*. Williams & Wilkins, Baltimore, 1927.

9. H. S. Jennings, *The Behavior of Lower Organisms.* Columbia University Press, New York, 1906. Reprinted Indiana University Press, Bloomington, 1962.
10. M. F. Ashley Montagu, *The Direction of Human Development.* Harper & Bros., New York, 1955.
11. Clellan S. Ford, *A Comparative Study of Human Reproduction.* Yale University Publications in Anthropology, No. 32, 1945.
12. *Ibid.*
13. M. F. Ashley Montagu, *Coming into Being Among the Australian Aborigines.* London, Routledge, 1937.
14. Baldwin Spencer & F. J. Gillen, *The Arunta,* 2 vols. Macmillan, London, 1927, vol. 1, pp. 39, 221.
15. George Devereux, *A Study of Abortion in Primitive Societies.* Julian Press, New York, 1955.
16. Kaj Birket-Smith, *The Eskimos.* Methuen & Co., London, 1959, p. 139.
17. A. M. Carr-Saunders, *The Population Problem.* The Clarendon Press, Oxford, 1922, pp. 222–223.
18. H. Stieve, *Der Einfluss des Nerven Systems auf Bau und Totigkeit der Geschlechtsorgame des Menschen.* Georg Thieme, Stuttgart, 1951; Horsley Gantt, "Disturbances in Sexual Function During Periods of Stress." In H. G. Wolff *et al.,* eds., *Life Stress and Bodily Disease,* Williams & Wilkins, Baltimore, 1950, pp. 1030–1050.
19. H. Schuermann, "Über die Zunahme männlicher Fertilitätsstörungen und uber die Bedeutung psychischer Einflüsse für die Zentralnervöse Regulation der Spermiogenese." *Medizinische Klinik,* Bd. 43, 1948, pp. 366–368.
20. D. H. Stott, "Cultural and Natural Checks on Population Growth." In M. F. Ashley Montagu, ed., *Culture and the Evolution of Man,* Oxford University Press, New York, 1962, pp. 355–376.
21. M. F. Ashley Montagu, *Prenatal Influences.* C. C. Thomas, Springfield, Illinois, 1962; M. F. Ashley Montagu, *Life Before Birth.* New American Library, New York, 1964.
22. John J. Christian, "Physiological and Pathological Correlates of Population Density," *Proceedings of the Royal Society of Medicine,* vol. 57, 1964, pp. 169–174.
23. *Ibid.*
24. John J. Christian & David E. Davis, "Endocrines, Behavior, and Population," *Science,* vol. 146, 1964, pp. 1550–1560.
25. A. Milne, "On a Theory of Natural Control of Insect Populations," *Journal of Theoretical Biology,* vol. 3, 1962, pp. 19–50.
26. W. H. R. Rivers, ed., *Essays on the Depopulation of Melanesia.* Cambridge University Press, Cambridge, 1922, p. 89.
27. *Ibid.,* p. 94.
28. *Ibid.,* pp. 101–102.
29. A. Lommel, "Notes on Sexual Behaviour and Initiation, Wunambal Tribe, North-Western Australia," *Oceania,* vol. 20, 1949, pp. 163–164.

30. Horsley Gantt, "Disturbances in Sexual Function During Periods of Stress." In H. G. Wolff *et al.*, eds., *Life Stress and Bodily Disease,* Williams & Wilkins, Baltimore, 1950, pp. 1030–1050.

31. W. B. Cannon, "Voodoo Death," *American Anthropologist,* vol. 44, 1942, pp. 169–181; Hans Selye, *Stress.* Acta Endocrinologica, Montreal, 1950; H. G. Wolff, *Stress and Disease.* C. C. Thomas, Springfield, Illinois, 1953.

2. *The growth of population*

Early Population Numbers

Man has been on this earth for some 2 million years. During almost the whole of that period his populations were very small indeed. The food-gathering hunting way of life, which was his principal way of earning a living during that period, cannot support more than a relatively small number of people. Prehistoric populations numbered from several score to a few hundred individuals. By a population is to be understood any contiguously distributed grouping of the species that is characterized by both genetic and social continuity through one or more generations. With the discovery of food production some 12,000 years ago, the first great industrial revolution, in which for the first time the reproduction of plant foods, as in agriculture, could be controlled and the reproduction of animals could also be controlled, as in stock-breeding, the first village settlements became possible, and a larger number of people could be supported. The evidence suggests that the principle of controlled reproduction was applied virtually simultaneously to both plants and animals, that is, to stock-breeding as well as to the cultivation of plants. The region in which these discoveries were first made appears to have been in Mesopotamia. It is not surprising that the second major industrial revolution, namely, the development of urban culture, is also first known to have occurred in the same region. Urban culture is characterized by a division of labor in which food is supplied in return for useful work performed in another occupation or industry, with or without the intermediacy of money. The oldest town thus far discovered, at pre-Biblical Jericho, dates back some 9,000 years.[1]

Urbanism and Population

Town life is characterized by the fact that it is artificial, highly organized, stratified, and increasingly removed from contact with nature. It sets free much energy for propagation, art, invention, power structuring, and increasing economic and social complexity. But the main thing is that it makes possible the support of increasingly large numbers of people, populations the size of which had never before existed in the whole history of man. It is with the advent of the second industrial revolution, the development of urbanism, that the population problem begins. And the point to remember here is that that problem has its origins in a revolutionary change in social life which occurred not more than 9,000 years ago. If we think of the history of man as written in a 2,000-page book, then the urban part of that history consumes less than the last two pages of that book. In the total history of mankind that is a very short period indeed. And yet the human damage and the damage to nature that has been done within that short period of time is immense. Whole populations have died out, fertile lands have been turned into deserts, civilizations have been destroyed, war and rapine have resulted in vast devastations, and millions of human beings have lived out their brief lives in misery and despair, in

> Blank misgivings of a creature
> Moving about in worlds not realized.

The average age at death of prehistoric man, it has been calculated, was thirty-three and one-half years,[2] an average which held for the greater part of the world of mankind right up to 1861. The figure of eighteen years for the average age at death which is sometimes given is based on the Greek cemetery data and should not be generalized. Compare thirty-three and one-half years with the expectation of life of seventy-three years for the average American, seventy-five years for the female and sixty-nine years for the male. In less than a hundred years the expectation of life for the sexes has more than doubled, and this has been almost wholly due to improvements in medical care, sanitation, and nutrition. Undoubtedly the expectation of life for both sexes will continue to rise.

But let us begin at the beginning. Man, we have already said, is some 2 million years old, and for the greater part of that 2 million years he was a food-gatherer and hunter. We have already stated that his population numbers throughout that long secular period of time were small. Let us attempt to answer one of the first questions frequently asked, namely, how many people have ever lived on the earth? Wellemeyer and Lorimer's calculations reported by Annabelle Desmond are based on the assumption that man first appeared about 600,000 years ago.[3] But this date is now outmoded by recently made discoveries and new dating methods, the sounder figure seeming to be nearer 2 million years. At the 600,000-year figure Wellemeyer and Lorimer estimate that some 77 billion human beings have been born. This estimate was arrived at on the basis of three time periods as set out in the table below.

THE POPULATION OF MAN FROM PREHISTORIC TIMES TO THE PRESENT

Period	Number of years in period	Number of births per year at beginning of period	Number of births per year at end of period	Number of births in period
600,000–6000 B.C.	594,000	"1"	250,000	12 billion
6000 B.C.–A.D. 1650	7,650	250,000	25 million	42 billion
A.D. 1650–1962	312	25,000,000	110 million	23 billion

Source: Annabelle Desmond, "How Many People Have Ever Lived on Earth?" *Population Bulletin,* February 1962.

At the base figure of 600,000 years for the age of man, these estimates seem sound enough, though most authorities would be inclined to put the beginning of the Neolithic nearer 7000 years B.C. than the 6000 of Wellemeyer and Lorimer's estimate. There is, however, more than a question concerning the validity of the base figure of 600,000 years. As I have already remarked, this should be nearer 2 million years. This makes no significant difference to the number of births per year at the end of this period, set at 6000 B.C., namely, 250,000 per annum, but it does considerably alter the figure of 12 billion births in the 594,000-year period. If we add only 1 million years to the base figure of 600,000 years, then for the 1,594,000 years involved, instead of 12 billion babies born before A.D. 6000 the number would be 32 billion, making the grand total an estimated 97 billion human beings who had been born up to the year 1962, or approximately 10 to the eleventh power. I believe that that is probably a more accurate approximation to the real numbers. At the lower estimate of 77 billion, today's population of approximately 3 billion would be about 4 percent of the total number of human beings ever born, while at the higher estimate of 97 billion the proportion would be about 3 percent.

This excursion in arithmetic is no idle exercise in curiosity, for it is a very necessary corrective to the statement frequently heard that there are more people alive today than the total number of human beings ever born. At the moment it simply happens to be untrue, but if we continue to reproduce at current rates it will not be long before it becomes true.

Up to the discovery of food production some 12,000 years ago, it is estimated that the total population of the earth was about 5 million and the birthrate about 5 per 100. Since that period man has increased his numbers some 700 million times to 3.5 billion people! This staggering increase received its initial boost with the discovery of food production and has been accelerating at a galloping rate ever since. By the beginning of the Christian era the world's population had risen to about 250 million, that is, in 7,000 years the population had increased fifty times. A thousand years later the total number was 275 million, an increase of only 25 million in a thousand years. This small increase reflects the population controls that come into play with crowding, mainly the effects of disease and high infant mortality. Plagues during the first millennium A.D., tuberculosis, malaria, and the terrible depredations of the Hungarians and the Vikings in Europe alone wrought havoc with the population. The havoc was not fortuitous; it was the direct product of the increasing pressures of population. This is a fact to underscore and never forget. In the year 1100 the population rose by 31 million to 306 million. A hundred years later (1200) by 42 million to 348 million. In 1300 by 36 million to 384 million. In 1400 it fell by 11 million to 373 million as a result of the bubonic plague of 1348–1350, when about 20 percent of the population died. In 1500 the population made a tremendous jump by 73 million to a total of 446 million, and by 1600 rose by 40 million to 486 million. Thus from the year A.D. 1000 up to the year 1600 the population increased at the average rate of about 40 million per annum, with a total increase of 211 million people in 600 years.

Between 1600 and 1700, the Age of Discovery, of exploration, of scientific and technological innovation, the birth, indeed, of the heroic age of science and the development of an intellectual ferment the like of which the world had never before experienced, the rate of population increase began to accelerate. By the middle of the seventeenth century the population had risen by 50 million to 545 million, and by 1750 by a tremendous leap of 183 million to 728 million. Fifty years later, in 1800, the increase had proceeded at double the rate of the preceding hundred years, by 178 million to a total of 906 million. Fifty years brings us to 1850 with an increase of 265 million to a grand total of 1 billion 171 million. All records for population increase are now broken: the world population rises for the first time to its first billion, and in fifty years 54 million more human beings are born than were born in the whole of the 600 years following the end of the first millennium A.D.! By the beginning of the twentieth century, in 1900, the world population has again doubled its rate of increase by 537 million to a total of 1,608,000,000. Twenty years later there were 202 million additional human beings on this earth, bringing the total in 1920 to 1 billion 810 million. In the twenty years following, up to 1940 the rate of increase has more than doubled, and there are an additional 436 million, bringing the total to 2 billion 246 million. Another twenty years brings us to 1960, with an addition of 726 million to yield a total of 2 billion 972 million.

In 1965, only five years later, we attained a population of 3.5 billion. In sixty years the world population has doubled itself. The present world population will be doubled in thirty-five years to 7 billion. At the present rate of increase, at the very conservative estimate of 2 percent per year, the world's population would continue to double every thirty-five years. Unless we do something to stop it, by the year 2035 there will be some 14 billion people on this earth.

If we go on multiplying at this rate, 5,000 years hence the world population will form a spherical mass which would be increasing with a radial velocity equaling the speed of light. Some forty years later, at the current rate of population growth, there would be two such spheres.

We, who have already drawn too many postdated bills on the Bank of Time, have no right to incur debts for others to pay. No one has the right by his present conduct to compromise the future.

These are staggering figures I have placed before you. They would have been even more staggering had man's current rate of increase prevailed since the beginning of the Christian era. At a rate of increase of 2 percent from A.D. 1, the world would now have contained 90 billion times 10 to the twelfth power, or 90 billion times a trillion individuals! Even though such figures may belong to the "Gee, whiz!" school of statistics, they should be sufficiently startling to induce some serious reflection.

During the period 1650–1750 population growth was at the rate of 0.3 percent a year; during 1750–1850 it was about 0.5 percent a year, and from 1850–1950 at 0.8 percent a year. Currently the rate is about 2.0 percent a year. This is a tremendous increase. Spelled out in detail this means that:

Every second on this earth 4 babies are born.

Every minute about 240 babies are born.

Every hour about 15,000 babies are born.

Every day about 360,000 babies are born.

Every week about 2.5 million babies are born.

Every month over 10 million babies are born.

Every year there are about 119 million births.

To balance these 119 million births there are some 56 million deaths a year. This means that for the four babies born every second, two persons die, and the world is by so much the more crowded.

At the present time China and India, the two must populous countries on the Asian continent, account for more than a third of the world's population. China alone, with a population estimated at over 650 million, accounts for close to a quarter of the world population. Yet in these two countries, already so crowded that many people are chronically on the verge of starvation, population is increasing faster than almost anywhere else. The population of India is increasing at the rate of 8 million a year. About 500 million Indians now live in an area about two-fifths the size of the United States. The average American earns in his first job in his first week a wage which is fifty times larger than the annual per capita income of India. If the present rate of population increase continues in India, by 1985 it will have a population of 775 million, and at least 1 billion by the end of the century! This excludes the present population of Pakistan, which is about 103 million and growing at a rate well over 2.0 percent.

Each night in Calcutta, 250,000 people sleep in the streets. In many parts of India dung collected for the village fires is carefully picked over for any pieces of grain which the cows may have failed to digest entirely. Any that are found are shared among the members of the family. In Mexico City urban workers in large numbers may be seen seeking food in the garbage bins of the rich.[4]

In general it is in the countries least able to support a large population, in the poorer and less developed regions, such as India and Latin America, that the population explosion is greatest. In 1965 the population of Latin America stood at 250 million. The annual rate of increase in Latin America is 2.8 percent. A population growing at such a rate will double in twenty-three years, so that by the end of this century the population of Latin America may be expected to reach 700 million. Similar increases may be expected in Oceania, Africa, and most of Asia. In Oceania the rate of increase is well over 2.0 percent, in Africa 2.5 percent, in Southeast Asia 2.7 percent, and in Southwest Asia 2.6 percent.

Among the newly developing countries, Mauritania in northwest Africa, one of the poorest countries in Africa, if not in the world, has one of the world's highest annual rates of population increase, 5.1 percent. With a present population of over 1 million, this means that the population of Mauritania will double every thirteen years! In a land of more than 400,000 square miles, which is mostly desert, such a rate of increase is calamitous.

Whereas in the past the countries that had the greatest rates of population increase were those that were economically the most successful, today it is the countries that are least economically developed, principally the agrarian countries, that have the greatest accelerating population growth. Ceylon (2.7), Taiwan (3.6), South Korea (3.3), and Malaysia (3.3); Costa Rica (4.3), Nicaragua (3.5), Venezuela (3.4) and Mexico (3.1); Turkey (2.7) and Syria (3.2)—these are some of the countries that will be doubling their numbers every twenty-three years. Mexico with a present population of more than 40 million will have more than 70 million in 1980.

From 1950 to 1975 it is estimated that the world population will have increased by 53 percent, and by 64 percent between 1975 and 2000, thus doubling in less than fifty years. During the twenty-five-year period from 1950 to 1975, it is estimated that the population of Latin America will have increased by 86 percent, Asia by 60 percent, Oceania by 59 percent, Africa by 52 percent, North America by 43 percent, and Europe (including the U.S.S.R.) by 31 percent. By 1975 the number of human beings added to the world population each year will be 77 million, and by the end of the century 126 million a year! From 1975 to the year 2000 this will represent an increase of 64 percent!

The Population Explosion

The accelerating rate of population increase constitutes "the population explosion." That expression has met with some objection on the ground that it is emotional and that it does not properly describe the conditions. I fail to see that the expression is an emotional one, and in any event I think it is high time that we stop taking dispassionate looks at things and get somewhat more deeply involved in them than we have been in the past. It has been argued that a rate of increase from 2 to 4 percent cannot be likened to an explosion. But that, it seems to me, is to miss the point altogether of what is happening. The term "explosion" in our present context is used as a metaphor, simply likening the rate of increase of human beings in the recent period compared to earlier rates to an explosion. If, having contemplated the meaning of the figures I have presented, anyone can think of a better metaphor, it will be a service to us all to have it made public. "Explosion" may not be the best term, but since it means "a blowing up," a "bursting," and that quite closely describes the rate of world population growth at the present time, we may properly continue to use the expression "the population explosion" to describe the facts. Metaphors when sensibly used can be illuminating and arresting. In a matter so urgent as population growth and its control, a matter literally of life and death, any legitimate means that may serve to call attention to the gravity of the problem should be encouraged, for the population explosion constitutes the most serious problem with which the world of humanity is today confronted. Not war, not nuclear tests, not hydrogen bombs, not even the threat of cobalt bombs, but the explosive growth of world population constitutes the most serious immediate and longterm threat to the welfare of humanity.

Malthus

In the most famous and most influential of all works on population, *An Essay on the Principle of Population As It Affects the Future Improvement of Society,* published in 1798 and in six massively revised and enlarged editions thereafter, Malthus argued that since the population increased in geometric progression and the food supply increased only in arithmetic progression, the number of human beings would always exceed the resources available to feed them, and many would inevitably die. The three great checks upon natural increase, according to Malthus, the Three Horsemen of the Apocalypse, are famine, disease, and war. Malthus subsequently added a fourth check, moral restraint or voluntary abstention from procreation.

The discussion and vituperation which Malthus' essay engendered has never ceased. In the context of the times in which he wrote, Malthus' *Essay* made a great appeal to the supporters of the *status quo*. It reenforced the *rentier* classes in their entrenched belief that wealth was a mark of divine grace and poverty its punishment, and that the poor were not entitled to claim relief as a right. On this important matter, for so gentle a man Parson Malthus had some very harsh things to say. In the second edition (1803) he wrote:

> A man who is born into a world already possessed, if he cannot get subsistence from his parents on whom he has a just demand, and if the society do not want his labour, has no claim of right to the smallest portion of food, and, in fact, has no business to be where he is. At nature's mighty feast there is no vacant cover for him. She tells him to be gone, and will quickly execute her own orders, if he do not work upon the compassion of some of her guests. If these guests get up and make room for him, other intruders immediately appear demanding the same favour. . . . The guests learn too late their error, in counteracting those strict orders to all intruders, issued by the great mistress of the feast, who, wishing that all guests should have plenty, and knowing that she could not provide for unlimited numbers, humanely refused to admit fresh comers when her table was already full.[5]

Malthus was persuaded to omit this severe judgment from subsequent editions of the *Essay*, but it is a viewpoint which he maintained to the end. As Beales has written, "Malthus has, especially in hard times, always had his admirers, but the main contribution of his school is that the essence of social policy is that there should be no social policy . . . or so it seems. And in retrospect that is of no great importance because society has turned it down." [6]

What is to be said of Malthus' theory in the twentieth century? In the first place it should be said that Malthus' views were not original. Almost forty years earlier similar views were expressed by Robert Wallace in his book, *Various Prospects of Mankind, Nature, and Providence* (1761). It matters not, for Malthus' *Essay* is the work that resulted in the impact that resulted in the great debate that has been proceeding ever since. Here a distinction must be made between Malthus' theory and Malthus' practical recommendations.

With respect to Malthus' theory it may at once be said that taken as a general statement it is a good theory, regardless of whether it is correct or not, simply because it has been a fruitful theory, fruitful of debate. Malthus' theory is, indeed, a fruitful error. The notion of overpopulation, for example, is not an absolute, as Malthus implied. Overpopulation is always relative, a relationship between man and his resources, and the resources imply much more than subsistence. Furthermore, it is today clear that population does not in fact grow faster than the supply of food, and hence that Malthus' principle theorem is unsound. Malthus' opposition to any artificial family limitation within marriage or any kind of "artificial and unnatural modes of checking population, both on account of their immorality and their tendency to remove a necessary stimulus to industry," [7] could scarcely have proved more wrongheaded. Malthus' population policy was simple: Moral restraint was the conduct by which the evil consequences of the principle of population were to be mitigated. By "moral restraint" Malthus meant, first, the postponement of marriage until the individuals involved were able to support a family and, second, abstention from all behavior before marriage that might lead to children. Society was to be so ordered as to provide the greatest incentives for the prescribed rules of conduct to be followed.

These ideas are quite as unsound as the last 150 years have proved them to be. Attitudes toward sex, marriage, the family, and society have undergone revolutionary changes. Premarital intercourse with or without conception is no longer regarded as the heinous moral offense it was in Malthus' day, and even in his day the contribution to the population made by children born out of wedlock was insignificant. That contribution is greater in the twentieth century than ever before, but this does not mean that artificial prevention of conception in premarital and marital intercourse cannot come to be regarded as perfectly moral and constitute a far greater check upon population increase than Malthus' unrealistic "moral restraint." It not only can, but there is not the least doubt that it is already beginning to do so in some countries.

Throughout his writings on population and economics Malthus made his belief unequivocally clear that Poor Laws, relief, create further poverty, and as population increases poverty increases. Again, the history of the last 150 years shows how unsound this idea is, even though it may not have been quite as unsound in Malthus' own day. In the first place, it is now clear that Poor Laws do not create poverty but that poverty creates Poor Laws, and that the answer to poverty is neither Poor Laws nor relief but raising the standard of living of the poor by the indicated means. By greater spending, increased opportunities for education, industrial development, and other necessary social and economic changes. What Malthus never understood, and what the English to this day, in contrast to Americans, fail to understand, is that the more one spends the more one earns. The adherence to the opposed viewpoint, with all its many consequences, has brought England to its present sad economic condition. England's present economic woes, allowing for the loss of its empire, are due not to the pressure of population so much as to the pressure of outmoded economic behavior in a rapidly changing world which is leaving England far behind. Instead of improvements in living standards producing a rise in birthrates, England constitutes the best example of the fallacy of that theorem. In 1851 the birthrate of Great Britain was 34.1 per 1,000, but by 1964 the birthrate had fallen to 18.5 per 1,000. And although there has been a remarkable decline in mortality rates, the annual rate of increase in population has fallen from 12.3 to 0.8 per 1,000 in the same period. There can be no doubt that this decline in the birthrate has followed upon the growing awareness that children are expensive and compete with other opportunities for development, and that their limitation is therefore desirable. And for the last hundred years there has been an increase in the use, in Great Britain, of artificial and other means of limiting conception and births. These changes in social habit and custom have been a direct consequence of the rise in the standard of living for the population in general. Much the same development has occurred in the rest of Europe.

Malthus' dismal theorem is, therefore, unsound where real efforts have been made to improve the living standards of human beings. It remains true only under conditions in which efforts are not made to improve the lot in general of human beings. It remains true where there is no foresight, the last of the gifts granted by the gods to man, and populations are abandoned to a natural increase in some lands, and increase is accelerated in others by the combined elevation of the survival rates of infants, mothers, and everyone else, and by increasing the expectation of life, by reducing the death rate. With increasingly greater efficiency this is exactly what we have been doing during the last century and a half.

Consider Ceylon, for example. With the introduction of the benefits of modern medicine and public health, chiefly through malaria control, the death rate dropped from 19.8 per 1,000 in 1946 to 12.3 in 1949. The death rate is now 8.5 per 1,000, well within the limits of Western levels, while the birthrate remains at its former high level of 36 per 1,000. In other words, in some ten years or so the death rate in Ceylon fell by about 70 percent, while the birthrate continues at its former high level. The population explosion in Ceylon is not proving beneficial to that country. *Too Many Too Soon* is the title of a film recently issued in Ceylon by the Family Planning Association—a title which simply and accurately describes the situation in Ceylon.

If, in Ceylon as elsewhere in the world, men had had the wisdom to foresee the consequences of a precipitous drop in the death rate without an accompanying drop in the birthrate and had assumed the responsibility of seeing to it that with the improvement in medical and sanitary conditions there was a simultaneous improvement provided in the understanding, purpose, and use of methods of birth control, Ceylon might have

41]

saved itself the serious problems with which it is faced today.

Puerto Rico presents a good example of the uses of foresight and planning. Since the 1940s Puerto Rico has experienced an even more spectacular increase in population as a result of a death-rate drop of 82 percent in one decade. This alarming increase in population has been slowed down by the government-initiated wide dissemination of knowledge and the easy access to the means of birth control. With a population of more than 2.5 million, the annual rate of increase is now 1.7 percent with a birthrate of 31 per 1,000, and with one of the lowest death rates in the world, 6.9 per 1,000. Puerto Rico has a long way yet to go, but it has made a good beginning; together with its economic progress, the auguries promise well for the future.

It requires to be thoroughly understood that population is a relationship between man and his resources, and that a moderate population increase of between 1 and 1.5 percent per annum is in most cases a desirable increase. Stationary populations are likely to grow stagnant, since the death rates go down and the old, in effect, replace the young, with a consequent reduction in the aptitude for progress. Up to a certain point the pressure of population has a stimulating effect. Beyond that point it tends to have the opposite, a depressing effect. And so every society must find its optimum population number if it is to function in a healthy manner. That optimum number will vary at different times with different conditions, and the Good Society, which is to be preferred to the Great Society, will always attempt to keep its human population in healthy equilibrium with the resources that are available to it.

REFERENCES

1. Dorothy Kenyon, *Digging Up Jericho*. Praeger, New York, 1957.
2. Henri Vallois, "La Durée de la Vie chez l'Homme Fossile," *L'Anthropologie*, vol. 47, 1937, pp. 499–532.
3. Annabelle Desmond, "How Many People Have Ever Lived on Earth?" In Stuart Mudd, ed., *The Population Crisis and the Use of World Resources,* Junk, The Hague, 1964, pp. 27–46.
4. William McCord, *The Springtime of Freedom*. Oxford University Press, New York, 1965, p. 11.

5. Thomas R. Malthus, *An Essay on the Principle of Population*, 2nd ed. J. Johnson, London, 1803, p. 531; 5th ed. J. Johnson, London, 1817, vol. 3, p. 393.
6. H. L. Beales, "The Historical Context of the *Essay* on Population." In D. V. Glass, ed., *Introduction to Malthus*. Watts & Co., London, 1953, p. 22.

3. Nostrums and prescriptions

DDT has in the last quarter of a century done more than deity, democracy, and demographers combined to decrease mortality rates. The use of a chemical substance synthesized in a Swiss laboratory, DDT, in many regions of the world—Ceylon, Cyprus, Greece, India, the Philippines, Sardinia, and Taiwan—has constituted the principal contribution toward the survival of millions of reproducing human beings who, in the absence of the work done in that Swiss laboratory, would never have survived.

Before the advent of modern medical and public health services, most human beings born never reached reproductive age. Today most do. When mortality rates were high, a high birthrate was essential to maintain the population. With this was associated social encouragements to early marriage and prolific reproduction. These were good ideas. But when mortality rates are reduced to a low level, a high reproduction rate is not only no longer essential—indeed, it becomes positively endangering.

The peoples who have been assisted to reduce their mortality rates have not been assisted to reduce their reproduction rates. We have ourselves continued and helped other peoples to perpetuate attitudes toward childbearing that have rapidly become outmoded by the changes in our ability to control death. We need today to control birth—but always with the preenvisionment of the consequences of such control. We have become very good at controlling death. In most civilized countries during the last hundred years the expectation of life of the average individual has more than doubled. We need to understand and to teach others that a revision of traditional attitudes toward childbearing in harmony with the changed conditions is urgently necessary. That when mortality rates were high, high childbearing rates were desirable, but that with the achievement of low mortality rates lower childbearing rates are desirable, and high childbearing rates are not only no longer necessary but undesirable.

Human beings must learn to control their own multiplication as part of their concern with the improvement, and maintenance of the health and wellbeing of their fellow men. The physical and mental wellbeing of human beings can be greatly improved and their longevity extended, but as a prerequisite to this the control of reproduction will always be necessary.

At this moment (1968) there are 69 million children in the United States under the age of eighteen, and of those 69 million children 12 million live in the most abject poverty. Eighteen out of every hundred children living in the most affluent country with the highest standard of living in the world, live under physical and moral and intellectual conditions which are nothing short of catastrophic. Most of these 12 million children should never have been born, for the simple reason that there was no one to give them the care they deserved. They are a disaster. No one cares for them. In 1964 three-quarters of a million children were arrested in the United States. In New York City alone in the same year more than 40,000 children were arrested. This is, of course, only a proportion of the total number of children who committed indictable offenses. The increase in the calendar of serious crimes—murder, rape, assault, arson, larceny, theft—has been spectacular.

These tragic children are not simple statistics but reflect the alienation and indifference of a delinquent society. Every one of those children is a human being who has been failed in the most basic of his rights, the right to fulfillment. A society unable to satisfy the needs for development of more than a limited number of its citizens should see to it that that number is never exceeded. And when that has been said, that is the long and the short of the story.

Birth control has been discussed and debated for well over a hundred years, and in some places the idea still meets with as much irrational opposition as it ever did. While it is perfectly true that there is no adequate defense, except stupidity, against the impact of some ideas, the impact of the facts of overpopulation has been such in recent years as to cause a perceptible and hopeful rise of interest in the heading-off of the disasters that overpopulation brings in its wake. In his State of the Union message in 1964 President Johnson said, "I will seek new ways to use our knowledge to help deal with the explosion of world population and the growing scarcity of resources." Former President Eisenhower has put the issue very clearly. "The population explosion," he said, "has become one of the critical world problems of our time. It threatens to smother the economic progress of many nations and endangers the free world struggle for peace and security. Greatly expanded public and private efforts must be undertaken to contain this human explosion." Progress is being made, but it must be accelerated. More and more persons practice birth control, increasingly greater numbers desire to, and many governments have recognized the pressing necessity of teaching their citizens to do so. Every government ought to have a Department of Population Control.* Governments have many departments organized to defend the people against threats originating from without their borders. But scarcely any have a department designed to protect the people against the most dangerous of all threats from within their borders. I say "the most dangerous" because I believe, in common with many others, that the devaluation of the quality of humanity by the uncontrolled increase in its quantity constitutes a vastly more tragic loss than the reduction in its numbers

* Such a department exists in Japan, the only land which has really satisfactorily solved its population problem, to the extent that a labor shortage threatens there! Japan reduced its birth rate, by control and legalized abortion, from 34.2 per 1,000 in 1947 to 17.2 per 1,000 in 1957 to 7.0 per 1,000 in 1964! In other words, in ten years the birthrate was cut in half and seven years later by more than half again.

by the evils of famine, disease, or war. Freedom and freedom for human development decrease as the square of the population increases, opportunities for growth and development are curtailed and frustrated, and self-realization assumes not even the form of a dream, and, like this insubstantial pageant faded, under conditions of overpopulation most men are destined to leave not a rack behind.

Napoleon it was who cynically remarked that God is on the side of the army with the heaviest artillery. It is no longer true. The heaviest artillery may be entirely bogged down and rendered ineffectual by the sticky mass of people that impede its progress. God is on the side of those who will treat life as the sacred thing it is. We have been talking a long time about the sacredness of human life. If we really believe that life is sacred, then it is time we began treating it as if it were, and not as some expendable thing that can be disregarded the moment it is brought into the world.

Man has been described as the only example of a 150-pound nonlinear servomechanism that can be wholly reproduced by unskilled labor. It is one way of looking at him. Another is as a creature full of promises and challenges to fulfillment.

The creation of a human being should surely be regarded as by far the most important activity of human beings, of human society, for the simple reason that every birth entails a birthright. For the simple reason that the birthright of every baby is development, the fulfillment of its capacities. It is a crime against humanity and against the person to deprive any individual of his right to the fulfillment of his potentialities. And yet this is precisely the deprivation that the pressures of overpopulation work upon untold millions of individuals. And this, especially, is the effect that we too often fail to emphasize when we discuss the population explosion. Nevertheless this is overwhelmingly the most significant of the disasters that overpopulation wreaks upon the individual.

Overpopulation is a problem which is usually discussed in relation to the food supply. It is said that uncontrolled growth of population is dangerous because it threatens our nutritional resources, that there will not be enough food to feed so many

47]

new mouths. This is to misplace the emphasis completely. In the first place it is quite unsound to argue that the food supply would be insufficient to feed the new mouths. The truth is that we already have the means to maximize the food supply far beyond the needs of any number of people. In the United States with a population of approximately 200 million we pay farmers millions of dollars not to cultivate their land. Other peoples could be taught to become as efficient in food production.[1]

It is not the resources of food but the resources of humanity that should be the main point of emphasis in discussions of the population explosion. Human beings do not exist to eat, they eat or should eat in order to live, and to live should mean to live as a fulfilled human being and not necessarily a filled one. Man does not live by bread alone. Bread is important, but not as an end, only as a means to one, to the fulfillment of the humanity that is within the capacities of every human being. And anything that impedes or threatens that humanity should be considered evil. The pressure of overpopulation constitutes the greatest of such evils. It is an evil that should therefore be attended to. Not by exorcism or recurrent unproductive genuflections to noble ideals, and still less by incantation, but by practice and by hard work.

With even larger populations than are threatened we could teach the developing nations how to increase their food supplies, their general productivity, their health, but the consequences of their learning to do so would render it increasingly more difficult for them to learn to master and fulfill themselves. Why? Because when the size of a population increases beyond the limits consonant with the requirements of individaul development, individual development is necessarily slighted. The very pressures for survival produce the atomization, the fragmentation of human relationships, disengagement, alienation, and indifference to the lot of others; a state in which everyone must sink or swim by his own efforts without expectation of support from others.

Increase in size tends, in human societies, to increase the complexities with which such societies are confronted out of all proportion to the actual increase in quantity. And one of the first things that suffers under such conditions is the quality of human relationships. Consider, for example, the United States. It is a big country. It has grown at a rapid rate. Our crime rates of every kind, our suicide rates, murder, lawlessness of every kind, disorder, disorganization, wastage, injustice, and vast numbers of other problems, are among the highest and the most complex in the world. We have grown too large too quickly. And the result has been that we have grown into the habit of paying more attention to things than to human beings. Human beings create the need for things, and the business of dealing in things yields greater cash returns—or, at least, so it is held by those who believe in consumerism—than enabling human beings to fulfill themselves. In this big country we have grown so used to thinking in terms of bigness that we have erected quantity into a value and tend to measure the value of things by quantity rather than by quality. We flatter ourselves that we have the biggest buildings, the longest roads, the most cash, the greatest store of armaments, the greatest number of and the largest colleges and universities, the most populous cities.

In all this worship of quantity we seem to have forgotten that the only genuine wealth of a people lies in the quality of those people. What is the sense of having 27,500 students in a university, with often more than 600 students in a class? Certainly it is possible to instruct such numbers, but it is scarcely possible to educate them. For in the process of education one is concerned with a dialogue between student and teacher. The student is recognized as a unique person, and the exchange that should be unhurriedly proceeding between teacher and student, should serve to minister to the individual needs of the student so that he may grow and develop as a human being, in the increase in his sensibilities, the broadening of his vision, in the deepening of his understanding, as well as in the enlargement of his mind and the increase of his knowledge. To do all this is difficult if not impossible under crowded conditions. Under such conditions the precious gift that lies within the power of the teacher to offer his students—his own personality—is aborted and diminished, if not altogether lost. And what is worse, so is that of the student, who is pressed into a mass conformity instead of being helped toward the development of his own individuality and the service of his fellow man, by the pressure of the overcrowded institutions in which he finds himself and which reflect the consequences of the general overpopulation of the country.

What happens to a country when it becomes overpopulated is in macrocosm what can be observed occurring on a smaller scale in a city that becomes overpopulated. It matters not how materially prosperous the country, the complexities produced by overpopulation constitute a human and social disaster for most of its inhabitants. Consider New York, Chicago, Los Angeles, Paris, London. What becomes of humanity in such cities? What will happen to human beings when populations double and treble in size? Altogether apart from the fact that we are already engulfed by automobiles and overcome by smog, the struggle for survival will become even more severe and there will be vanishingly less time and thought available for the development of the individual. The individual, indeed, will tend to get lost in the crush. Schools and teachers will be insufficient to take care of the swelling masses of unplanned children; schools and classes will be even more crowded than they are today, with a consequent lowering of standards. Parents will be able to pay even less attention to their children than they do today. Delinquency and crime and poverty will increase, and social disorganization rather than organization will grow.

It is not generally realized that there are more people alive today than there have been ever before, and this is undoubtedly true for delinquency and crime rates of every kind. Less than thirty-two years from now there will be an estimated 350 million Americans. The number of automobiles will have increased from the present 90 million to 190 million. If anyone desires to see what future America will look like, let them go to California, that land of perpetual pubescence where cultural lag is mistaken for renaissance and the destruction of the land or increase in real-estate values is equated with advancing civilization. In California there are the largest, biggest, and most complex freeways in the world, where often to drive under seventy-five miles an hour is to court death, a land into which pour 1,600 people a day, one half million a year, where for every 1,000 increase of population 238 acres of arable land are lost to asphalt or buildings,[2] where it is expected that, and one can actually see, 3 million acres of open land will disappear under the inundation of people. It all looks like a tentative preface to extinction, and especially of the human spirit, as recent political and social events in California serve only too gloomily to testify.

The rights of man should beyond all others include freedom and freedom of individual development. Irresponsible and unplanned reproduction is not freedom; it is the abuse of freedom and a principal cause of the loss of freedom. Poverty and ignorance are the greatest enemies of freedom, and overpopulation is today the greatest single cause of poverty and ignorance. And indiscriminate reproduction is most generally a consequence of poverty and ignorance.

An education geared to the needs of society and raised standards of living are the beachheads that must be secured if responsible parenthood is to become a reality. But the establishment of such beachheads takes time, and time is running out. It is important for us to understand that in most of the lands, such as those in Latin America, in which the population will double every twenty-three years, there is no longer time for education if the population growth is to be controlled. Even if the fertility rate were halved in the next thirty-two years, the population of southern Asia will still double itself in those same years. Insofar as education is concerned in such lands, the point of no return was reached long ago. We, and by "we" I mean humanity, must now begin to consider other means of birth control. Voluntary birth control cannot be depended upon in such countries, not at least until the educational and living standards of the people have been raised, and this will take several generations. We cannot wait until then and allow ourselves to be inundated by the tidal wave of births which are bound to come. Incantation and ritual declarations of hope in the future are not enough. More heroic measures than education will be necessary in such countries.

51]

There are still people who protest and resist vaccination against epidemic diseases. Such people endanger the lives of others as well as of themselves. Recognizing this, the laws of most lands make vaccination obligatory. The public health services do not spend years attempting to persuade people during an epidemic that they should be vaccinated; they require and if necessary force them to be vaccinated, and with our approval. Overpopulation may be likened to an epidemic disease, and it is far more effectively dealt with by preventive than by any other means. It is better to prevent disease than to be compelled to cure it. Mankind, it is to be feared, with respect to overpopulation is now in the stage of having both to cure it and prevent the possibility of its ever becoming epidemic again.

In India, with a population of 500 million, the rate of population increase is a staggering 1 million a month. After twenty years of family planning there is not the least evidence that the rate of population growth has decelerated in a single Indian state or in more than a handful of the country's 500,000 villages. In 1967 India's new Minister of Health and Family Planning, Sripati Chandrasekhar, proposed the idea that all males with two or more children should be subject to compulsory sterilization. This would entail cutting the vas deferens, a simple operation which can be performed within 10 minutes, and perfectly harmless, but perfectly workable in the control of the male's ability to produce conception. Whether this proposal will be adopted in India remains to be seen.

As both cure and preventive of the threat of overpopulation in some lands we must today seriously consider the use of chemical additives in food or water that will produce temporary sterility. If antidotes were available to offset the antifertility effect of such additives, there could be no reasonable objection to the sterilization of whole populations, since fertility could be restored at will. Compulsory control may be undemocratic, but if it is then so is compulsory education, the compulsory draft, compulsory taxes, compulsory vaccination, and compulsory obedience to the law. Egypt, with a birthrate of between 40 and 44 per 1,000, no longer has the time to educate its people in the urgent necessity of no couple having more than two children. Its annual rate of increase of 2.7 percent per annum will bring all its schemes for improvement to nothing. It is not a plague of frogs or of locusts that will destroy peoples like the Egyptians, but the plague of its own proliferating numbers.

Contraceptive substances added to food and water may yet prove to be one of the greatest blessings to humanity. Such antifertility agents should be given the most serious consideration. In the high-income countries the population is generally educated enough to learn to change its ideas about family size without the necessity of compulsion. In the low-income countries there must be a fundamental change in values, attitudes and motivations before married couples will voluntarily come to control fertility. Knowledge and availability of contraceptives are not enough. And this is not a problem restricted merely to the low-income countries. There are millions of individuals in the United States, for example, who cannot be persuaded to control their fertility voluntarily. They cannot be reached by education, and these are just the people whose fertility is by far the highest in the land, and from whose ranks, understandably enough, the largest number of delinquents and criminals come. Since experience shows that such individuals cannot be expected to control their own fertility, it will be necessary for society to control it for them. There is, I suggest, a simple rule to be followed: Anyone unable to support a child by the fruits of his own labor or income should not be permitted to have a child. The right to have a child should be earned as a privilege, and anyone who has not earned the right to have a child should not be permitted the privilege of having one. With rights go duties, obligations, and anyone unable to fulfill his duties, his obligations, should not enjoy the rights which entail such duties. Having a child is no longer a matter of private will but of public welfare. Whatever endangers the public welfare should, therefore, be carefully regulated. If a person desires to drive a car, he must first prove that he is able to do so, and then only after he has obtained a license and periodically renewed it may he drive a car. But anyone who wants to produce children or to indulge himself in ways that lead to children is perfectly free to do so. As Dr. F. H. C. Crick has said, "Do people have the right to have children at all? Is it the general feeling that people do have the right to have children? This is taken for granted because it is part of Christian ethics, but in terms of humanist ethics I do not see why people should have the right to have children. I think that if we can get across to people the idea that their children are not entirely their own business and that it is not a private matter, it would be an enormous step forward." [3] As, indeed, it would. And I think that the idea of responsibility should begin to replace the irresponsibility with which so many millions of children are brought into the world. No one should be permitted to practice medicine and surgery who has not undergone the proper training and been licensed by society. In the much more delicate business of operating upon the lives of countless human beings, we allow anyone, without the slightest qualification or responsibility, to become a parent. Becoming a biological parent, *parentage,* is a matter of a few minutes; becoming a responsible parent, *parenthood,* is something else again, a matter of adequate preparation. The unqualified, the unprepared, the quacks should not be permitted to wreak their havoc upon the innocent. Ignorance and irresponsibility, whether involuntary or voluntary, are the same in their effects, and they must be corrected.

As I have already remarked, if life is sacred, it is time we began treating it as such, and not as if it were something expendable, to be thrown away or treated with the inconsideration of vague intentions. Every birth should be regarded as a contribution to society as well as to the family and to the child that has been born. A gift to be treated with gratitude and reverence, so that every child may be from birth assured of the optimum conditions for development and fulfillment. Anything short of this is to disinherit the newborn of his birthright and to deprive his society of a cooperating and contributing member of society. The worthiness of every human being is such that it should be considered a crime to bring a child into the world under conditions in which his worthiness cannot be properly respected. Human beings are not objects, commodities, expendable sources of energy, to be haphazardly brought into the world to live miserable and unfulfilled lives. If intercourse is the only pleasure that millions of miserable human beings are able to enjoy, then without depriving them of that pleasure it should be prevented from continuing to be the direct source of untold miseries in others.

To be a human being essentially means to know, to understand, and to control. Knowledge and understanding appear to be the essential prerequisites of control. But as we have already remarked, it is too late in some regions of the world to wait upon the development of knowledge and understanding. While these must be taught, while they are being taught, sterilization by some such artificial controls as food additives will, in the interim, have to be resorted to. Pills, intrauterine devices such as rings, spirals, loops, and the like, sterilization of the male either permanently by vasectomy or temporarily by tying off the vas deferens or by drugs, the use of diaphragms, condoms, and other contraceptive devices like foams, jellies, and so on, should all have their uses taught in every community. Every community should have a population control office, just as it has a water control board, a fire department, and a police department, where everyone can go for advice and instruction in population control. This should mean not alone learning to control the births in one's own family but also helping others control the births in theirs. Not only this, "the facts of life," as they are euphemistically called by a hypocritical society, should be taught from an early age in the home and in the schools, beginning with the nursery school and continued throughout the educational system.

The lesson is a simple one. The function of human life is to live it, not in misery but in the joy of human realization, of fulfillment, not so much in material as in human qualities. And if we are to realize the potentialities of human quality, then it is indispensably necessary for us to attend to the control of human quantity. Economic, technological, scientific, and social development should always be regarded as secondary in importance to the much more significant development of human beings. As Professor Harold A. Thomas, Jr., has put it, "Human development means cultivation of the innate potentialities of the individual, time for work and time for leisure, food, shelter, and vitality of family life." [4] These possibilities should constitute the basic birthright of every human being born into the world. Anything less should be considered an offense, antisocial and antihuman, and treated as such. The best way to treat such offenses is to prevent them. And the best way to prevent them is to enable each person to know and understand why and how such offenses can be prevented. Teaching human beings to know and understand their responsibility for themselves to others and the means of accomplishing this is, I am sure, the most effective way in the long run of solving, among others, the population problem.

It is the moral obligation of every intelligent person to do what he is able as a responsible person to ensure, by whatever reasonable means he can, the practice of population control himself and the diffusion of the knowledge of it as widely as possible. Superstition, ignorance, fear, poverty, and sheer Machiavellianism constitute formidable barriers in the way of population control. But they can be overcome. The Catholic Church and the Communists, for much the same reason, have opposed birth control. In 1959 the Catholic Truth Society of London put the matter unequivocally clearly in a pamphlet addressed to Catholic wives: "Our faithful Catholic mothers are doing a wonderful work for God. In time, if contraceptive practices continue to prevail amongst Protestants, their number will decrease and the Catholic race * will prevail, and thus England might again become what it once was, a Catholic country." [5] Thus, official doctrine among some Catholics at least is that population control must be left to non-Catholics in a breeding contest in which the Catholics will emerge victorious. It is not an accident that the birthrate in such regions as Latin America is so highly correlated with the power structure and dominance of the Catholic Church. But fortunately not all Catholics follow official Catholic doctrine, and it is a remarkable fact that by far the larger part of the clientele of many birth-control advisory

* Catholics are, of course, not a "race" but a religious group.

agencies is Catholic. Also many Catholic churchmen no longer subscribe to the Church's outmoded antipathy to birth control, and there is every hope that official Catholic policy will change in the humane direction.[6]

The Communists oppose any form of birth control for peoples other than themselves for the simple reason that the more misery they can encourage by overpopulation the more readily they believe they will be able to take over such peoples. Mao Tse-tung has stated that poverty is an asset to the Communists because it breeds "revolutionary fervor." The Russian Communists have opposed all attempts at birth control for peoples other than themselves. As Professor Philip Appleman has remarked in his book *The Silent Explosion,* "Although they claim to be against population control on principle . . . the Communists are nevertheless taking steps to check their own population growth, apparently in order to improve economic conditions; and although they preach 'the sanctity of life' to underdeveloped countries, their official opposition to population control is actually making life in such countries more and more degraded and miserable. Thus an ostensible Marxist belief does double duty as a ruthless Cold War tactic." [7]

A Church which has so often been governed by the principle of expediency may yet persuade itself that by its antipathy toward population control it is playing directly into the hands of its greatest enemies, the Communists.

It is necessary for all of us who are interested in the future of humanity to be aware of the forces at work which, whether through ignorance, vested interest, misguided judgment, or self-seeking, stand in the way of a humane population policy. If we would assure humanity's future we must pay attention to the conditions in the present that will ensure that future. If anyone cares to ask, as Bernard Shaw once put it, "What has posterity done for me that I should do anything for posterity?" the answer is that it is not enough to be clever—Satan was not wanting in cleverness; furthermore, that Bernard Shaw left no posterity and wouldn't have known anyway, but that what humanity will always stand in need of is involvement in its past, present, and future; for those of us who live now are the heirs of the past, the beneficiaries or victims of the present, and the makers of the future.

It is man's moral obligation to be intelligent, knowledgeable, understanding, and committed to the welfare of his fellow man. Faced with new challenges, it is necessary for us to think out the appropriate responses to them. New challenges require new responses that usually require a deepening and more active enlargement of our moral values. To love our fellow man we must understand what love is. Within the framework in which we have been speaking, and within any other for the matter of that, love is behavior calculated to confer survival benefits in a creatively enlarging manner upon others.[8] Whatever stands in the way of enabling our fellow men to live more fully and to realize their potentialities to the optimum must be regarded as evil. Overpopulation is the greatest of the evils impeding the progress of individual fulfillment and must be unequivocally regarded as such. It is for this reason principally that all of us as responsible human beings must do everything in our power to see to it that the cancer of overpopulation is brought under control, and kept under control, so that its ravages may be mitigated and repaired and human beings at long last may enjoy a chance to become what they have it in them to be.

REFERENCES

1. William and Paul Paddock, *Hungry Nations.* Little, Brown & Co., Boston, 1964. William and Paul Paddock, *Famine 1975!* Little, Brown & Co., Boston, 1967.
2. James P. Degnan, "California: The Bulldozer Crop." *The Nation,* March 8, 1965, pp. 242–245.
3. F. H. C. Crick, "Discussion." In G. Wolstenholme, ed., *Man and His Future,* Little, Brown & Co., Boston, 1963, p. 275.
4. Harold A. Thomas, Jr., "Orientation, Thrust and Goal of the Harvard Center for Population Studies," *Harvard Public Health Alumni Bulletin,* vol. 22, 1965, p. 18.
5. A Catholic Woman Doctor, *A Talk to Catholic Wives.* Catholic Truth Society, London, 1959, p. 26.
6. Dorothy Dunbar Bromley, *Catholics and Birth Control.* Devin-Adair Co., New York, 1965; John T. Noonan, *Contraception: A History of its Treatment by the Catholic Theologians and Canoninsts.* Harvard

University Press, Cambridge, 1965; Editorial, "The Vatican and the Population Crisis." *Population Bulletin,* vol. 21, 1965, pp. 1–15.
7. Philip Appleman, *The Silent Explosion.* Beacon Press, Boston, 1965, p. 91.
8. M. F. Ashley Montagu, *The Direction of Human Development.* Harper & Bros., New York, 1955.

4. *Wilderness and humanity*

There is a pleasure in the pathless woods,
There is a rapture on the lonely shore,
There is society, where none intrudes,
By the deep sea, and music in its roar:
I love not man the less, but Nature more.

—Byron, *Childe Harold's Pilgrimage*
Canto IV, Stanza 178

Recently a cartoonist, clearly painfully aware of what has been going on around him, produced a cartoon showing two over-stuffed and obviously opulent men standing amidst a host of oil derricks and the splintered remnants of trees by a pool filled with oil slick and debris. With evident pride, one of these instruments of destruction, surveying the devastation they had jointly wrought, remarked to the other, "And to think that only a few weeks ago all this was wilderness."

That cartoon faithfully recorded an incident which must have been repeated scores of thousands of times in the United States alone, not to mention other lands. A short time ago I read in the New York *Times* an account of a developer who had announced his intention of erecting a housing project on one of the last remaining woods on Long Island. The residents, revolted by the threatened destruction, called a meeting of protest at which the developer presented his case. He failed to understand, he said, how there could possibly be the least objection to his proposed leveling of the woodland, and with a

sincerity that could only have sprung from the deepest conviction he pleadingly intoned, "But look what beautiful houses,
streets, roadways, and gas stations there would be where now
there is only wilderness." It was, in its way, really quite touch-
ing, for I am informed that he had a catch in his voice. He
doubtless felt as Milton might have done had his *Paradise Lost*
been rejected by an uncomprehending editor. What the outcome of the meeting was I do not know, but I suspect that the
developer won out and that for him the destruction of the woodland and its replacement by a development assumed the form of
Paradise Regained.

Like Peter Bell,

> A primrose by a river's brim
> A yellow primrose was to him,
> And it was nothing more.

There can be little doubt that there are among us, in numbers saddening to reflect upon, many who when they see a blade
of grass or a tree immediately feel how nice it would be if it
could be bulldozed out of existence and a surface of asphalt put
in its place. Wilderness is equated to wasteland, and with the
pressures of population being what they are, there remain few
among us who seem able to contemplate with equanimity good
land going to what they consider to be waste.

Contemporary man in relation to the wilderness is well de-
cribed in A. E. Housman's "improvement" on Frances Corn-
ford's poem "To a Fat Lady Seen from the Train."

> O why do you walk through the fields in boots,
>   Missing so much and so much?
> O fat white person whom nobody shoots,
> Why do you walk through the fields in boots,
> When the grass is soft as the breast of coots
>   And shivering-sweet to the touch?
> O why do you walk through the fields in boots,
>   Missing so much and so much?

It was not always so. Man has been on this earth about two million years, and for almost the whole of that time he lived in the wilderness; it was his home and his world. And of that world he considered himself a natural part. He was a food-gatherer and hunter, and he saw and experienced the world as a web of intricate interrelationships of which he, in common with every other living thing—and all things were animated by some spiritual essence, whether animals, rocks, clouds, pools or mountains—everything, indeed, in nature was an inseparable and connected part. Such peoples—and there are still a fair number of them in existence today—living as close to nature as they do, entertain a wholly different conception of their relation to the world in which they live from that of the town-dweller of civilized societies. Indeed, the modern urbanite is so far removed from the world of nature and his views of his own relation to the world in which he finds himself differ so profoundly from those of peoples living close to nature, he usually finds it difficult if not impossible to understand the meaning of such peoples' beliefs. He therefore tends to treat them as odd, curious, esoteric, primitive, savage, wild, and strange. So far has urban man departed from life in the wilderness that he comes to regard it as something crude and rude, "wild" in the pejorative meaning of that word. Like his conception of "wild" animals, his view of the wilderness is as far removed from the realities as it could possibly be. A strong case might, in fact, be made out for civilized man being the only "wild" animal in existence. Animals in the state of nature do not make war upon their own kind; they have no Attilas or Hitlers; and, not to put too fine a point upon it, animals seldom if ever exhibit the kind of savagery that civilized men exhibit toward one another. Civilized man, especially in the Western world, has projected the image of his own violent self upon the screen of nature. Without in any way wishing to diminish the great contribution of Darwin toward our understanding of nature, his view of nature, as Patrick Geddes was the first to point out, was substantially a projection of conditions prevailing in nineteenth-century industrial Europe upon the backdrop of nature. One of Darwin's favorite phrases in *The Origin of Species* was "the warfare of nature." It was an idea that Darwin inherited from earlier thinkers and from his environment. The conception of nature as a gladiatorial show is one which the followers of Darwin even more than Darwin himself helped to perpetuate. For most people today the idea of nature as the "wild," the "jungle" in the Darwinian sense, is the only idea of nature they know.

The myth of the beast and the myth of the jungle, as the mythological beliefs relating to wild animals and nature may be called, profoundly affect the attitudes and conduct of those who adhere to such myths toward what the combination of those attitudes apperceives as the "wilderness." Through the distorting glass of their prejudices the wilderness is seen as something unruly, something to be civilized, brought under control. The best way to do that is, of course, to get rid of it and turn its vacant acres to profitable use. Under the pressures of expanding populations this has everywhere been the history of the destruction of the wilderness. Under the increasingly accelerating pressures of population everywhere in the inhabited world, millions of acres of wilderness are destined to be destroyed. It is, therefore, all the more necessary to do what we can now to make clear to everyone what such devastation is likely to do to humanity. In this way, perhaps, we may yet be able to save some remnants of the wilderness and perhaps also help to revitalize and renew man's necessary relationship to it.

Man, it cannot too often be pointed out, is a wild animal who has, in civilized societies, domesticated himself. Urban man especially lives under highly artificial conditions far removed, in most cases, from the wilderness. Millions of such urban dwellers have never seen an apple on a tree, and the only animals they know are domestic ones and those they may have seen only in zoos. This virtual complete separation from nature leads to a view of it which is wholly disengaged, even alienated, and frequently hostile. This is a pathological state, a morbid dissociation from what should have been a vital involvement in relation to the whole of nature. Man's 2 million or so years spent in close interrelationship with the wilderness helped to form him and make possible everything he has since done, and yet I believe with Benjamin Rush that "man is naturally a wild animal . . . taken from the woods, he is never happy . . . till he returns to them again." This should not be taken to mean that there exists anything like an archetypal species memory, but what I think it should be taken to mean is that man is a part of the wilderness, a part of nature, and that his relation to it is not merely one of natural harmony, of ecologic necessity but, in his urban condition especially, one of civilized health. A healthy relationship to the wilderness is not in the least incompatible with civilized living. Indeed, I believe it to be an indispensable condition thereof; that no man is truly civilized unless he is involved in and cares for the wilderness. To live in the city can be quite wonderful and enlarging, but not if it renders one insensitive to the meaning of the wilderness. Detachment from the wilderness means detachment from the world of nature, an exchange of the one for attachment to the world of things. Most people feel this; hence the strong urge that so often comes upon them to return to the wilderness. The enormous number of people who enjoy camping with their families in the wilderness, and even those who prefer more sophisticated reversions to the wilderness such as a country or seashore hotel or those Isles of Illusion, Palm Springs and Las Vegas, constitute a significant testimony not merely to the desire for a change of scene but to the deep-seated need to get out into the open. It is a feeling beautifully expressed in Keats' sonnet:

> To one who has been long in city pent,
>   'Tis very sweet to look into the fair
>   And open face of heaven,—to breathe a prayer
> Full in the smile of the blue firmament.
> Who is more happy, when, with heart's content,
>   Fatigued he sinks into some pleasant lair
>   Of wavy grass, and reads a debonair
> And gentle tale of love and languishment?
> Returning home at evening, with an ear
>   Catching the notes of Philomel,—an eye
> Watching the sailing cloudlet's bright career,
>   He mourns that day so soon has glided by:

E'en like the passage of an angel's tear
That falls through the clear ether silently.

Perhaps no other poet has put it better than Wordsworth in
his "Lines Written a Few Miles Above Tintern Abbey, on
Revisiting the Banks of the Wye During a Tour, July 13, 1798."

> For I have learned
> To look on nature, not as in the hour
> Of thoughtless youth, but hearing oftentimes
> The still sad music of humanity,
> Nor harsh nor grating, though of ample power
> To chasten and subdue. And I have felt
> A presence that disturbs me with the joy
> Of elevated thoughts; a sense sublime
> Of something far more deeply interfused,
> Whose dwelling is the light of setting suns,
> And the round ocean, and the living air,
> And the blue sky, and in the mind of man,
> A motion and a spirit, that impels
> All thinking things, all objects of all thought,
> And rolls through all things. Therefore am I still
> A lover of the meadows and the woods,
> And mountains; and of all that we behold
> From this green earth; of all the mighty world
> Of eye and ear, both what they half create,
> And what perceive; well pleased to recognize
> In nature and the language of the sense,
> The anchor of my purest thoughts, the nurse,
> The guide, the guardian of my heart, and soul
> Of all my moral being.

To be cut off from the wilderness is to suffer a spiritual im-
poverishment and abridgment of life which the understanding
and appreciation of the wilderness and the kinship with nature
and everything in it bring. It is not the notion of the wilderness
for its own sake that is of value, but the awareness of one's
relatedness to, one's unity with it, that deepens and extends the
scope of human life. The aesthetic life and the enjoyment of
the merely picturesque often lead to a sybaritic self-indulgence

rather than to spiritual exaltation. And neither the one nor the other is enough, for what is necessary is the recognition of the simple fact that our wholeness as human beings depends upon the depth of our awareness of the fact that we are a part of the wholeness of nature and that the standards of dominance we have erected for ourselves in relation to it are artificial and destructive. As Immanuel Kant remarked long ago, evolution has been anthropocentrically envisaged as "a very long ladder created by man to place himself on the highest rung." And so we have created categories of "higher" and "lower" animals, a kind of race prejudice from the folly of which the so-called highest may justifiably do with the so-called lowest whatever they opportunistically desire. It is alleged that man is made in God's image, but that the beast is made in the image of the brute. Man, it is alleged, is loving and intelligent, the most successful of all creatures, and therefore superior to all other creatures, who act from instinct and not from intelligence, from selfish appetites and not from love. These are among the most entrenched beliefs of the learned as well as of the ignorant.

It is all very well awarding ourselves prizes for extreme, even excessive, cleverness, but if that cleverness leads to the kind of destructiveness that man has been practicing in the recent period, man's cleverness may yet prove itself to have been the most selectively disadvantageous trait ever developed by any creature in the whole history of animated nature.

Man prides himself on the variety of his inventiveness, but the variety of animated nature is far greater than that achieved by man. If man would simply have the grace to come off it and with appropriate humility acknowledge himself the made-over ape that he is, a creature whose kinship is with the whole of animated nature, he might be able to see the world of which he is a part in truer perspective. Like most self-made men, man, who has made himself, is an outstanding example of unskilled labor, a very imperfect creature indeed, and the lack of skill he exhibits in the making of human beings is prodigious. Indeed, that lack of skill threatens to put an end to us all. What man has made of man and of the world in which he lives is a sorry

story. What animal, indeed, has created as much devastation?
It is written in the Book of Job:

"Ask now the beasts and they shall teach thee; and the fowls
of the air, and they shall teach thee:

"Or speak to the earth, and it shall teach thee and the fishes
of the sea shall declare unto thee.

"Who knoweth not in all these that the hand of the Lord
hath wrought this?

"In whose hand is the soul of every living thing, and the
breath of all mankind."

And in the Koran it is written, "There is no beast on earth
nor fowl that flieth, but the same are a people like unto you,
and to God they shall return."

Without accepting these words in their literal sense, the
fundamental truths they express are beyond dispute, namely,
that we can learn from these other "peoples," and that we
ought to respect them for what they are, our kin.

Who but a few have ever given any attention to the profound
meaning of those words? Saint Francis of Assisi, whose love for
all living creatures is a part of our tradition, is regarded as an
eccentric who carried things too far and to whom, at best, we
offer up the smoke of incense as before an empty shrine.

Man may yet restore himself to health if he learns to understand himself in relation to the world of nature in which he
evolved as an integral part and comes fully to appreciate the
meaning of his relationship to the world of nature. He has for
too long diminished himself by his prejudiced and false views
of himself in relation to that nature, and in so doing he has
diminished and devastated so much of the rest of the world. He
has everything to gain from taking a fresh look at the world of
nature and making it a part of life as essential to him as he is
essential to it. The lessons man may learn from the study of
nature are of at least as great significance as any he can learn
from the purely human tradition, for as Wordsworth said in
the poem already quoted from him:

> Nature never did betray
> The heart that loved her; 'tis her privilege

MAN OBSERVED

Through all the years of this our life, to lead
From joy to joy: for she can so inform
The mind that is within us, so impress
With quietness and beauty, and so feed
With lofty thoughts, that neither evil tongues,
Rash judgments, nor the sneers of selfish men,
Nor greetings where no kindness is, nor all
The dreary intercourse of daily life,
Shall e'er prevail against us, or disturb
Our cheerful faith that all which we behold
Is full of blessings.

5. Crime and society

Crime and criminals are the inventions and products of society, and criminals are the instruments and the victims of that invention. It is the logic of the criminal and delinquent society to blame its crimes and delinquencies upon the criminals and delinquents and then to punish them for the offences it has, in most cases, caused them to commit.

A crime is whatever a society chooses to define as such. What may be considered a crime in one society may not be considered so in another. But whatever may or may not be considered a crime in any society, all societies define crime as an act committed in violation of a law prohibiting it or omitted in violation of a law ordering it. Hence, it is the society that defines the criminal, *not* the criminal who defines himself. And it is my suggestion here that it is almost invariably the society that makes the criminal; that criminals, indeed, are made, not born.

There have, of course, been many views arguing the contrary standpoint, from Lombroso through Lange to Hooton. Lombroso and Hooton have long been thoroughly discredited.[1] Lange's studies on the criminal behavior of twins are rather more worthy of respect.[2] Lange showed that identical twins who become criminals are significantly more likely to take to such a way of life than nonidentical twins. From this Lange and others drew the conclusion that genetic factors play a role in the disposition to commit crimes. Not that there are genes which determine individuals to commit crimes, although this *has* been maintained by some, like Hooton and others,[3] but that there are genes which under certain environmental conditions will render it likely that their possessors will more easily be disposed to criminal behavior than those who do not possess such genes. This is, however, a very different thing from saying that there exist such entities as "criminal genes" which, do what you will, will express themselves in criminal behavior. The idea of "criminal genes" is so highly improbable that for all practical purposes it can be dismissed as absurd. Absurd, because genes do not determine anything. What genes do is to influence the physiological or functional expression of a trait or a behavior, but a significant factor in influencing that expression will be the environment in which the trait or behavior undergoes development.[4]

The pathetic fallacy or, as it is more often called, the reductionist fallacy is to attribute human behavior either exclusively to the action of genes or to the exclusive action of the environment. Both the biologistic and the environmentalist positions are unsound for the simple reason that all development is the result of the interaction between genetic constitution and the environments in which those genes undergo development. That, in fact, is what heredity is. Not what is received in one's genes from one's parents or what one is born with, but the genes and the environments one receives undergoing development in interaction with one another. The genotype being as variable as it is, it is possible that some individuals may be born with genes which under certain environmental conditions would make it easier for them to become lawbreakers than for other individuals to do so who do not possess such genes.

It should be clear that all that this means is that genetically influenced differences in response to the environment exist a between different individuals. That under the same environmental conditions individuals will tend to respond somewhat differently, idiosyncratically, and that under the stimulus of different environmental conditions will tend to respond differently. Given the nature of the genes, whatever their potentialities, those potentialities will not develop unless they are environmentally stimulated to do so. So supposing the possibility that in some individuals some genetic or other organic conditions existed which, under certain environmental conditions, caused them to commit acts defined as crimes by their societies, it is surely evident that a society alive to such possibilities would see to it that the environmental conditions likely to facilitate the expression of the undesired behavior would as far as possible be reduced or eliminated. Just as, for example, we make environments virtually impossible in which the polio virus can work its havoc within human beings, so, too, we could make social environments virtually nonexistent in which crime could flourish. For just as it is the favorable environment that makes it possible for the polio virus to prosper, so it is the environment favorable to crime that causes crime to thrive.

The point I am trying to make here is that if—and it is a very big "if"—there are any genetic factors which under the appropriate environmental conditions may more readily result in criminal behavior than in the absence of such genes, it is highly probable that such genetic conditions either are (1) widely distributed among human beings, or (2) more or less rare.

I expect to be completely misunderstood when I say that I take the first view, namely, that all human beings carry genes which under certain conditions are likely to express themselves in behavior which some society or another will call criminal. By this I do not mean that anyone is endowed with or born with "criminal genes." What I do mean is that all individuals, no matter what the nature of their genes, will under certain environmental conditions tend to respond with behavior which in their society is considered criminal. Stated in this manner, and not for a moment underestimating the importance of the genes, it will be understood that the environment in which those genes develop constitutes by far the most important factor in the production of criminal behavior.

I am devoting so much attention to this aspect of the problem of crime in order to dispose as early as possible of the biologistic or hereditarian argument. Whatever there may or may not be in that argument, the fact is that by far the most important

necessary condition in the genesis of crime is the environment—
the social environment.

Many years ago I pointed out that from my standpoint as a
social biologist, habitual crime appeared to me to be a trade or
profession, licitly or illicitly pursued, like any other, in many
cases the only one that was open or possible to those who followed this way of life—socially open, not biologically open.[5]
However, I went on to add that habitual crime was in most, if
not in all, cases an adaptive form of behavior in the struggle of
the individual to survive. While from the social viewpoint such
behavior may be considered undesirable and unallowable, it is
perfectly normal behavior in most cases, in the sense that it
cannot be distinguished from any other *normal* form of adaptive behavior of the organism. I emphasized the idea of nor-
mality because I wished to draw attention to the fact that
behavior called criminal is, from a biological standpoint, as
normal as any other form of adaptive behavior. Crime is, in
most cases, an attempt on the part of the individual to make
himself secure. The security need not be physical, it may be
emotional or both.[6]

If anyone doubts the adaptive value of crime for the habitual
criminal, let him read Robert Allerton's autobiography, *The
Courage of His Convictions*,[7] the most intelligent, articulate,
and humane autobiography of a professional criminal ever
written, a criminal who spent twelve and a half of his thirty-
three years in prison and fully intends to continue in his life of
crime, even though he has to spend a third of his life behind
bars. It is a book that every moralist should read, and every
student of crime should consider the rather awkward questions
it raises.

It is clear that whatever the motivations that lead the individual to achieve security through behavior which his society
calls criminal, it is security in the manner that is acceptable to
himself that he seeks.

I should not like the idea of the search for security to be
accepted in an oversimplified sense as an explanation for all
crime. But as a working hypothesis which may be of practical
service in understanding some of the conditions and motiva-

tions which lead to crime, it is worth considering. The exceptions can, of course, be considered separately.

If it is the society that fails to provide the conditions for security, whatever those conditions may be, then clearly—however oversimplified it may sound—crime can be, if not altogether eliminated, then at least substantially reduced by providing every developing human being with the security-giving satisfactions which are so necessary for healthy development. This may sound very naïve to some people, particularly those who believe that man is born with aggressive hostile drives which, do what you will, will seek expression and often find expression in antisocial criminal behavior. Listen to what the doyen of English psychoanalysts, Dr. Edward Glover, in a book published in 1960 entitled *The Roots of Crime,* has to say on the subject. He writes:

> Expressing . . . more technical discoveries in social terms, we can say that the perfectly normal infant is almost completely egocentric, greedy, dirty, violent in temper, destructive in habit, profoundly sexual in purpose, aggrandizing in attitude, devoid of all but the most primitive reality sense, without conscience or moral feeling, whose attitude to society (as represented by the family) is opportunist, inconsiderate, domineering and sadistic. And when we come to consider the criminal type labeled psychopathic it will be apparent that many of these characteristics can under certain circumstances persist into adult life. In fact, judged by adult social standards the normal baby is for all practical purposes a born criminal.

In a footnote to this revelation Dr. Glover adds, "At the close of this lecture, the lady Chairman and magistrate, Mrs. St. Loe Strachey, remarked: 'But doctor, the dear babies! How could you say such awful things about them?' " [8] Dr. Glover made no comment on Mrs. Strachey's remark, but I will.

I, of course, am completely on the side of Mrs. Strachey and thoroughly disagree with Dr. Glover. Dr. Glover belongs to the school of psychoanalysts who are addicted to mistaking their prejudices for the laws of nature. What the "technical discoveries" may be to which Dr. Glover refers, and upon which, presumably, he bases his description of the human infant, he never tells us. They are, no doubt, the "technical discoveries" proceeding from the method of postulating facts to fit theories. In this way, as psychoanalysts themselves have only too often shown, one can build a perfectly logical system to fit one's rationalizations. Nothing, of course, exceeds like excess. But this is not science. It is the Higher Horoscopy. I challenge anyone to produce a single piece of evidence that would withstand more than a moment's critical examination, which would in the slightest degree lend support to Dr. Glover's astonishing statements. But they are not really as astonishing as all that, for what they represent is a contemporary form of the doctrine of what our Victorian ancestors so charmingly called "innate depravity." [9]

It is a notion akin to that of the "wild beast," the "savage," "the jungle," and the concept of "instinct." This whole system of rationalizations has infected the Western world for more than two millennia, and it goes like this. The state of nature is one of internecine conflict, with beast against beast. Man originates from the beast and carries in his structure the relics of his bestial ancestry. This bestial inheritance expresses itself in aggressive behavior of various kinds, which explains to a large extent juvenile delinquency, crime, war. Like the belief in "instincts," this is all very comforting because it explains everything and relieves the true believer of those feelings of guilt he might otherwise entertain were he to believe that he was responsible for himself to others. The belief serves much the same function as going to church on Sundays serves for many people. On Sundays in church one can fall upon one's knees and receive absolution for one's sins committed during the week; one can then go out and fall upon one's neighbors during the rest of the week and, returning to church on Sunday, repeat the whole cycle again. It is very gratifying to some people, just as the belief in "innate depravity" or "instincts" is to others. Man, the mythmaker, creates his unreal myths as explanations which comfort him in an insecure universe, and proves again and again how much more real the unreal can become than the real. Man, unable to face the crippled image of himself, projects it upon the state of nature. But there are no wild beasts in the state of nature; there are no jungles in the state of nature. If you want to see wild beasts and jungles I can tell you where to look for them: in the towns and cities of the civilized, especially Western, world! There are very few "savages" among nonliterate peoples, but there are millions among so-called civilized peoples. However, we like to think that "we" are "civilized" and that the others are "savages." But it is simply not true, if by civilization we are to understand the conquest of violence by reason and the art of being kind. By such measures, even at the risk of being once more considered softheaded and dewy-eyed, I repeat, with Jean Jacques Rousseau, that large numbers of human beings in the Western world are degenerate as such, compared to the so-called savage, "the noble savage," as he came to be called in the later eighteenth century.

Millions of human beings in Western society have for centuries, nay, millennia, been deprived of their birthright, which is development, and been caused to become very different creatures from what they had it in them to be. And this is the great tragedy, the real evil, that befalls so many human beings, whose misfortune lies in the difference between what they were capable of becoming and what they have in fact been caused to become.

Whatever the causes of crime may be, I think we would be best advised to take the view that their elimination can more effectively be achieved through social means, by social change, than through any other means. If genes are in any cases significantly involved, then what genes can do the appropriately designed social environment can effectively control. Insofar as the education and control of development, of behavior, is concerned, I don't think any other position is possible. Man's principal mode of evolution and adaptation has been through culture, and it is through cultural means alone that he must continue to make those changes that will contribute to his healthy development. And this, of course, holds equally true for any modifications that may be attempted of his genetic constitution.

Such a position does not make us environmentalists, in the

sense that we believe that all man's behavioral traits are environmentally determined, but it does make us culturalists, in the sense that we believe that in whatever ways man's behavioral traits are influenced we can influence those traits to develop in the desired direction by cultural means.

At the present stage of our knowledge and ethical development I think we may safely ignore genetic change and concentrate on the means most likely to secure the desired individual changes, namely, by social change.

Having uttered what I hope will strike everyone as a series of grand platitudes, we may now proceed to a closer examination of the causes of crime and go on to suggest the remedies that may be prescribed.

The motivations that lead individuals to commit crimes are as numerous as the leaves in Vallombrosa. Any attempt to say less would constitute a gross oversimplification. But there are certain conditions underlying such motivations which can, I think, be broadly generalized, at least, as a working hypothesis. These are two. The first is the psychosocial conditions in which human beings develop, and the second is the socioeconomic conditions in which individuals develop. The two groups of conditions in many cases are so closely interrelated that they are virtually indissociable from one another. However, there are numerous cases in which they are not closely interrelated; hence the necessity of dealing with each group separately. The evidence seems to me beyond question that if we could bring these two groups of conditions more closely into harmony with the inborn needs of the person for development, we would achieve a major revolution in the incidence of crime.

A first step in the right direction would be to drop the usage of such terms as "delinquent" and "criminal." Those who engage in behavior termed "delinquent" or "criminal" fall into no specific diagnostic category psychiatrically and do not constitute conditions such as diseases or disorders which themselves require treatment. They are not clinical entities but the names we give to norm-violating behavior, which we then treat with legalistic responses, which are somehow expected to put wrong right.[10] The traditional mode of dealing with the wrongdoer is to commit a socially sanctioned wrong against him, and this will somehow alleviate the situation, if not set things right. This archaic practice is, of course, based on the idea of retributive justice—which is no justice at all. When a society commits a sanctioned wrong, no matter whether it be called justice or by any other name, what it is doing is to sanction wrongdoing in a much more significant manner than any wrongdoer could possibly do by his wrongdoing. If society can kill a man for taking the life of another, surely that provides a model for those who make their own laws? I daresay that public executions made many more murderers than they ever prevented.

Punishment for human error, it seems to me, is itself the greatest of errors, for when human beings err what they are direly in need of is compassion and understanding—not punishment. I think almost everyone will agree that our penal systems have monumentally failed in their attacks on the problem of crime. And there's the rub: If they had *attacked* less and *approached* more with proper compassion the problems with which they were confronted, they would have stood a better chance of understanding them and doing what was required. It was Sir Thomas Noon Talfourd, the English jurist, who many years ago wrote, "Fill the seats of justice with good men, but not so absolute in goodness as to forget what human frailty is." Alas, we have not had many such jurists. On the other hand, we have had far too many who have been much more devoted to the letter of the law than to its spirit, than to the conception of law as love digested through reason, ruminated love.

I am trying to make a complicated subject simple without oversimplifying it. As the libraries of volumes which have been written on it will testify, my effort is foredoomed to failure, but, nothing daunted, let me venture on. Society enjoys its criminals and delinquents, as it calls them. From Socrates, Jesus, Tycho Brahe, Michel Servetus, and innumerable others, scapegoats have served the frustrated and the insecure as objects upon which their accumulated aggressions could, with every social sanction, be expended. The yellow press, which battens on blood, murder and crime, has for long been aware of this need in its readers and panders to it. The publicity given to crime in our public media serves many purposes in addition to that of making fortunes for the owners of the media. The criminal serves as a target for the individual and collective aggressions of the society, but also society often enables the individual to identify himself vicariously with the criminal and, of course, in many cases also with his victim. In any event, the emotional dividends are not inconsiderable. In our own day the so-called juvenile delinquent has become a target for adult aggression, and the mythology about him, fed by mass media, has become a self-fulfilling prophecy. It is a requirement of society that juvenile delinquents exist, for a certain number of young people must fill the niches that adults have created for them. "Whatever is the younger generation coming to?" Parents, teachers, social critics, experts of various kinds, and various other agents, all combine to perpetuate the myth of the juvenile delinquent. In fact, they have invented him.

Norm-violating, bizarre behavior is expected of the young. It is predicted. It is described, condemned, and threatened with punishment—and it should be no surprise that it materializes in the predicted forms!

Just as the Southerner often loves the Negro because the Negro provides him with a readymade scapegoat, a target for one's aggressions, and just as the policeman finds his most meaningful relationships with the lawbreaker, a creature who must exist if the policeman is to exist, so many adults see their relationship to the young, as corrective agents, as discipliners and disapprovers, as policemen of the lowly drives with which they assume the young are endowed.

All young people, at one time or another, exhibit norm-violating behavior. When such behavior violates legal norms, it may come to the attention of the law-enforcement agencies and be characterized as juvenile crime.

Now, what is the meaning of juvenile crime? Why do juveniles commit crimes?

The reasons are many, but principally it is because they have been failed by their society. The society has failed the individuals who become parents, and the parents who have been failed by society in turn fail their children, and the children in turn fail their society and will usually in turn fail their own children, and so the vicious cycle will continue to be perpetuated.

Our society fails large numbers of human beings because it not only fails to understand the nature of man, the nature of human needs, but because more positively it subscribes both covertly and overtly to the most damagingly unsound views concerning human nature and human needs. Those views I have already mentioned, namely, that man is born an aggressive creature and that a certain amount of that aggressiveness will find expression. And that, therefore, in bringing up children we must police and discipline these lowly aggressive drives so that the child grows up into at least the facsimile of a decent human being, that is, someone like his elders.

But whether children are conditioned on the basis of such theories or not, if they are frustrated in their needs for development they are likely to grow up as disorganized, disordered individuals, insecure, unable to relate warmly toward others, and lacking in social feeling.

Man has evolved in a unique way, as the only creature whose principal means of adaptation to the environment is through culture, through the man-made part of the environment. It is an altogether new zone of adaptation which called upon the highest development of certain traits: the increasing supremacy of problem-solving behavior, that is, intelligence, and the concomitant decrease in the power of instinctual drives; the great extension of the dependency period necessary to learn all that one must in order to function as a human being, the very high premium placed upon the mother's ability to minister to the dependent needs of the child, the father's cooperativeness, and the extraordinary importance of maternal love in the socialization of the human being.

The enormous importance of satisfying the dependency needs of the infant cannot be overemphasized, for those needs must be satisfied if the individual is to develop as a healthy human being. And by health I mean the ability to love, the ability to work, and the ability to serve. As Alfred Adler put it in his great and too little known book, *Social Interest: A Challenge to Mankind* (1938):

> The child's inclination to cooperation is challenged from the very first day. The immense importance of the mother in this respect can be clearly recognized. She stands on the threshold of the development of social feeling. The biological heritage of social feeling is entrusted to her charge. She can strengthen or hinder contact by the help she gives the child in little things, in bathing him, in providing all that a helpless infant is in need of. Her relations with the child, her knowledge, and her aptitude are decisive factors. . . . It may readily be accepted that contact with the mother is of the highest importance for the development of human social feeling. . . . *We probably owe to the maternal sense of contact the largest part of human social feeling, and along with it the essential continuance of human civilization.*[11]

It does not have to be the biological mother; a surrogate mother will do. But what the child must have is love for the first half dozen or more years of his life. And to the extent that he is failed in this, the most important of all the needs for human development, the need to be loved and so to grow in the ability to love others, to that extent he will fail to develop as a healthy human being. Whether by neglect or pampering, in whatever manner the failure to meet the needs of the dependent human being has come about, he will suffer and will spend the rest of his life attempting to compensate for his failures of development. He will be hungry for attention, for means of establishing his own worth, for the respect that has been withheld from him, for the gratification of immediate impulses without any concern for the long-term consequences. Not having been loved himself, he will not love others. Not having been trusted, he will not trust others; and having been unsympathetically treated by others, his sympathies will hardly be stirred by others whom he may harm. Life itself may not be highly valued, and it matters not to such individuals whether they or anyone else lives or dies.

Is such a state of mind criminal? I believe not, even though it is the state of mind that readily leads to the commission of acts called criminal. I believe, on the contrary, that such a state of mind is a sickness just as real as any sickness induced by vitamin deficiency and generally more serious in its effects, and I therefore believe that such conditions should be treated as sickness—sicknesses which are best prevented by the proper prophylactic treatment or which can be ameliorated, at least in a sufficient number of cases to make the effort worthwhile, by the proper treatment instituted as early as possible. The failed human being, as he may be called, embarks upon behavior calculated to restore him to those states of being he seeks. It is a kind of homeostatic adaptive behavior, even though it might be antisocial in its effects. Aggressive behavior, for example, is almost invariably a signal of the need for attention. A great deal of so-called delinquent and criminal behavior is of this kind. What it calls for is not the traditional meeting of aggression with counteraggression—which only worsens things—but love. And by love I mean behavior calculated to confer survival benefits upon others in a creatively enlarging manner. The greatest of all crimes committed by society, not listed as a crime at all, is the failure to provide the conditions for the realization of that birthright. The human being is born as a highly organized creature with all his potentialities ready for development under the stimulus of the expected satisfaction of his needs. He is born as a creature oriented in the direction of healthy development. That is what he is born *as*. What he is born *for* is the realization of those potentialities as one who lives as if to live and love were one. Any individual and any society that stands in the way of that development commits the greatest of crimes not only against the individual whose development they obstruct and disorder but against the society of which he is a member; against, indeed, the whole of humanity, for the individual, his fellows, society, and humanity are deprived of the unique qualities that every individual has it within him to develop. In this way not only are great human riches lost to the world, but great and proliferatingly noisome damage is done to the world of humanity and of nature.

The irreverence with which we regard human life is evident from the way in which it is irresponsibly proliferated, so that the most perilous problem with which humanity is today confronted is not the hydrogen bomb but the population bomb. There should, surely, never be a time when any child is conceived unless he can be guaranteed his optimum fulfillment as a human being. We must seriously ask ourselves whether any human being ever has the right to less than the fulfillment of his birthright. To so deprive a human being, even to the least degree, is to dispossess him of his sacred right to development. To secure that right, the right to fulfillment, should be the first duty of a sane and humane society. Hence, the most urgently necessary step in that direction must be the control of conception so that children are permitted to those alone who are capable of discharging their obligations to them. Those obligations will consist principally of giving their children the love and the steadfastness that human beings require for healthy development.

Is this a utopian pipe dream? If enough of us continue to think that it is, it will continue to be so. But if enough of us believe that dreams are the stuff of which reality is made, we, who have achieved so many magnificent conquests, will surely be able to make this exigent conquest of ourselves.

> If there were dreams to sell
> Merry and sad to tell,
> And the crier rung his bell,
> What would you buy?
> —Thomas Lovell Beddoes
> *Dream-Pedlary*

It is for old men to dream dreams and for young men to see visions, visions of the city beautiful, for the only true realists are the visionaries who endeavor to make the world over in the image of their dreams.

We need to revalue the meaning of parenthood and cease confusing it with parentage. The one is an art, the other is the consequence of a physical act. We need to revalue our miscalled educational system and turn our schools into institutes for the training in the art and science of human relations. By these means, I am convinced, we will achieve the most significant advances in the establishment of healthy human beings in a healthy society.

In the overcrowded societies of this world, where the competition for the symbols of success are so strongly emphasized and where the conditions of life under the oppression of which so many millions live constitute urgent pressures to escape from them, it is clear that many will take whatever avenue of escape they can. This is an aspect of the discussion of crime which has been examined by innumerable authorities, and I need not underscore it any further here, except to say that such avenues of escape are perfectly understandable forms of adaptive behavior. When they result in a "smart operator" or a robber baron, we find the achievement not uncommendable. But when the escapist fails, he is condemned as much for failing, if not more so, than for the offense he has committed. For, in fact, the judges appear to believe that there is no offense so blameworthy as the offense of getting caught. This opinion is also shared by those who get caught, as is evidenced by some verses from the pen of a lady who was incarcerated in the Massachusetts Reformatory for Women. The verses begin:

> I'm walking about a prison,
> What do you think I see?
> A lot of dumbells doing time,
> While all the crooks go free.

The disinherited, failed individuals of our civilized societies are caught up in a ruthless struggle for existence in which from the very outset they have so many strikes against them the marvel is that any ever emerge from it without a criminal record. The supreme emphasis placed upon success, especially in the Western world and most particularly in America, success externally validated, principally by money, makes this the basic value of the culture. Hence, whatever means are available leading to the achievement of success are likely to be adopted. It is no accident that virtually all crime rates are greater in the United States than in any other part of the civilized world. The

anomic conditions of such a society were clearly described by
Merton many years ago:

> It is only when a system of cultural values extols, virtually
> above all else, certain *common* symbols of success *for the popula-*
> *tion at large* while its social structure rigorously restricts or com-
> pletely eliminates access to approved modes of acquiring these
> symbols *for a considerable part of the same population,* that anti-
> social behavior ensues on a considerable scale. In other words,
> our egalitarian ideology denies by implication the existence of
> noncompeting groups and individuals in the pursuit of pecuniary
> success. The same body of success-symbols is held to be desirable
> for all. These goals are held to *transcend class lines,* not to be
> bounded by them, yet the actual social organization is such that
> there exist class differentials in the accessibility of these *common*
> success-symbols. Frustration and thwarted aspiration lead to the
> search for avenues of escape from a culturally induced intolerable
> situation; or unrelieved ambition may eventuate in illicit at-
> tempts to acquire the dominant values. The American stress on
> pecuniary success and ambitiousness for all thus invites exag-
> gerated anxieties, hostilities, neuroses, and antisocial behavior.[12]

And as Merton further points out, in such a society "the-
end-justifies-the-means" view of life becomes a principle for
both survival and for something more than mere survival when
the values of that society exalt the end and its organization
limits the possibilities of recourse to the approved means. This,
of course, is what leads to *anomie,* that is, personal and social
disorganization, to normlessness.

Quite clearly, then, allowing for all the multiple causes of
crime and the forms it assumes, if crime is ever to be reduced to
reasonable dimensions, if not entirely eliminated, it is the
disparities that exist in societies between the ends that are held
to be desirable and the means to their achievement that will
have to be reduced. These changes will involve changes in both
ends and means, but principally in means. In short, our efforts
must be directed toward the evolution of conditions in which
every human being will be enabled to achieve the ends of fulfillment as a human being within whatever range of capacities
with which he has been endowed.

Briefly set out, I would suggest these efforts be directed first toward the limitation of the birth of children only to such persons who are able to prove their ability to help children toward fulfillment of their capacities for being human. This implies a drastic program of birth control humanely and intelligently conducted. Second, I would reorganize our whole instructional system as a genuinely educational system, in which training in the theory (the science) and practice (art) of human relations constitutes the core and the basis of the process of learning to grow and develop as a human being. Third, I would abandon all punishment and treat all lawbreakers as persons in need of help, and then give them the indicated assistance, even if that entailed forcing them to remain in a therapeutic institution.

I do not believe that those who commit crimes are as a rule mentally ill. I do think that they are frequently suffering from an expression of the social sickness of which their society is the vector, and hence I strongly feel that it is not so much the criminal who is in need of treatment as his sick society. However, the sick society sees in the criminal a precious victim whom it needs as a scapegoat upon which to project its own sickness and, through the whole apparatus of the penal system, law, and practice, ritually cleanse itself of the sins it has committed. However, too much of a good thing is always too much, so that now that crime has grown to such proportions that it has gotten out of hand, the sick society is readying itself for even greater follies than it has committed in the past. It will pass laws and go through the motions, with the help of the National Rifle Association, of doing something about the indiscriminate sale of arms, it will stiffen penal procedures, it will spend millions of dollars—all to no purpose. For it is not in weapons or their easy availability or in weak laws that crime has its roots, but in the failure to understand what it means to be human. And until that is understood, and we do what is necessary about that understanding, we shall go on committing the greatest of all crimes—the crime against the human spirit.

REFERENCES

1. Robert K. Merton and M. F. Ashley Montagu, "Crime and the Anthropologist." *American Anthropologist,* vol. 42 (July–September, 1940), pp. 384–408.
2. J. Lange, *Crime and Destiny.* Knopf, New York, 1930.
3. Earnest A. Hooton, *Crime and the Man.* Harvard University Press, Cambridge, 1939.
4. Ashley Montagu, *Human Heredity.* World Publishing Co., Cleveland, 1964.
5. Ashley Montagu, "The Biologist Looks at Crime." *Annals of the American Academy of Political and Social Science,* vol. 217 (September, 1941), pp. 46–57.
6. Emile Durkheim, "Crime as Normal Behavior," in his *Rules of Sociological Method.* Free Press, New York, 1950, pp. 67–73.
7. Tony Parker and Robert Allerton, *The Courage of His Convictions.* W. W. Norton, New York, 1962.
8. Edward Glover, *The Roots of Crime.* Imago Publishing Co., London, 1960, p. 8.
9. For the critical examination of these views see Ashley Montagu, *The Direction of Human Development,* Harper & Row, New York, 1955, and the same author's *On Being Human,* 2nd ed., Hawthorn Books, New York, 1967.
10. National Education Association, *Delinquent Behavior,* Washington, D.C., 1959; Milton L. Barron, *The Juvenile in Delinquent Society,* Knopf, New York, 1954; Ashley Weeks, *Youthful Offenders at Highfields,* University of Michigan Press, Ann Arbor, 1958; Isidor Chein *et al., The Road to H,* Basic Books, New York, 1964; David Abrahamsen, *Who Are the Guilty?* Grove Press, New York, 1952; David Abrahamsen, *Crime and the Human Mind,* Columbia University Press, New York, 1960; S. R. Slavson, *Re-Educating the Delinquent,* Harper & Bros., New York, 1954; Nigel Walker, *Crime and Punishment in Britain,* Aldine Publishing Co., Chicago, 1965.
11. Alfred Adler, *Social Interest: A Challenge to Mankind,* Putnam, New York, 1938.
12. Robert K. Merton, "Social Structure and Anomie," *American Sociological Review,* vol. 3 (October, 1938), pp. 672–682.

6. *The long search for euphoria: drug addiction*

The history of drug-taking is almost as old as the story of man. Wherever beset by anxiety, frustration and tension—fear of the gods, fear of enemies, fear of failure in life—some people have sought sanctuary in drugs. For most of them the refuge has turned into a prison or at best an illusion. To scorn these fugitives from reality is to forget that there, but for the force of circumstance, goes any one of us.

Man is a creature of habit, always has been, and could hardly survive from one day to the next if he were not. Many of his habits, like signaling to another driver for a turn, help keep him alive. Some, like saying good morning, are merely pleasing and harmless. Others, like overeating, are harmful but still socially acceptable. And a few, like taking certain drugs, can be shortcuts to eternity.

People become addicted to almost anything, and do. It is when they abandon themselves to a habit that we say they are addicted to it. Smoking, one of the most widespread addictions in the Western world, is made up of a whole complex of habits —motor, gustatory, olfactory, psychological, biochemical, social— all of which contribute to an addiction so compelling that it is surpassed in its driving imperiousness only, if at all, by those other compelling habits, eating and overeating. Food is a necessity, but that is not the reason why most people eat in civilized societies. For the most part, they eat because eating represents a reducer of tensions to which they have become habituated. Eating, in fact, does not constitute a condition of survival—it is food that does. Eating is pleasurable as an act in itself, and pleasure is taken in food as savored by eye and palate, but scarcely ever is food relished in civilized societies for its contribution to survival. Most men in civilized societies would be appalled by the thought that there was nothing to eat but food, or that one might drink only when one was thirsty.

The most habitual of all our habits, eating, in fact constitutes an addiction to which most men are completely enslaved. They therefore overeat. Among alcoholics and other addicts there is a frequent history, as children, of an addiction to candy or soft drinks. Quite frequently habitual overindulgence in candy, ice cream or soft drinks does become an addiction, though such habits are seldom so described. Such addictions are, of course, not as damaging as the true drug addictions nor are they as compelling; they are, however, not infrequently the precursors of later, more serious addictions.

The point I am trying to make is that strong dependence on anything, whether emotional, physiological, or social, is an addiction, and that true addiction is merely an unfortunate special case of a rather universal human tendency to become habituated to some form of support or behavior upon which one then becomes dependent. In true addiction, withdrawal symptoms become evident following abstinence, the symptoms varying with the nature of the practices to which one has become addicted. The psychological dependence upon eating or chewing gum, smoking or biting one's fingernails may be quite as strong, and the withdrawal symptoms upon ceasing the habit may be almost as disturbing as in true drug addiction. It is not easy, in many cases, to distinguish between a psychological craving and a physiological addiction, although there can be little doubt that in the case of the addictive drugs the physiological changes induced operate powerfully to influence the addict's behavior. Physiological changes are not, of course, absent in common habituations or even in relatively uncommon ones, such as addiction to enemas or polysurgery in which the individual seeks to have as many surgical operations as he can manage to secure. The difference is that in these latter kinds of habituations the drive is mainly of psychic origin, whereas in the true drug addictions the drive is mainly physiological, and therefore organically extremely compelling.

If any societies ever existed in which drugs of some sort were not taken, then they belong irrecoverably to the far reaches of prehistory. Every nonliterate society investigated by anthropologists, with the possible exception of subarctic and arctic societies, has utilized drugs in one form or another, largely for their hedonistic effects.

Anthropologically the history of drug-taking is rather more than unusually interesting. Among the nonliterate peoples living at the most undeveloped levels of society, at the food-gathering and hunting stage, the use of drugs seldom leads to serious addiction, although when habit-forming drugs such as tobacco and alcohol are introduced to these peoples, they often develop a strong craving for them. It is among more settled peoples, agriculturalists and pastoralists, that one begins to encounter the use of various plants as anodynes to which one may become addicted.

Among the food-gathering and hunting peoples of Australia, men, women, and children often chewed the leaves of the pitjuri plant (*Duboisia hopwoodii*). The men prepare the leaves in their own way by mixing them with burnt acacia (*Acacia salicina*) ash. The alkali in the ash liberates the alkaloid piturine from the crushed pitjuri leaves when these meet in the presence of the moisture supplied by the aborigine's spittle. Piturine has much the same action as nicotine. The aborigines eagerly testify to the stimulating benefits they derive from chewing pitjuri, as a pick-me-up, especially when they feel off color and tired. Pitjuri chewing, they say, is a comforter which fosters mirthfulness and friendly-fellow feeling.[1] Pitjuri leaves, packed in woven string-bags, were traded for hundreds of miles for spears, boomerangs, and other articles along what came to be known as "pitjuri roads."[2] While pitjuri-chewing aborigines experienced much the same craving for the leaf as smokers do for tobacco, the pitjuri-chewing habit never led to a morbid addiction.

The Bushmen of the Kalahari Desert and the Cape Hottentots used to smoke dagga, the herb *Leonotis leonurus*. This had a markedly intoxicating effect. Because of its injurious consequences, its cultivation and sale is now strictly controlled by the government of South Africa. The Bushmen and Hottentots are now pipe smokers of tobacco, a weed that was introduced to them by Europeans.[3]

In tropical South America coca plants are cultivated and their leaves chewed for their stimulating and narcotic effects. The natives claim that "it satisfies the hungry, gives new strength to the weary, and makes the unhappy one forget his troubles." There are many records of Indians going without food for days while working at the most exhausting tasks and enduring incredible hardships, living on nothing more than coca leaves. No wonder, then, that these people consider the coca leaf a gift of the gods and revere it accordingly. The soothing effects of the cocaine, except when taken in excess, clearly make life a great deal more endurable than it would otherwise be for these Indians.

Peyote or mescal buttons in the form of the infusion derived from them were similarly used throughout Central America and Mexico. During the nineteenth century a North American Indian religious cult developed around the worship of the spheroid top of the peyote button. Many Indians regarded it as the vegetal incarnation of a deity and used it to induce visions as well as to achieve ritual purification.[4]

Mescaline produces no pronounced addiction or withdrawal symptoms. The color visions and transcendent states it is capable of producing have been described not only by Indians but by such experimenters as Havelock Ellis, Aldous Huxley, and Allen Ginsberg.[5] The hallucinations produced by mescaline are quite pleasant and often give rise to a good deal of uncontrollable risibility.

It is a fact worth noting that narcotics and stimulants were much more developed and widely used among the South American Indians than those of North America, and not used at all among the natives of the arctic and subarctic.[6] Perhaps the most celebrated of all drugs, tobacco, the very name of which is derived from the Arawak Indian term for cigar, originated in South America. Members of Columbus' crew observed the natives of Cuba and Hispaniola smoking huge cigars. The Indians declared that the habit removed the fatigue from their limbs, made them sleepy, and lessened their weariness. In 1558 the explorer André Thevet reported that the Indians in the vicinity of what is now Rio de Janeiro, Brazil, stated that tobacco "is very good for loosening and carrying off the superfluous humors of the brain." [7] The rest is history. Carried by Columbus to Europe, tobacco soon became the most popular drug in the world. Its immediate and temporary psychological and physiological benefits are such, and its deleterious effects so long delayed, that its use has spread like a contagion.

Herodotus, some 2,400 years ago, mentioned the use of Indian hemp (hashish) as a drug "smoked" among the Scythians of Asia Minor. Herodotus tells how the men gather the plant *Cannabis indica,* "which bears the strangest produce. When they are met together in companies they throw some of it upon the fire round which they are sitting, and presently, by the mere smell of the fumes which it gives out in burning, they grow drunk, as the Greeks do with wine. More of the fruit is then thrown on the fire, and, their drunkenness increasing, they often jump up and begin to dance and sing. Such is the account which I have heard of this people." [8] The Scythians also used hemp seed to produce the conditions of a vapor bath. As Herodotus described it, "creeping under the felt coverings, [they] throw it upon the red-hot stones; immediately it smokes, and gives out such steam as no Grecian vapor bath can exceed; the Scyths, delighted, shout for joy, and this vapor serves them instead of a water bath." What Herodotus may have been here describing was the custom of ritual purification from the taint of contact with a corpse.

In the Middle East, northern and central Africa, in Asia Minor, in India, and also in Mexico hashish or its cousin, marijuana, is widely smoked in either pipe or cigarette. Hashish is also available as an oil which may be taken orally. Théophile

Gautier, Baudelaire, and Bayard Taylor, among others, have left us glowing accounts of the phantasmagoric effects of hashish.[9] Everything appears in a brilliant light. Every sensation is enriched. One laughs, one feels exhilarated, intoxicated. Again, a gift of the gods to lighten the burden men bear on earth. As for marijuana, some accounts glow, but others simply bore. Its effects depend on the taker, who may feel exhilarated, intoxicated—or nothing. It is not an addicting drug but can be a dangerous one, for experimentation with it may lead the experimenter to narcotics in further search of thrills. Among American troops in Vietnam the smoking of marijuana is widespread (New York *Times*, 26 October 1967).

The intoxicating pepper kava *(Piper methysticum)*, chewed or taken in the form of a beverage and widely used throughout Oceania; the betel-nut chewing (a bit of areca nut, a betel leaf, and some lime) of Malaysia, India, Polynesia, and the east coast of Africa, very similar in its effects to tobacco in having both a stimulating and a soothing effect; the khat tea *(Catha edulis)* of northeast Africa and southwest Arabia, which reduces the need for sleep and produces a feeling of contentment and excitement, like tobacco and alcohol, are all drugs to which men and women, and even children, have become addicted. And there are numerous others.[10]

Opium was first cultivated *(Papaver somniferum)*, undoubtedly for its hedonistic effects as a drug, in Sumer about 4000 B.C. The Sumerian ideogram for opium is HUL.GIL; HUL stood for "joy" or "rejoicing," and GIL for "the plant opium." The meaning is obvious: "The plant that produces delight." From Sumer knowledge of the narcotic qualities of the white poppy spread to Asia Minor, Egypt, and Greece. Homer speaks of "the intoxicating poppy, the poppy saturated with lethal slumber." There is clear evidence of the use of poppy seeds among the Lake Dwellers of Switzerland (2800 B.C.).[11] In the Middle East the uses of the white poppy established themselves very widely, and the knowledge of it was carried from Persia (Iran) by Arabs to India and China. Contrary to a widespread belief, the fact is that opium-smoking did not begin in China until the seventeenth century; up to that time it had been used in China exclusively as a remedy for dysentery. Owing to the demoralizing effects, opium-smoking was forbidden by the Emperor Yung Ching in 1729, but the prohibition had little effect. In Turkey and Persia the preferred way of consuming opium was to eat it.

The most eloquent of opium-eaters, Thomas de Quincey, in his *Confessions of an English Opium-Eater,* 1822, has left us a remarkable account of the effects of opium upon the addict. De Quincey took his opium in the form of laudanum. Said to have been invented by Paracelsus (1490–1541), laudanum is opium tinctured with alcohol. In this form it is taken in "drops," and was widely used throughout Europe as an anodyne for pain. It was as a remedy for toothache that de Quincey first became acquainted with the drug. Having obtained the drug and arrived at his lodging, de Quincey wrote:

> It may be supposed that I lost not a moment in taking the quantity prescribed. I was necessarily ignorant of the whole art and mystery of opium-taking; and what I took I took under every disadvantage. But I took it; and in an hour, O heavens! what a revulsion! what a resurrection, from its lowest depths, of the inner spirit! what an apocalypse of the world within me! That my pains had vanished was now a trifle in my eyes; this negative effect was swallowed up in the immensity of those positive effects which had opened before me, in the abyss of divine enjoyment thus suddenly revealed. Here was a panacea, a *pharmakon nepenthes* for all human woes; here was the secret of happiness, about which philosophers had disputed for so many ages, at once discovered; happiness might now be bought for a penny, and carried in the waistcoat-pocket; portable ecstasies might be had corked up in a pint-bottle; and peace of mind could be sent down by the mail.[12]

And he concludes another rhapsody with the words, "Thou only givest these gifts to man; and thou hast the keys of Paradise, oh, just, subtle, and mighty opium!" [13]

De Quincey's book is credited with launching many a reader on the road to addiction.

Another distinguished English opium-eater was Samuel Taylor Coleridge. Writing to his brother in April 1798 he says, "Laudanum gave me repose, not sleep; but you, I believe, know how divine that repose is, what a spot of enchantment, a green spot of fountain and flowers and trees in the very heart of a waste of sands!" That haunting poem, *Kubla Khan,* one of the most beautiful in the English language, was written by Coleridge in 1798 under the influence of opium. John Livingston Lowes has explored the crowded chambers of Coleridge's vision in a memorable book.[14] There can be little doubt that the marvelously phantasmagoric imagery of *Kubla Khan* was not unrelated to the effects of opium. Coleridge is known to have experimented with several other drugs. The addiction to laudanum (four or five ounces a day) later became the "accursed habit," "this wretched vice," "a species of madness . . . a derangement, an utter impotence of the *volition,*" the cause of his "blighted utility," the waster of his talents, and of the "barbarous neglect" of his family. In a letter to a friend dated 19 September 1809, Coleridge wrote, "The practice of taking opium is dreadfully spread. Throughout Lancashire and Yorkshire it is the common Dram of the lower orders of People—in the small town of Thorpe the Druggist informed me, that he commonly sold on market days two or three Pound of opium, and a Gallon of Laudanum—all among the labouring Classes. Surely, this demands legislative interference." [15] For about the same period it is reported that "in a district of Manchester, three pharmacists sold not less than 41 liters [10 gallons] of *tincture opii crocata.*" [16]

Voltaire's phrase defining religion as "the opiate of the masses" suggests how widespread the opium habit had become among "the lower orders of People" of Europe. There can be little doubt that it was a habit encouraged by the upper to keep the lower orders of people somewhat happier in their misery. The trade in opium for the French and particularly the British had been very lucrative. The greater quantity of the opium introduced into Europe as well as into China came from British India. At the conclusion of the first Opium War (1839–1842) the English forced on China the continuation of the trade in opium, a trade which the Chinese had declared illegal. In the second Opium War (1856–1858) the English and the French further consolidated their gains at the expense of the Chinese, literally forcing millions of Chinese into moral and physical degradation. It was not until 1906 that the decision was reached to order compulsory limitation of the cultivation of the poppy in China and to make clandestine cultivation subject to the heaviest penalties. It was only then that the English import from India officially stopped.

Opium-smoking found its way into the United States by way of San Francisco soon after the Civil War. Prior to the war it had been confined to the Chinese community. The consumption of opium was virtually uncontrolled in the United States until the passage of the Harrison Anti-Narcotic Act in 1914, though some effort had previously been ineffectually made to limit its importation by the imposition of a heavy tax. The figures on the amount of opium imported annually into the United States indicate that the consumption of opium had spread widely.[17] While for a time opium-smoking by Americans followed the Oriental practices, it soon changed its character when it found its way into the underworld. It then began to lose much of its mystical significance and appeal and assumed, in popular opinion, the dimensions of a menace.

Several other factors contributed to the growth of drug addiction in the United States. In 1806 Friedrich Wilhelm Sertürner had discovered morphine, and in 1853 the hypodermic syringe or needle had been invented. This was first used by its inventor, C. G. Pravaz of Lyons, for the injection of iron perchloride into an artery for the relief of an aneurysm, and by Alexander Wood of Edinburgh, independently, for the subcutaneous injection of morphine.[18] The hypodermic use of morphine spread rapidly, especially among the armed forces in the Civil War, indeed to such an extent that morphinism became known as the "army disease." This problem continued unabated after the war and resulted in many chronic addicts. It had, however, one beneficial result in that it served to awaken medical men to the dangers of indiscriminate use of the hypodermic needle. But it was not till the beginning of the present century that the medical texts began to warn the practitioner of the need for caution.

In 1898 diacetylmorphin, or heroin, a derivative of morphine, was first produced in Germany. At first the drug was lauded as "a safe preparation free from addiction-forming properties," but with experience the harmful effects of heroin were noted and its use restricted to physicians. It is at this point that heroin slipped into the hands of the underworld, where it has remained to this day. The underworld found heroin-sniffing cheaper, more convenient, more adaptable to many conditions, and easily concealed from friends, public, and authorities.

In heroin addiction, euphoric states are experienced during the first weeks, but after that the addict achieves only brief periods of comfort or none at all. When abstinence symptoms begin to appear he reaches for the drug again, at any cost, to himself or anyone else. Hesse quotes a heroin addict as saying, "In contrast to hashish heroin produces cowardice, impertinence, and immodesty. Its direct effect is sleepiness and total indifference. Lately I have injected it into my veins only—not much, but not less than 0.5 g. When I had more, I injected more, up to 4–5 g. daily. I would not hesitate to risk my life to get hold of one single dose. After getting used to the drug, I felt repulsion and repugnance against women." [19] The effect of heroin is to produce a moral dementia. The end is a complete physical breakdown.

The history of heroin addiction in the United States shows a pattern of dips and one upswing. From 1914 to the mid-forties there was a distinct downward movement. This was due to the passage of the Harrison Act in 1914 and the Supreme Court's interpretation of this law in the 1920s, as a result of which addicted persons were cut off from legal supplies of narcotics. During the Second World War there was a complete cessation of heroin imports. After the war there was a perceptible upsurge. Shipping lanes opened everywhere, and the racketeers moved back into the field of trafficking as a major criminal enterprise.

Although drug addiction is decreasing in the United States— about 1 in 4,000 persons is addicted today compared with about 1 out of 400 persons in 1915—it is increasing as a business. Three hundred and fifty million dollars are spent annually by addicts for supplies at the street level.[20] The circuitous method of shipping heroin to the United States no doubt is one factor. Opium produced in Turkey for medical purposes finds its way to the illicit market where it is smuggled into Syria and Lebanon and processed into a morphine base. This is smuggled to France, where it is transformed into heroin in clandestine laboratories. According to former Narcotics Commissioner Harry J. Anslinger, heroin is becoming widespread in the Far East. He estimates that Hong Kong's heroin addicts number about 150,000; that is, 1 out of every 15 inhabitants of Hong Kong is a heroin addict. Hong Kong is believed to be the biggest consumer market for narcotics in the Far East. A government white paper states that "drug addiction is one of Hong Kong's greatest social and economic problems."

Stanley Karnow, *Time* bureau chief in Hong Kong, states: "Unlike American junkies, who 'mainline' with hypodermic needles, Asian addicts use more elementary devices. They 'chase the dragon' by heating heroin granules on tinfoil, inhaling the fumes through a straw or a bamboo tube. Breathing in heroin through a matchbox is called 'playing the harmonica.' . . . An emaciated factory worker recently explained that he allotted $26 of his $42 monthly salary for heroin. Why? He tapped his chest: 'It relieves my pain.' How did he eat? 'When I chase the dragon I'm not hungry.' "[21]

In Western societies addiction to barbiturates and amphetamines has greatly increased in recent years. The barbiturate addict becomes sluggish and confused, memory and judgment are impaired, and delusions and hallucinations, and even suicidal tendencies, may develop. The amphetamines include such drugs as benzedrine and dexedrine, as well as others. These drugs are medically used to stimulate the nervous system, elevate blood pressure, and reduce appetite. They are also available in combination with barbiturates as "purple hearts." Like all stimulants, the amphetamines are also depressants, and when their stimulant effect wears off, or even before, they may produce extreme depression, aggressiveness, and ill temper.

The amphetamine addict is not usually content with the normal prescription of 25 mg. a day, but may take more than

ten times that amount. The result of such doses is wild excitement and irritability, impulsiveness, and disorientation. The
amphetamine addict tends to develop hallucinations and delusions of persecution, but these end effects do not worry him;
what he enjoys are the "kicks" he derives from his addiction.
Like most addicts, his dependence on drugs is usually due to
some inherent defect of personality which disables him from
meeting the normal stresses and strains of everyday living in a
responsible manner.

Surveying mankind "from China to Peru," it becomes very
evident that the tensions incident to daily living almost everywhere drive men to seek some sort of flight from their weari-
some company. Life as a food-gathering hunter in some cases
provides its own relief from such tensions, but even at this level
of social development most people seek some relief from the
stress of life. At more sedentary stages of socioeconomic development, greater tensions may accumulate, and tension reducing drugs tend to be increasingly cultivated for consumption.
Among urban dwellers, who so constantly suffer the anomic
reminders of hope deferred and success unachieved, the tendency to resort to anodynes of various sorts is increased. The
most widely distributed and, fortunately, among the most harmless of these anodynes is alcohol. Alcohol, taken in moderation,
is not only harmless but beneficial.[22] We need not dwell on it
any further here.

Accumulating tensions, it is known, unfavorably affect the
functioning of the neurohumoral system of the body.

The neurohumoral system consists of the interacting nervous
and endocrine glandular systems. Exhaustion of this system by
stress, strain, or tension leads to depression of vital activities,
breakdown, illness, and often enough death. It is, therefore, not
surprising that under such conditions men have sought relief—
whether in the jungles of South America or in the urbanized
ones of North America—from the dark and sordid oppressions
of this world by resorting to anodynes that are the illusory keys
to Paradise. Some seek the obliviating effects of drugs which will
remove them if only for a little while from the reverses and
disappointments of the struggle for life; others seek their

exhilarating effects, while still others seek to experience the enchanting visions they have heard are produced by drugs.

The realities of life, good and bad, are not that easily trifled with. Psychologically and physiologically, drugs do a temporary and wholly illusory job on the individual's damaged ability to meet the challenges of his environment. But in so doing drugs cause increasing psychological and physiological havoc. They are sadly self-defeating. The repairs, therefore, have to be done with greater frequency, until that time arrives when there is nothing left to repair and the whole structure collapses. Among the South American Indian coca-chewers, these things are fully understood. The Indians refer to the addicts as *coqueros*—"living corpses." Drugs are the keys not to Paradise but to the gates of Hell.

In our own time we have witnessed a completely new development in the use of drugs. For some younger people they have become a way of life. Among boys and girls of high-school and college age there has been an alarming rise in the resort to such drugs as marijuana, LSD (lysergic acid diethylamide), DMT (dimethyl tryptamine), "68" or "sex juice," and most recent of all a new megahallucinogen, STP, an atropinelike drug. The letters STP are said to stem from a motor fuel additive named "scientifically treated petroleum." The use of this drug appears to have commenced on a wide scale in California about May 1967.

Marijuana is not addictive, but potentially harmful because it may serve as the introduction to experimentation with more dangerous drugs. When smoked by unstable personalities, there is evidence that it can be very disordering indeed. LSD is extremely dangerous because, in addition to producing severe disorientation and profoundly disorganizing disturbances in mental function, it also produces damage to the transmitters of heredity, the chromosomes. Research has shown that when administered to rats in early pregnancy LSD has produced gross malformations in the offspring.[24] Examination of the chromosomes of LSD users has revealed a bizarre series of abnormalties.[25] Furthermore, there is now considerable evidence that the

99]

damage done to both mind and chromosomes may be long-enduring and in some cases permanent.

A "trip" with LSD lasts from eight to twelve hours; a "trip" with DMT about two hours; one with "68," three to four hours, initiated by violent epileptic seizures. A "trip" with the super-hallucinogen STP lasts three to four days, during which the "tripper" is really "turned on." STP produces mania, excitement, extreme disorientation, dilated pupils, rapid pulse, dry mouth, blurred vision, and respiratory difficulties. In mid-June 1967 upwards of 5,000 capsules of STP were distributed free at a mass meeting of "hippies" in San Francisco. One of the great dangers of STP is that it may be combined with chlorpromazine, which LSD users often take after a "trip" to calm themselves down. Chlorpromazine accentuates the effect of STP, and the combined effect of the two drugs can be fatal. Already many STP users have been hospitalized, but despite the known dangers of the drug its use is likely to spread, for there are only too many immature young people who feel that the simplest way to solve their problems is the easiest way—by "tuning in, turning on, and dropping out." This is, of course, no solution at all; it is an irresponsible evasion of the problem—a sick response to the stresses of a sick society.

REFERENCES

1. Herbert Basedow, *The Australian Aboriginal*. Adelaide, F. W. Preece & Sons, 1925, p. 156.
2. Baldwin Spencer, *Wanderings in Wild Australia*, vol. 1. London, Macmillan, 1928, p. 159; T. Harvey Johnston and J. Burton Cleland, "The History of the Aboriginal Narcotic, Pituri," *Oceania*, vol. 4 (1933), pp. 201–223, 268–284.
3. Isaac Schapera, *The Khoisan Peoples of South Africa*. London, Routledge, 1930, p. 101, p. 241.
4. LaBarre, Weston, *The Peyote Cult*. Yale University Publications in Anthropology, No. 19, 1938.
5. See David Ebin, ed., *The Drug Experience*. New York, Orion Press, 1961, for a collection of firsthand accounts.
6. Harold E. Driver, *Indians of North America*. Chicago, University of Chicago Press, 1961, pp. 87–104.
7. André Thevet, *France antarctique*. Antwerp, 1558.

8. Herodotus, *The History of Herodotus.* London, The Nonesuch Press, 1935, Book I, p. 201; Book IV, p. 75.
9. See Reference 5.
10. Erich Hesse, *Narcotics and Drug Addiction.* New York, Philosophical Library, 1946.
11. Ferdinand Keller, *The Lake Dwellings of Switzerland, and Other Parts of Europe.* London, 1866.
12. Thomas de Quincey, *The Confessions of an English Opium-Eater,* Part II. London, 1822. Nonesuch Edition, p. 786.
13. *Ibid.,* p. 801.
14. John Livingston Lowes, *The Road to Xanadu.* Boston and New York, Houghton Mifflin Co., 1927.
15. Samuel Taylor Coleridge, *Select Poetry and Prose.* London, Nonesuch Press, 1933.
16. See Reference 10, p. 27.
17. "Organized Crime and Illicit Traffic in Narcotics," Report of the Committee on Government Operations, United States Senate, 4 March 1965.
18. Barbara M. Duncan, *The Development of Inhalation Anaesthesia.* London, Oxford University Press, 1947, pp. 76–78.
19. See Reference 10, p. 57.
20. See Reference 17.
21. Cable from Stanley Karnow, 16 April 1963.
22. Morris E. Chafetz, *Liquor: The Servant of Man.* Boston, Little Brown & Co., 1965.
23. See Reference 10, p. 59.
24. George J. Alexander *et al.,* "LSD: Injection Early in Pregnancy Produces Abnormalities in Offspring of Rats." *Science,* vol. 157 (1967), pp. 459–460.
25. Samuel Irwin and Jose Egcozcue, "Chromosomal Abnormalities in Leukocytes from LSD-25 Users." *Science,* vol. 157 (1967), pp. 312–314; J. Thomas Untergleider, "The Dangers of LSD." *Journal of the American Medical Association,* vol. 197 (1966), pp. 109–112 (389–392); Robert Auerbach and James A. Rugowski, "Lysergic Acid Diethylamide: Effect on Embryos." *Science,* vol. 157 (1967), pp. 1325–1326; Doris H. Milman, "An Untoward Reaction to Accidental Ingestion of LSD in a 5-Year-Old Girl." *Journal of the American Medical Association,* vol. 201 (1967), pp. 821–824; Hans Zellweger, J. S. McDonald, and Gisela Abbo, "Is Lysergic-Acid Diethylamide a Teratogen?" *The Lancet,* vol. 2 (1967), pp. 1066–1068; R. G. Smart and K. Bateman, "Unfavorable Reactions to Lysergic Acid Diethylamide (LSD): Review of the Available Case Reports," *Canadian Medical Association Journal,* vol. 97 (1967), pp. 1214–1221.
26. "The Drug Scene: Dependence Grows," The New York *Times,* Jan. 8–12, 1968.

7. *Social change and human change*

An embarrassment of clichés would, perhaps, be the fairest description of what most people conceive to be the nature of human nature. Such stereotypes as "You can't change human nature," "It is only human nature," and that we shall always have with us wars, juvenile delinquents, murderers, politicians, poverty, and pornography, because it is in the nature of the beast, are only too banally familiar.

All these disorders, and many others, are taken to be expressions of human nature. But they are not. They are expressions of a learned, an acquired nature. And, indeed, it were better not to speak of nature in this connection in order to avoid any possible confusion between genuinely natural phenomena and artifactual learned or acquired behavior.

The only thing natural for man as a behaving human being is to be unnatural. It is because of his ability to be unnatural that man has been able to make the natural do his bidding, to put a noose around the natural and draw it to himself. Man is human because he has transcended the natural in himself and in his environment; because he has made himself and he has made the human environment, and in large part remade the natural environment. Man is human because he has moved into a wholly new zone of adaptation, the dimension of the man-made part of the environment, the extrasomatic environment of communication through symboling, that is to say, *culture*.

Beyond all other creatures man is the creature who adapts to his environment entirely through learned, that is cultural, responses. The "entirely" here does not, of course, refer to such complex responses as respiration, food and liquid intake and the other basic responses without the satisfaction of which the organism could not survive. But even these basic needs are in many fundamental ways affected both in their expression and satisfaction by cultural pressures.

Whatever a human being comes to know and do as a human being he must learn from other human beings. Man is, as a result of his peculiar and unique mode of evolution, the most plastic, the most malleable, and the most educable of all creatures. If one were to settle upon the one trait which beyond all others distinguishes man from everything else in the world, it is man's educability.

Having been abandoned by the trees, man's forest-dwelling ancestors were forced to adapt themselves to a life on the savannas, the open plains. This entailed the transition from a herbivorous to an omnivorous diet and to hunting instead of merely food-gathering. Hunting puts a high positive selection pressure upon problem-solving abilities and a negative selection pressure upon unthinking automatic reactions. Success in the hunt is impeded by instinct and advanced by quick thinking, by intelligence, that is, by the ability to make the appropriate response to the particular challenge of the environment.

In response to such challenges man's genetic system gradually changed in a feedback relation to the cultural demands. The cultural challenges, having produced changes by selection in the genetic constitution (the genotype), were in turn challenged by the carriers of the new gene combinations, so that as cultural advances were made in this way there was a continuing selective pressure exerted upon the genotype, resulting in further genetic change.

It is only in recent years that this feedback relation between culture and genotype has come to be recognized.[1] What this means is that man's social behavior has played a fundamental, *the* fundamental, role in the evolution of man as a human being and as a physical organism. That is to say, even man's peculiar physical traits have been significantly influenced in their evolution to their present form by cultural factors.

What, in brief, the selective pressures that have been operative in the evolution of man have produced is a creature who can learn to live in any environment in which it is possible to live. There is only one creature on this earth that can do that, and that is man. This extraordinary creature, unique in the history of our world, prospers best in environments in which he is challenged to acquire, to learn his *responses,* rather than to react to those challenges with fixed and inappropriate *reactions.* What a world of meaning lies in those statements for all who have anything to do with the education, the making, of human beings! A matter to which we shall return.

In all animals genes determine potentialities and the limits of their possible development. The realization and ultimate expression of those potentialities are to a large extent determined by the environment. In no animal is that anywhere nearly as true as it is in man. Thus heredity is the result of the interaction between the genetically determined potentialities and the environmental stimulations which those genic potentialities undergo. Genic potentialities for being human are not enough to make a behaving human being; for *that* the behaving human environment, actively provided by other human beings, is necessary.

Hence, no matter what the normal limits of the genically determined potentialities may be, given those potentialities for being human, the most important and indispensably necessary condition for the development of human behavior is the socializing human environment provided by human socializers. Without one or more such socializers there can be no social human beings. As Aristotle remarked more than 2,000 years ago, "The nature of man is not what he is born as, but what he is born for." And what man is born for is the realization of his potentialities in adaptation to whatever environments in which he finds himself. And with a genetic constitution that enables him to adapt himself to every possible environment, he is abundantly able to do that—*provided he is adequately taught.*

As an instinctless creature man comes into the world naked and with a cry, and just as his body is clothed or not according to the customs prevailing in the culture in which he is born, so his potentialities are tailored into the required behaviors according to the patterns of culture prevailing in his particular segment of society. Man is custom-made. The product of the cultural patterning or organization of his raw potentialities constitutes human nature, and that human nature will vary according to the cultures in which it has been conditioned.

That being so, and since cultural or social change occurs in all societies, changes in human societies will be reflected by changes in human nature. The record of man's history abundantly testifies to that fact. Indeed, changes in human nature must always depend upon social changes. Human change *is* social change. These quite elementary, simple, and verifiable statements are fundamental. They at once provide us with the surgent hope and the constructive foundations for a creative approach to the making of human beings.

I have said that man is the creature who prospers best when he is challenged to acquire, to learn and develop his responses rather than to react with stereotyped and inappropriate behaviors. And what a challenge those words should constitute to every educator! Intelligence, the ability to make the most appropriate response to any particular challenge, the supreme problem-solving ability, has been a vitally important factor in the evolution of man. It is an ability as vitally important today as it ever was—if anything, even more important. And it is as vitally necessary for the healthy functioning of the organism today—indeed, even more vital than it ever was. And yet our so-called educational systems specialize in training students in an incapacity to think, in the absorption of large quantities of facts learned, for the most part uncritically, and regurgitated upon certain ceremonial occasions known as examinations. Such individuals go through life regurgitating stereotypes under the impression that they are engaged in thinking. We pride ourselves on the fact that we can make machines that think like human beings and overlook the fact that we have long been making millions of human beings who think like machines.

Lack of skill in thinking can be lethal. A stereotype regurgitator has become a servo-mechanism, a starting device for initiating automatic reactions. Such starting devices are now proliferating at a disastrously accelerating rate and threaten the continuing quality of humanity as never before. Through thinking soundly man changes for the better. By thinking unsoundly or not at all man changes for the worse. And it must always be remembered that by virtue of his educability man is capable of learning not only more sound things but also more unsound things than any other creature, and that the result of this is not intelligence but confusion. So that social change may be sound so that human change shall be sound, the primary requirement is teaching the young how to think critically, originally, imaginatively, and daringly.

In the nuclear scientific age we need to teach children to understand why it is that nuclear science is far too important to leave to the nuclear scientists; and why, indeed, all science is too important to leave to scientists; that science is not enough; that science must be controlled by humanity, just as humanity must, in a feedback relation, be in continuous reciprocal interaction with science, for the mutual enrichment of both and of mankind.

The best guarantee of advancing social change is the ability to think; and by the ability to think I mean the ability to think soundly. The future, no less, of the world depends upon our ability to teach the young how to think soundly from their earliest beginnings.

Indispensably necessary as the ability to think is, it is not sufficient; for man is not alone a thinking creature, he is also a feeling creature. And just as he has to be taught to think, so, too, he has to be taught how to feel. The potentialities are there, but they require education; and by education I mean *educare,* to nourish and to cause to grow, those potentialities for being able to relate oneself warmly, lovingly, and creatively toward others. This group of potentialities, the capacity to love, is developed in precisely the same way as are one's other social capacities, by learning. And one learns to love in only one way: by being loved.

The growth and development of the ability to love has played a major role in the evolution of the human species. With the loss of instincts and the increasing dependency upon others for learning how to be human to which this loss led, a deepening of involvement—as a capacity and an ability—in the welfare of the dependent child became a trait of correspondingly increasing survival value.

I have repeatedly urged that in view of the evolutionary facts and what we have learned of the nature of human development our educational institutions, to be worthy of the name, must become institutes for the training in the science and art of human relations. That all else must be regarded as secondary to this, and that the three R's must come to be regarded as secondary skills in the service of the primary of all skills, the art of creative interaction with others. Toward this end I conceive the educator's function to be that of one who joins learning to loving-kindness in himself and in his pupils. There is nothing in the innate nature of man which constitutes in any sense a barrier toward the achievement of this end. On the other hand, innate nature has an orientation and a directiveness which seeks realization in just that way. And nature is so malleable, so plastic, so educable a thing, that it can be adjusted to any kind of social change considered desirable.

REFERENCES

1. Ashley Montagu, ed., *Culture and the Evolution of Man*. New York, Oxford University Press, 1962; Ashley Montagu, ed., *Culture: Man's Adaptive Dimension*. New York, Oxford University Press, 1968; Ashley Montagu, *The Human Revolution*. New York, Bantam Books, 1967.

8. *The current values and changing needs of youth*

The world has moved so rapidly during the last fifty years, and values have been so much shaken up, it has become for many people a problem beyond their capacity either to solve or adjust to. And being rather more than less comfortable in them they tend to cling to their conformities with a strength which is generally inversely proportional to the weakness of their position, and which varies in opposition to new ideas and social change as the square of the distance from their comprehension of what is in fact going on and what is in reality required. This is rather a formidable psychosis for an enlightened adult to be faced with and an even more difficult one for a teenager. There is, of course, a teenage problem, but that problem is not the teenager but the adult. The teenager's problem is the adult's confusion and lack of understanding. Many adults behave as if they expected the adolescent to embrace adult values and to live by them quite early in life. When the adolescent declines to do so and embarks upon his own exploration of the new world in which he hopes to discover himself, his experiments and attempts at self-realization are condemned and deplored. Adults expect teenagers to be better than themselves, not understanding that adolescents cannot and should not live as adults do.

Teenager a Scapegoat

The only cure for adolescence is maturity, and that takes time. Every group which is unsure of itself requires a scapegoat, and the teenager has become the scapegoat of the adult world. Upon the teenagers adults frequently project their own weaknesses, and then censure the objects of their projection for exhibiting them. They then go on to predict the consequences of the teenagers' disregard and flouting of adults' expectations of them, and in this manner, in a sort of self-fulfilling prophecy, they produce the very behavior they specify and expect.

Teenage behavior, unlike adult behavior, is somehow conceived to constitute a threat to adult life. The implicit assumption is that teenagers constitute a social problem, one which must be dealt with before it gets out of hand, and that therefore considerable attention must be concentrated on the minutiae of teenage attitudes and behavior. Once the facts are codified, it is felt, that teenage "bizarre" behavior becomes less threatening and, hopefully, more manageable.

Families Fail Youth

Such attitudes are absurd, but they are much worse than absurd because, as Voltaire put it, those who believe in absurdities will be capable of committing atrocities, and adults, alas, are perpetually committing atrocities against the young. Hence, the necessity of understanding that it is not so much the young, teenagers, adolescents, or by whatever name we call them, as adults and adult behavior that requires the focus of our attention if the adolescent is to mature in an undeformed, untraumatized, healthy environment. Standing between two worlds—the experience of childhood and the uncertainties of the prospective condition of adulthood—the adolescent only too often finds himself isolated from both worlds, finding solace and support only among those of his own age group but for the rest failed by his environment. Too often the teenager appears to be a sort of sequestrum not *in* but *on* the family, which the family, not knowing how to deal with, attempts to throw off like some foreign body, either by closing him out in the varieties of ways parents and others are able to do or by abandoning him to the school. Unfortunately, in too many schools conditions are often not much better than they are at home, as anyone will know who has experienced such schools actually or vicariously by reading such a report as Edgar Friedenberg's "The Modern High School: A Profile" in his excellent book *The Dignity of Youth and Other Atavisms*.[1]

The adolescent is, for the most part, denied civil rights so that the restraints and petty restrictions to which he is subjected often are exercised with the peculiar license that those who consider themselves above the law so frequently enjoy. Such injudicious exercises of authority are likely to engender little respect for regulations or the justice of the regulators. In such homes and schools adolescents have the feeling that they are in custody, and quite normally they react to such custodial control by attempting to break out of it. This, in the adult world, constitutes a punishable offense. The only thing that militant authority can think to do in a mutiny is to repress it. What a splendid thing it would be if those who hand down the tablets of the law would understand that simply because they were incised on marble and are repeated and pronounced with solemnity, they are not necessarily sound, and that one should be grateful to those who from time to time cause us to hang question marks on the things we take most for granted and who induce us to question our first principles.

Rebellion Shows Independence

Rebellion and defiance are the marks of independent spirits, but some adults prefer surrender and obedience as evidence that progress has been made. But this is not progress; it is defeat. Youngsters who have been so defeated seldom ever really grow up. Their defeat has been calamitously damaging to them. They have yielded to and settled for the requirements of their discipliners. The character structure of the Germans represents a good example of the consequences of such lack of rebelliousness and defiance of parental authority by children. The fear and respect (*Ehrfurcht*) which is demanded by the father, the obsessional sense of duty (*Pflicht*) which seems to serve the German as a substitute for what elsewhere develops as conscience, the command of the father observed as inflexible law, the unquestioning obedience expected of children and inferiors, the discipline and regulation, the lack of freedom, the enforced passivity of the child—these are the factors in the socialization process of the German child that made so many millions of Nazis possible, and will, it is to be feared—unless the German family is thoroughly democratized—make the reappearance of some neo-Nazi or other form of human disaster in Germany merely a matter of time. For a fuller discussion of this subject reference may be made to Bertram Schaffner's *Father Land*,[2] and David Rodnick's *Postwar Germans*.[3]

Few greater disasters can befall a human being than to be obstructed and halted in the need and the striving to grow, to grow in integrity and as an interdependent dependent spirit. Those who have the courage to test themselves by declining to be mere echoes of their elders' voices, who have the spirit to rebel and to strike out originally on the way they make for themselves, hope that their challenges will be met with sympathy and understanding, for this is what they deserve. When understood as they should be, the so-called rebelliousness, the defiance, the insubordination, will be seen for what they are: acts of integrity, the effort to move forward in growth toward independence. While making reasonable demands upon the artificers of such acts of integrity, evidences of the desire to grow, every encouragement should be given the entrepreneurs.

Revolt Not Revolting

When it is understood for what it is, adolescent rebellion need no longer cause adults to feel threatened. With anxieties relieved they can then begin to elaborate the techniques and skills which will enable them to meet the challenges of the younger generation creatively and with wisdom. The adolescent revolt is revolting only to those who do not understand it. For those who do it is seen to be a perfectly healthy and most necessary expression of a sensitively responsive growing and developing being, a vitally active creature enthusiastically engaged in an adventuresome creative interrogation in the process of becoming what he is striving to be.

Neither prudence nor piety is a deity to cultivate in youth. As Robert Louis Stevenson put it, "A full, busy youth is your only prelude to a self-contained and independent age; and the muff inevitably develops into the bore. There are not many Doctor Johnsons, to set forth upon their first romantic voyage at sixty-four. If we wish to scale Mont Blanc or visit a thieves' kitchen in the East End, to go down in a diving dress or up in a balloon, we must be about it while we are still young. It will not do to delay until we are clogged with prudence and limping with rheumatism, and people begin to ask us: 'What does Gravity out of bed?' Youth is the time to go flashing from one end of the world to the other both in mind and body; to try the manners of different nations; to hear the chimes at midnight; to see the sunrise in town and country; to be converted at a revival; to circumnavigate the metaphysics, write halting verses, run a mile to see a fire, and wait all day long in the theatre to applaud Hernani." [4]

Forcing Adult Values

In America the pressure to make the child adopt adult values as soon as possible begins even before adolescence, American parents finding it especially amusing to dress their children in clothes which are in no way distinguishable from those of adults at as early an age as possible and to encourage them to indulge in adult patterns of behavior as early as possible. Thus, children who have not yet reached their teens are encouraged to date, the boys to take corsages to their dates, and so unhappily on. Adolescents tend to be the more admired the more they resemble adults in every respect. As a consequence of such pressures, not too subtly applied, the whole period of childhood and adolescence tends to be foreshortened, telescoped, and compressed into a relatively short period, so that child and adolescent do not, frequently, enjoy the opportunity to grow and develop at their own rates, in a steplike process, from childhood through adolescence to maturity. The young tend, only too often, to be rushed through these stages at a rate which exceeds the speed limit of development with resulting irreversible damage to the machinery. This is the chief reason, I suspect, why there are so many technical adults about us who are really no more than arrested children and retarded adolescents, for they have never enjoyed the freedom to mature from one phase of development into the other. It is a necessary condition of maturation that the individual must grow and develop into behavioral statuses and roles. Such complexly developed roles cannot be assigned to anyone, except on the most superficial and unrealistic of levels. Such roles must be earned.

What makes things so much worse is that, while pushing children toward the adoption of adult values and conduct, adults are at the same time making it only too evident to children that they are still children who must attend to the catch-words of their elders simply because the latter are no longer as young as they once were. It all makes for the sorriest of confusions.

World a Textbook?

If the passage of time is the cure of adolescence, the adolescent has himself been rendered impatient by the pressures to achieve adulthood that have been applied to him. He would like the cure to be immediate, although there are happy evidences that many adolescents are beginning to enjoy their teenageism and are learning to postpone the promise of immediate satisfactions for long-term gains. "Just why," asks a seventeen-year-old girl, "just why is everything being made to go faster and faster? You have to have this math bit by the time you're five. That's funny. And this great shift to stuffing people with education early so that by the time you get to college you see this world as a big, vast . . . textbook!" (*Newsweek,* 21 March 1966, p. 70).

That, I think, is a very telling criticism. The world is *not* a big, vast textbook. Yet this is often how the young are conditioned to look at it in school. What could be more unrealistic than the formalistic, uncritical manner in which so much teaching is conducted in the schools? I shall never forget reading the complaint, many years ago, of a bright-eyed Italian "problem kid" in a Brooklyn trade school. One day he had to be kept in after class, and this is what he said to his teacher:

My whole seven drives is to fly like on the wings of an angel. It must feel great to be up in the stars.

So what happens? They shove me into this dump and gimmie coveralls. Now I'm a putter-upper and taker-downer. And I'm in the X class. The mystery class. They tell me in public school I can be anything I want to. So I'm in the X class.

You read a hundred of these dry books in school. You know less than before. They wanna learn us, don't they? So why don't they give us the right kind of books, huh? Like "The Ancient Mariner." Honest, teach', that book stinks. It's falling apart. They're too old or something. Ain't there no new books? Some new kind? . . . What kind? I don't know. Something real. About facts, like. About life.

Now don't think I'm talking about myself. I'm a lug. I know it. But teach', why? I wasn't born like that, was I? What made me that way, huh? Take my old lady, for instance. She works like a horse. But some other ladies on my block go to the country. You should see what them sourpusses look like. And my old man, he says he's gonna drop dead any day now. But he ain't so old; he's about forty. Now why? You know Goldstein? He's got you in the sixth period. He says to me: "How ya expect to have brains if ya eat spaghetti?" He's a dog, that bonehead. What's he eat? Gefulte fish. But anyway, if there's so much to eat in the stores, why can't we get some of it? Why we gotta eat spaghetti all the time? Huh? Romeo, that dumb gorilla. You don't know him. He used to be my pal. I meet him in the street, he tells me he joined up with the army. What for? My uncle joined up and he got a brass plate in his head.

You see what I mean? Everything's shot to hell, like. And we gotta read "The Ancient Mariner."

They're trying to make a dope of us around here.

Ain't this a school? Ain't they supposed to learn you the truth around here? So why they keep us guessing all the time, huh? The teachers mark you wrong on your paper but they don't tell you what's right.

It's haunted, this place. They're always talking about school spirit. I never seen it. All I know—I take a lotta guff for eight periods.[5]

School Role Needs Rethinking

And there is much else, to the same effect. This was more than a quarter of a century ago, but it still goes on. Where was, and where is, the help for these bright-eyed children who have been so failed by their elders? If it is not to be the school, as I think it should be, where else are they to look to for help? Traditional conceptions of the function of the school have long been outmoded. The notion that school is the factory in which one acquires a competence in the three R's is still widespread among us, even though there have been rumors abroad that elsewhere in the world school is also regarded as an important agent in the formation of character. The truth is that today more than ever it is necessary to reconsider the role of the school in helping young people to meet the challenges of the world in which they are going to live. This will necessitate not merely instruction in the three R's but the revaluation of the purposes of education and the assumption by the school of the role of the therapist in repairing damage done to the student's psyche and in assisting him to achieve the mental health he would otherwise be in danger of losing. The school counselor constituted a first recognition that something this way needed to be done. But the school counselor, as every school counselor must recognize, is a mere palliative. Every teacher must play the role of a counselor if he is to fulfill his task as a teacher—not merely as an instructor who imparts knowledge and skills but as an educator who is engaged in the most important of all social services in bringing out the latent talents and uniqueness of the student and of preparing him for the most important skill, the skill of human relations. And this is done by edu-*caring*, which is the root meaning of the word from which *education* is derived—*educare*, to nourish and to cause to grow; and this can be achieved only if the educator cares. It seems to me that current values in so-called education have for a considerable time been failing to meet the changing needs of youth, by adhering to an antiquated conception of the meaning and purposes of education and by failing to revalue its values in adaptation to the substantive social changes that have taken place during the last fifty years.

The school should be the place in which youth is enabled to take full advantage of its educability, as the challenging environment in which each human being, seen as a creative part of an interconnected network of human relationships, is beyond all else assisted to develop all those qualities of humanity, in the application of which the skills and techniques he acquires in school will be designed to serve.

Must Set Selves in Order

The abstract inconsideration of good intentions is not enough, nor is the ritual making of recurrent unilluminating genuflections at annual meetings sufficient, nor is the obsessive inadvertence with which we continue to compound the errors of our predecessors, which practical men call experience and others the name they give to their mistakes. What is required is, among other things, the recognition that before we can mean much to anyone else we must first mean something to ourselves; that setting oneself in order is the principal basis for practicing good human relations; that it is personal influence that determines the size of a life, not words or even deeds; and that, therefore, as the unacknowledged legislator of the world that he is, the educator stands in a critical position in relation to the making of humanity. For it is through his personal influence that he can act upon the world of youth to make the world of man what it ought to be. What we need to do is to remove the burden of our focus of attention on youth and transfer some of it to ourselves, for if we would make order in others we must first set our own houses in order. It is important for educators to realize that theirs is a magnificent responsibility, a responsibility that begins with remaking oneself as one ought to be in order that one may discharge the responsibility of being to others what we may help them in their own unique way to become.

Youth Needs Guidance

The world is in a parlous state, and the condition of youth is, if anything, more rather than less stressful than it used to be. While it is true that stress is life, youth needs to be given some guidance in the matter of meeting stress. It requires no assistance whatever in the multiplication of unnecessary stresses, usually produced by misguided and misunderstanding adults. It may be folly to expect adults to do what they may reasonably be expected to do, and as everyone should know, when everything has been said and done, more will have been said than done, but is it too much to expect that some adults will take a good look at themselves and reexamine the foundations of their attitudes in the midst of which they sit pat as in so many citadels of solidified infallibility? The disenchantments of age constitute no sort of preparation for dealing with the illusions of youth. In the best circles, I am told, it is no longer believed that youth is an offense or a malady, although it is not considered culpable to act as if it were so. It would be unfair to blame all educators for being short on ideas. Ideas are an affair of the mind, and there are too many educators who tend to distrust the mind in education, who favor the conservative approach. Conservatism, in essence, rests on doubt in human nature. It distrusts improvement, clings to traditional institutions and prefers the past to the future. Such persons tend to see youth through the distorting glass of the doctrine of innate depravity, instincts, and drives which cause the teenager to behave in the trying ways in which he sometimes does. Seeing the world according to the kingdom that is within them, they recreate it in their own image in the young in the forcing house they call the school. In that disaster area known as California their supporters appoint Dr. Max Rafferty Commissioner of Education and elsewhere in the land the nearest available individual with a doctorate in the Lower Phrenology, that is, Physical Education, is appointed a school principal or school superintendent. Not that I regard the Lower Phrenology as unimportant. Developing the proper bumps on one's biceps, good habits of physical exercise early established, are greatly to be encouraged. I am all for physical education. But I do not believe that the kind of training that leads to a diploma in that subject is an adequate preparation for an educator and still less for a position of leadership in education. What *is* needed is training in the art and science of human relations.

I have spent so much time discussing the educator because I strongly believe that if youth is to find its proper place in today's society and that of the future, it will largely be the doing of those educators who have the vision to see that they are themselves a part of the problem they are trying to solve. And they must ask themselves whether they are going to continue to be part of the problem or whether they are going to make themselves part of the solution.

"Teenager" Is Belittling

Having said so much with reference to the educator let me now return to the teenager. One of the first things we need to do is to get rid of the term "Teenager." It has developed a sort of pejorative meaning, so that it has become an *opprobriquet,* if I may be allowed to coin a word, a term of opprobrium. What we need to develop is a new respect for youth, and not continue to treat young people as so many of us do as if they were isolates, segregates, belonging to a so-called "inferior race." In short, we need to cultivate the view in everyone, and particularly in youth, that youth is an especially blessed period of life, and to make it so. In the "Ballad of Middle Age" Andrew Lang wrote,

> Our youth began with tears and sighs,
> With seeking what we could not find;
> We sought and knew not what we sought;
> We marvel, now we look behind:
> Life's more amusing than we thought.

Our task should be to take the unnecessary tears and sighs, the directionlessness and unknowingness out of the experience of youth, and render it as conscious and unfloundering as is reasonably possible. I don't by any means wish to be understood as desiring the computerizing of youth, or featherbedding it, but I do mean that if we could help youth to understand more clearly its own nature and the nature of the world in which it is living, that we would in this way be helping it to perceive more steadfastly the direction in which it should itself travel. I don't mean to take frustration, and tears and sighs, and trial and error out of the life of youth, but I do mean that it would be highly desirable to reduce them to reasonable proportions, and not, with the best of intentions maximize them unnecessarily.

Youth Questions

The adolescent asks himself a thousand and one questions. "What sort of a person am I?" "Are my thoughts and feelings similar to those of other people or am I quite different?" "Am I better or worse than other people?" "Would people want me if they knew what I was really like or would they reject me?" "What sort of people are my parents?" "How do they compare with other children's parents?" "What do my friends think about me?" "What do I think about my friends?" "What sort of person do I wish to be?" and so endlessly on.

This interrogation of himself and of his environment should be made as fruitful as possible, a creative interrogation, and not what it so frequently becomes, a traumatic and unsatisfying delayed reaction to the eventual movement into technical adulthood. In comparing himself with others the adolescent tends to focus on externals, on good looks, appearance, physical attractiveness, clothes, possessions, in short, external validations of his worthiness. And this, of course, is in keeping with the supreme values at the altar of which most of his elders worship. It is here precisely that the great job of repair work is called for. For it is here that we have the immediate opportunity of teaching youth that it is not external values that matter so much as internal ones, and that the external values are valueless unless they are supported by the internal ones. The eternal values of love, integrity, courage, the ability to think clearly and soundly so that one may know what knowledge is for, and the necessary skills, techniques, and knowledge which will enable one to realize oneself through one's fellow men more fully.

If one could but see the necessity of being adolescent during adolescence as a healthy part of development and help the adolescent to be so, great strides would be made. By thinking about the thinkable and doing what requires to be done with understanding and with compassion, no problem is insoluble— not even that of the adult who has missed out on his own adolescence. By his uncomprehendingness the adult has forced youth into an autonomous culture of its own in which there is little profitable communication between the two cultures. It will take a great deal of hard thinking, revaluing of values, and hard work if this situation is to be remedied. That it can be done, I have no doubt. That it will be done will depend upon the number of people who are willing to take this problem seriously.

REFERENCES

1. Edgar Friedenberg, *The Dignity of Youth and Other Atavisms*. Beacon Press, Boston, 1965.
2. Bertram Schaffner, *Father Land*. Columbia University Press, New York, 1948.
3. David Rodnick, *Postwar Germans*. Yale University Press, New Haven, 1948.
4. Robert Louis Stevenson, "Crabbed Youth and Age," in *Virginibus Puerisque*. Chatto & Windus, London, 1902, pp. 96–97.
5. Hyde Partnow, "For Crying Out Loud." *Direction*, vol. 3 (1940), pp. 8–9.

9. *Has chastity a chance at college?*

Our young women, especially those in college, appear to have almost completely achieved the noble goal of "emancipation." They exercise the right to choose their clothes, friends, cars, and college curricula; they may now aspire to careers almost as various as men. But the very scope of their emancipation may contain a tragic flaw: The young women of America may be losing the right to say no.

Certainly many college girls, who may be both bright and beautiful, prefer to abstain from sexual intimacies before marriage and succeed in doing so. Indeed, the abstainers may even be a majority. Yet there are massive social pressures, applied not just by ardent young men but by a host of cultural forces, to participate to the full in premarital sex experience. The right to chastity appears to be in jeopardy.

As one college dean has said, "The pressure of the football weekend is simple and direct: the young man manages to convey the idea that if sex is not part of the package, the young woman will not be invited back." Meanwhile a substantial number of motion pictures and much of the modern literature and art which college students are expected to examine chronicle a marvelously diverse parade of extramarital sex.

The concern over morals on the campus has both college

authorities and parents quaking in a clammy grip. Impulses on what to do about it range from making an all-out effort to reimpose and reinforce traditional standards of morality with steely strictness at one extreme, to capitulating to the highly vocal young men and women who claim that chastity is passé at the other.

Both extremes are clearly unacceptable. The first is unworkable—unless the automobile is removed from American culture and sons and daughters are chained to radiators in separate dormitories. The second would quickly be found undesirable even by young people themselves; they would discover that free love is often not freedom at all and carries with it new bonds and burdens. The girl who believes that sex experience will make her into "a woman" often ends up as a sexually proficient but panicked little girl. The Sweetheart of Sigma Chi becomes the Plaything of Fraternity Row, and sex is reduced to a meaningless sport.

At the same time, the extremely sensitive and groping young people at our colleges are justifiably unwilling to wander indefinitely in a sort of amoral wasteland between the two conflicting sets of values now at work. So there is an essential need, which must be met, for a new code of sexual responsibility in America. I believe that most college women, from the avowedly promiscuous to the adamantly virginal, would welcome such a code. They are talking so much about sex these days mainly because they are seeking help. They seek it from each other: "Should I?" "Do you?" "What do you think is right?" They seek it from their parents, most of whom, however, have been too reticent, confused, or afraid to state convictions of their own in this direction. And they seek it from their college administrations even while they rant against them.

How rapidly is the rate of premarital intimacy increasing? How typical are the talkative coeds of their college generation? How much sex talk on campuses is just plain bravado—glib verbal embroidery based on little actual experience? Precise answers to these questions would be most helpful, of course, in working toward redefinition of sex standards that are both moral and tenable. But in all honesty, there are no exact answers. No one claims to have studied a national cross-section sample of today's college youth on this subject, as compared with studies of twenty or thirty years ago. Nor is it possible to determine whether the statements casually given by students to interviewers accurately describe the students' behavior. When Kinsey conducted his extensive studies of American sexual behavior in the 1940s, he knew that personal statements about sex could not be taken at face value. Some people are too shy to say what actually happened; others fulsomely describe escapades that never occurred. So Kinsey and his associates built numerous cross checks—trick questions—into their question-naires to help catch and eliminate inconsistencies and exaggera-tions. Current interviewers have not attempted so carefully to separate behavior from bravado.

Nevertheless, in the plethora of open sex talk on campuses today, in the earnest though sometimes exhibitionistic responses to interviewers' questions, and in the ferment of debate over dormitory visiting rules and the like, we find what is genuinely new in the college sex situation today—and the clue to its real meaning.

To deal first with the actual behavioral situation: It is cer-tainly clear, from all published studies, that the breakaway from traditional sex morality has been going on for several decades in America. Most authorities trace the beginning of this "sexual revolution" at least to World War I. There is evidence that the past half century has witnessed an increasing incidence of premarital sex relationships among all classes of young people, including college students. (The same studies, it should be pointed out, have also revealed that the extent of premarital sex has been lower among college youth, age for age, than among noncollege youth). When Kinsey did his research, he discovered that most men in the United States, and perhaps half the women, have sexual relations before marriage. It would not be surprising, therefore, if this long-term trend in American society has continued during the past twenty years and if more college boys and girls have premarital experience today than a generation ago. But the important thing to recognize is that the recent changes have not been nearly as great as all the talk and

fragmentary interviews may suggest. This is not the first generation of college youth to find the traditional standard of chastity
before marriage wanting.

But where the previous college generations seemed satisfied
to confront and perhaps disregard the traditional standard
privately, this generation seems almost anxious to affect the
confrontation in open bull sessions, the larger the better! In
this way they are perhaps being more candid and forthright
than their elders, and though their candor may not be to our
tastes, we should recognize that it has its positive aspects.

For one thing, it is part of a very healthy process which has in
every generation engaged some of youth's special talents—the
intensive scrutiny of adult life as it is and as they themselves
will experience it shortly. The agonizing preappraisal delves
into many aspects of social life and challenges some of our most
cherished values, including our *stated* values in regard to sex.
And today's young people are quite smart enough to perceive
that there is a yawning gap between our professed creed and the
sexual behavior many of us exhibit.

They divine, to be blunt, that they have been the recipients
of the most hypocritical, contradictory and confused view of
sex it would be possible to imagine that a society could offer.
The orthodoxy is that sex is a private and sacred relationship—
yet it is blatantly displayed on billboards across the length and
breadth of the land to merchandise everything from automobiles to underwear. The orthodoxy says sex is to be reserved
for one special spouse—but we manage to convey to our eleven-
and twelve-year-olds that the time has indeed arrived when they
must wiggle sensuously into the race. The orthodoxy says sex
has to do only with love—but it also has to do with money,
power, status and your future way of life. (How many mothers
have sent their daughters fly-casting with the admonition: "It's
just as easy to fall in love with a millionaire as with a pauper"?)
And, of course, the old chestnut which worked wonders (or did
it?) for many generations of college girls—"nice girls don't"—
soon becomes converted when tested in the actual crucible of
life, to the Radcliffe junior's bitter contention that, alas, "nice
girls do."

It appears, therefore, that the youngsters, rather than simply rebelling against the traditional standards, have discovered that the code, *as applied in American life,* offers precious little guidance to follow. Their boisterous sex talk can be seen as a brash but genuine effort to establish new guides for themselves by direct confrontation of much that the older generation preferred to avoid. This quest for meaningful values deserves understanding rather than denunciation, even if the language of the discussion is not ours.

Unquestionably, however, the open sex talk of today's college generation does have its morbid consequences. By the sheer pressure of words from their voluble contemporaries, boys and girls are being forced, not strictly by their own needs or desires but by the campus society in which they live, to indulge in behavior which they may not welcome or be ready for. This is perhaps but a continuation of the peer-group pressures which, at an earlier age, propel our children into Little League, the Girl Scouts, bouffant hairdos and rock and roll. But at the college level, it occurs in the context of a far more significant activity.

It is by no means a healthy situation—and this has nothing whatever to do with whether a particular boy and girl actually engage in premarital intercourse. It is unhealthy because, in the name of freedom, boys and girls are actually being robbed of their freedom of choice. The decision is not theirs, freely made for reasons which seem (and may even be) good and sufficient. The decision is made by the group, and the pressures to conform may be overwhelming, not just during the "football weekend" but in almost any automobile on a spring or autumn night. In lieu of an experience in responsible decision-making (which at least might have some maturing effects), our youngsters often find their behavior shaped by shoddy rationalizations, like the pseudo-Freudian argument that all repression is unhealthy, which represent the very antithesis of free choice.

In defense of the collegians, it must be pointed out that the pressures to conform in sexual behavior are only partly of their own making, for here too the adult world still plays a considerable role. Indeed, the ardent physical pressures applied by a young man in a car may be easier for a college girl to deflect than the psychological pressures exerted by her parents at a distance. A mother may be substantially, though unconsciously, contributing to the loss of her daughter's virginity, even while demanding that college authorities protect her from losing it. One college president I know cites the case of a sorority house in which by midyear at least half of the senior residents were pinned. The other seniors in the house, he said, began to panic —worried on the one hand, apparently, about the narrow spectrum of job possibilities open to them as liberal arts graduates and on the other about becoming objects of embarrassment in their own homes. "Their mothers, don't you forget it," the president said with some heat, "are born matchmakers and constantly needle their girls with such questions as 'Whom have you been out with lately?' And their fathers, without quite saying so, may often convey the idea that daughters in graduate school are not only an expense but a disappointment. Such a man wants to be the father of the bride, not of a Ph.D. candidate, and the girl is painfully aware of this." In one such sorority house, through combined peer-group and parental pressures, he said, sixteen out of eighteen seniors were pinned by the time of graduation.

What has this to do with chastity? A great deal—because the European pattern of sexual intimacies following the engagement is now one of the principal ways in which American collegians have been trying to resolve the moral conflict presented them. Nor are the social pressures, direct or oblique, applied only to the girls. A study was made not long ago of the male college students without experience in sexual intercourse. When asked if anyone had ever discussed their sexual behavior with them or indicated approval of their virginity, these young men said they had received no compliments, no approval, no support from the adults around them, and furthermore they felt there was much more prestige connected with having experienced premarital intercourse than abstaining from it. When fathers tell their college sons, "If you can't be good, be careful," it often carries the clear implication that there is more manhood and sophistication in virility than chastity.

In an effort to cope with this problem, colleges have promulgated a creative, if not always effective, array of regulations to govern heterosexual relations among students. At Oberlin, according to one student, "The closest thing a boy and girl can have to privacy is a bicycle built for two." This may be an exaggeration, but the faculty did turn down a request by student leaders that "honor sections" be established in dormitories where young women could be in company with young men without supervision during certain hours. The episode is fairly typical of the student cry for what has become known as "semi-private social space," and of college authorities' reluctance to grant it.

At Columbia, after much deliberation, a new rule became effective in 1963 under which coeds are allowed to visit men's dormitories—for the first time in the 209-year history of the institution. But the portcullis between the sexes was not raised very far: visiting hours under the rule are only from 2 to 5 P.M. on *alternate* Sundays. And dorm room doors must not be closed. A university authority interpreted this requirement by suggesting that doors remain open "a space comparable to the width of a book." He did not specify what kind of a book, so matchbooks quickly became the norm.

As if observing all this from across the continent, Reed College in Portland, Oregon, now carries a few quiet lines in its Parents' Information Sheet as follows: "Men may entertain women and women may entertain men during certain visiting hours each day, unless a living group has decided among themselves to restrict these hours. There is no rule about keeping doors open or other similar devices to keep young people from unacceptable behavior. Such regulations are relatively ineffective. Rather, we state quite clearly (in agreement with the Student Council) that promiscuity is unacceptable on campus."

Nor do all restrictions emanate only from college administrators. One Eastern girls' college two years ago decided that upperclassmen should be given maximum responsibility and therefore permitted them to stay out all night if they chose. But there has been much student dissatisfaction with the rule, I gather, because it deprived the girls of a considerable protec-

127]

tion beyond their own conscience and stamina. And at another school for women, the students asked that a liberal new 2:30 A.M. curfew be moved back to 1:30 A.M. The local night clubs closed at 1:00 A.M., and many of the girls evidently felt their mental and physical endurance was inadequate to protect their honor in a parked car for ninety minutes.

Viewed in aggregate, there is much variety in college rules dealing with morality—from punitive regulations to careful neutrality. So, to a degree, parents of collegians can pay their money and take their choice. But I think it can be safely generalized, as Margaret Mead has said in part, that most college rules are defined not so much to protect the students from immoral behavior as to protect college executives and faculty from attack by their more conservative supporters and alumni. I am convinced that this need not be the case, that many—indeed, most—parents would welcome colleges frankly confronting the problem of sex on the campus with more attention to providing students with authentic information and thoughtful guidance on the meaning of sex in the total context of life and less attention to such nonsense as slightly open doors. The latter demeans both the students and the college administrators and accomplishes nothing.

Fortunately, the picture is not all bleak. Many colleges, even those with strict boy-girl rules, are offering more and more information and guidance on sexual behavior. Oberlin, for example, in 1964 initiated a series of three lectures for students, using guest speakers of distinction—the first lecture on the biology of sex, the second on its psychological aspects, and the third on sex ethics. Vassar continues its sensitive and useful "sex panels" for freshmen, designed to provide both facts and advice by answering *all* questions submitted anonymously in writing. Barnard (the women's college of Columbia) holds informal discussion groups in dormitories at which deans and other college spokesmen including the president talk with—and listen to—the students. Duke University, as scores of other colleges now do, provides general information and guidance on sex in the context of family life and marriage preparation courses. In addition it offers special seminars for "pinned

:ouples"—those planning to be married shortly. And the student organization at Princeton, not waiting for the college administration to act, offers a series of ten lectures dealing broadly with sex, utilizing university professors and other authorities as speakers.

I do not mean to imply that in these courses or lectures professors or deans are preaching a "new morality," an explicitly permissive code of sex behavior. On the contrary, because they know young people and can speak with compassion, their emphasis is on giving chastity more than a fighting chance and helping to relieve some of the pressures on the students themselves. Thus they help place sex in a wholesome, even reverent, context; in addition, by imparting needed basic sex facts, they doubtless help straighten out twisted attitudes with which many young people enter college.

It is intriguing, and certainly gratifying, that much of the leadership in sex education today is being exercised by religious groups. The National Council of Churches, for example, through its Family Life Department, has done much to foster sex education classes and counseling in both churches and colleges. The council, of course, makes no compromises in its support of premarital chastity. At the same time it recognizes the church's responsibility in helping young people to make traditional morality useful for them, and it advises forgiveness and help, not puritanical punishment, for young people who have strayed.

While collegians certainly do need moral guidelines, as the gentle but authoritative voice of Millicent McIntosh points out, they will only scorn restrictions they believe to be punitive. And Miss McIntosh, who retired in 1963 as the president of Barnard, thinks it is the college's job to give positive, sympathetic guidance: "We should expect—and the students have a right to expect—colleges to represent the best our society knows about what makes a good personality and a good marriage. This is a responsibility college administrators cannot avoid. But by saying that you are going to throw students out if they don't meet these standards infallibly, you spike your guns ahead of time." In short, if the message is simply disciplinary, the stu-

dents aren't listening, or if they are, their reaction is hostile, so
receptive communication is never established through which
genuine guidance can take place.

On what moral platform can such guidance be given? Dr
Lester Kirkendall, professor of family life education at Oregon
State College, early in 1964, offered in the professional journal of
college deans, some most incisive comments on this: "With the
collapse of the negative fear-evoking deterrents, the older social
controls must be replaced with individual internalized control
which will stabilize family life and promote personal fulfillment even in the midst of conflict and change. This means that
our sex standards must have a foundation in loyalty and devotion to some loved one, based on a high-commitment relationship."

The phrases "internalized controls" and "high commitment"
are crucial here: As sexual freedom has increased over the past
four decades despite the continued lip service to traditional
morality and the shrill persistence of strict college rules, such
external controls obviously do not work. Only controls based
on carefully cultivated moral standards in the hearts and minds
of the individual stand a chance: internalized controls. And
these must emerge from a sense of self-respect and respect for
others in which the gift of sex is not given or taken lightly, but
only when there is a true sharing of commitments to one another. Such a sharing has been traditionally expressed in our
culture by the vows of marriage, founded on mutual protection,
growth, permanence and responsibility.

This is possible—the development of a new code of sexual
responsibility along such lines. Anthropologists have gathered
substantial evidence to indicate that while men develop conflicting impulses within them which can be labeled "good" or
"evil" according to almost any moral yardstick, their cooperative, other-person-respecting impulses tend to predominate if
given the opportunity. The respect for the right (and the right-
ness) of a girl—or a boy—to abstain from sexual intimacies can
be reestablished, I firmly believe. Colleges alone cannot do this,
but colleges along with parents, churches, the mass media and the
young people themselves can again build belief in the practi-

ality, as well as the virtue, of responsibility and restraint before marriage.

When the sound beginnings of such a code are evolved, unmarried young men and women will begin to have an enormously useful and reassuring way of arriving at sensible decisions about sex instead of having little but erotic arousal and physical opportunism to guide them.

But this is not possible unless, as Miss McIntosh suggests, there is authentic two-way communication between parents, faculty and college administrations on one hand and students on the other. While parents must approach the problems their children face with sympathy, communication will also be advanced if the younger generation comes to realize that the confusion of values about sex is not something for which their parents are totally to blame. Surely the adults who grew up between the two world wars confronted many critical problems and inherited deep moral dilemmas which were not of their own making either and with which they grappled, perhaps, as best they could.

Thus the situation calls for a high degree of mutual understanding and cooperation between the generations in which the emphasis is not so much on the problem of sexual passion as on the need for mutual compassion—respect of one generation for the other; respect of one sex for the other.

Parents would do well to recognize also that sex education, and the cultivation of judgment on sex, is not something that can be taken up all of a sudden and disposed of neatly at college, like a course in calculus or Greek literature. Orientation lectures, panels and discussion groups can be increasingly helpful but cannot replace the need for providing basic sex information and molding wholesome sex attitudes in the home. In recent decades, parents have progressed considerably in giving frank and appropriate answers to the inevitable questions of children on sex biology. Now they must be courageous enough to move on to what has become an even more embarrassing sphere—the question of sex *ethics*. Parents who fear their children (and there are many) will hesitate to be explicit on the

subject. Others will find that their "old-fashioned" ideas don'
sound too "shocking" when expressed.

This is easier said than done, to be sure. But it can be accom
plished, and without relying solely on the blunt "Don't." It car
be based on three premises: First, sex is a healthy force and it
discussion and expression should be kept healthy and no
driven underground. We may not want promiscuous sons anc
daughters, but we also do not want their approach to sex to be
so stunted and warped that they can never know its glories
Second, like any strong natural force, sex must be channelec
and disciplined in its enjoyment. It is in the nature of being
young to push new experience to its limits. But with sex, as witl
automobiles, going too far, too fast, too soon can be disastrousl
destructive. And third, as a divine gift for the expression o:
love, sexual intimacy should not be debased by behavior tha
can make a man and woman feel unloving about each other o
unhappy about themselves. In marriage, sexual fulfillment ca
grow to become a source of continuing mutual strength; before
marriage, it can become merely a lottery of impulse.

Chastity *must* have a chance. Sex is too good to squander

10. *The quest for self*

In his Gifford Lectures of 1929, *The Quest For Certainty*, John Dewey wrote,

> The time will come when it will be found passing strange that we of this age should take so much pains to control by every means at command the formation of ideals of physical things, even those most remote from human concern, and yet are content with haphazard beliefs about the qualities of objects that regulate our deepest interests; that we are scrupulous as to methods of forming ideas of natural objects, and either dogmatic or else driven by immediate conditions in framing those about values. There is, by implication, if not explicitly, a prevalent notion that values are already well known and that all which is lacking is the will to cultivate them in the order of their worth. In fact, the most profound lack is not the will to act upon goods already known but the will to know what they are.[1]

It does seem to me that things are not very much better than when Dewey uttered those words so long ago. The will to know what the basic values are seems, sometimes, even less of a human concern than making oneself comfortable with the world of things. Things today are even more in the saddle and ride mankind than they were when Emerson commented on the fact, while the supreme value, life itself as lived and realized through the self, has become confused, irresolute. This *is* the Age of

Anxiety, of Uncertainty, of Violence, to which the words of
Matthew Arnold, in "Dover Beach," seem, if not precisely to
describe the facts, at least to define the contemporary mood:

> Ah, love, let us be true
> To one another! for the world, which seems
> To lie before us like a land of dreams,
> So various, so beautiful, so new,
> Hath really neither joy, nor love, nor light,
> Nor certitude, nor peace, nor help for pain:
> And we are here as on a darkling plain
> Swept with confused alarms of struggle and flight,
> Where ignorant armies clash by night.

The mood expressed in these words of Arnold, indeed, reflects
the condition of contemporary man, as well as anyone has
ever described it. But sad as the human condition is in our time
and seriously disordering as it is, it is far from irreversible or
hopeless. Indeed, as a student of the origin and evolution of
man and his behaviors, I believe that his present condition was
clearly predictable from those complex developments which
followed the urban revolution some 10,000 years ago and which
have proceeded even more complexly at an ever accelerating
rate down to our own time.

What went wrong? The answer to that question is simple.
What went wrong was the growth and development of the conception of man as a creature who exists in order to enjoy the
maximal physical comforts with which he can provide himself
during his temporary sojourn on this otherwise comfortless
earth—the view of man and his life so well and irreverently expressed by that distinguished American Fred Allen: "You only
live once, but if you live it right, once is enough."

In the Western world the quest for self has for several millennia assumed the form of an introverted aggrandizement of
the self, a self-centeredness in which the individual becomes the
greater part of the whole and the remainder of the human
world exists largely to minister to his needs.

Without the least doubt the worst offender in the perpetua-
tion of this diseased version of the self is the Western family.

The Western family is an organization for the training of each of its members in self-centeredness and the production of a high frequency of mental illness; and for the inculcation, by systematic training, in the individual of aspirations which end with self, the focus of attention upon the individual's realizing himself not in relation to others but in realizing the satisfactions of what his family and his culture tell him are his needs. It is not generally recognized that the Christian family of the Western world, consisting of mother, father and their children, a self-contained unit, atomized and dissociated from other similar units, is an aberration. In other sections of the world of man people live together as members of extended families or families that are interrelated with other families, socially and by no means necessarily genetically. Emphasis is placed on the quality of human relationships, rather than on the quantity of external validations of "success" that one can learn to acquire. When one is brought up in a socially interrelated group, one develops a self and a conscience which seek expression through the group and with involvement in the group. When one is socialized within a family psychologically isolated from other families, in which parental attention is concentrated upon a more or less rigorous conditioning of the child in what is expected of him by others and what he has a right in turn to expect from them, such a child will emerge as an individualist who will tend to regard the rest of the world as his oyster.

Something of the factors involved and the effects they produce in two different culture areas has been perceptively stated by Felix Greene in his book *The Wall Has Two Sides.* He writes:

The Chinese developed their society for four thousand years uninfluenced by Western concepts and behavior patterns. Is it possible that the highly separate individualist consciousness . . . has never had to evolve here? In other words, that the consciousness of *I* being separate from *you* is not so sharp there as it is with us? *Me* and *not-me* tend to merge into the collective *we.* . . . The Chinese have long been aware that personal rivalry and personal protectiveness both lead to individual alienation. The

Chinese appear to be finding their basic psychological security
not in the search for personal possessions but in the quality o.
their relationship with each other.[2]

These views are fully supported by the Chinese-Americar
anthropologist Professor Francis L. K. Hsu of Northwesterr
University, in his book *Americans and Chinese: Two Ways o;
Life*.[3] As Profesor Hsu points out, the Chinese finds satisfac
tion within the primary group, while the American finds nc
assurance or permanent security in human relationships anc
therefore seeks satisfactions elsewhere.

The fact appears to be that when children are brought up ir
a family within an interdependent group which each is inter
dependent in relation to the other, in which mutualism rathe*
than individualism and the competitiveness that is associatec
with it are the rule, such children are likely to grow up a;
persons who consciously and rationally, as Stephen Coates ha;
recently written, choose cooperation in place of competitior
and altruism in place of destructiveness. In the Westerr
family, while the focus is on the individual and the growth ir
egocentricity, strong emotional ties are usually developed be
tween parents and children in a usually far from healthy man
ner. Intensely developed constellations of emotions, which
become repressed and remain unconscious, arise in relation tc
the parental figures. The incorporation of the imperatives o*
these parental figures by the child tends toward the production
of an over-rigid conscience which, together with repressed
hatreds and anxieties, may later play havoc with such a person';
ability to function in a healthy manner. The threads of the
personality, whatever their genetic potentials, are woven upon
the loom of the family, and in the creation of the self it play;
the fundamental role.

The quest for self as inculcated in the Western family struc
ture is based on an erroneous conception of the idea of man,
of what man is born as, and what man is born for. And if we
are ever to understand what man is born for, we had better
begin reexamining some of our most strongly held unexamined
beliefs concerning the nature of man and what he is born as

It should at this late date be clear that the doctrine of "original sin" or innate aggressiveness can no longer be seriously entertained. Man has an evolutionary history which renders it certain that the behavioral traits which have continuously been at the highest premium are intelligence with the concomitant loss of instinctual mechanisms, and the increasing development of cooperation and love. In the cultural evolution of man there has been a continuous feedback between genetic selection for such traits and the behaviors which these traits then rendered possible. All this contributed to increasing plasticity and educability and thus greater general adaptiveness to the cultural and physical environments.

As a consequence of his long, complicated, and peculiar evolution, man is born with a highly organized system of needs which constitutes the inbuilt value system of the organism. These are the basic needs: the need for oxygen, for food, liquid, sleep, rest, activity, bowel and bladder elimination and the avoidance of noxious and dangerous stimuli. These needs are called basic because they must be satisfied if the organism is to survive physically. We have learned, however, that insofar as healthy mental functioning is concerned the most important of all the needs which must be satisfied is the need for love—not merely the need to be loved but the need also to love others. As stated on an earlier page, love is behavior calculated to confer survival benefits upon others in a creatively enlarging manner. In this conception of love we have an invaluable unifying principle, which combines under one simple rubric the evolutionary facts, the facts of individual development, and the facts of individual and social mental health. From whatever standpoint the principle of love is viewed, it turns out to have the highest adaptive value in the development of both the group and the individual. Indeed, the principle of love is a grand generalization like the principle of evolution itself, which not only serves to explain and bring together a great disparity of apparently unrelated phenomena, but serves also as a touchstone for the development and conduct of human beings.

In his individual behavioral development the human organism repeats the development of the species. From the symbiotic

relation with the mother in the womb to the continuing symbiosis after he is born, the human organism unequivocally
clearly exhibits a directiveness in his behavioral growth and
development in which growth and development of the self
proceeds interconnectedly with increasing growth and development in interdependence, in relations with others. The directiveness of the organism is toward growth and development in
the realization of his need for relatedness. Toward this end all
his needs are so structured as to require stimulations which will
enable the organism to realize his capacities for relatedness and
turn those capacities into acted-out abilities. The self grows in
relatedness, and develops by what it feeds on. No one is ever
born with a self, though all of us are born with genetic potentialities for realization of a self, genetic potentialities which are
never alike in any two individuals with the possible exception
of "identical" twins. Allowing for the genetic differences, those
genetic potentialities will enable the individual to develop a
self only insofar as they are exposed to the appropriate environmental stimuli.

Clark Moustakas has written, "The individual is not a fixed
entity but a center of experience involving the creative synthesis
of relations. The central force for this becoming nature of man
is a basic striving within the human being to assert and expand
his self-determination, to create his own fate." [4] I wish this were
true, and I think it could be made to be true, but it is certainly
not true in a culture such as ours, in which we impose a self
upon the individual rather than help him toward the creation
of his own self. I believe, with Moustakas, that the evidence
indicates that the organism is oriented in the direction of self-
creation, but the evidence which is all about us also shows that
we only too rarely permit human beings to create themselves.
Instead of providing the child with those stimulations and
conditions which will equip him with the skills necessary for
that "creative synthesis of relations" which will enable him to
"create his own fate," we generally train the child in an incapacity to do any of these things, and far from teaching him to
create his own fate we teach the child to follow within the pre-
destinate grooves etched out upon him by his socializers. Intrin-

sic nature is overlaid and suppressed by extrinsic conditionings, and the extrinsic conditionings become "second nature." In this process of socialization intrinsic nature is lost.

Self-actualization in the optimal, if not the maximal, realization of one's potentialities is just as much a gift which others bestow upon us as is the burden which they may impose upon us of a self which is incapable of actualizing itself. It is, therefore, of the greatest importance for us to understand that selves are not born but made, and that they are made according to the pattern prevailing in the culture or particular segments thereof in which the socialization process takes place. We must squarely face the fact that in our culture we do not form selves in such a manner as to provide them with the skills and tools designed to enable them to continue to make themselves, as a sculptor works upon his material to produce the finished sculpture, but that what we do is to attempt to make selves that will conform to a common mold. We effectively produce stereotyped minds that go through life repeating clichés and stereotypes under the impression that this is what one means by thinking. We produce unquesting and unquestioning minds in frightening numbers, minds unable to evaluate evidence critically for themselves. Training them in the rote repetition and regurgitation of "facts," we deceive them into the belief that this is learning, and that what they have learned in this way is both knowledge and wisdom. We fail to understand that such teaching is the very antithesis of what teaching should be: learning the continuous adventure of thinking analytically, critically, and independently for oneself, of continually questioning basic principles and what is taken for granted or is held axiomatic. We teach them hypocrisy by ritual lying and group incantation and forget that knowledge, learning, courage, and love, are the four great chords of might, and that what is implied by these words means not so much what we have been prepared to get from the group as what we each can do for its betterment. "One nation under God, indivisible, with liberty and justice for all" is a fine ideal, but it is an abrogation of it if one fails to teach the lesson that fine words are nothing but ritual incantations unless they are followed by action. The meaning of a word is the action it produces, and the natural purpose of words is to put and keep human beings in touch with one another and not to divide them by setting up ideals which satisfy our need for ritual but at the same time render possible behavior of an opposed kind. Finally, we treat our schools as if they were institutions for the teaching of the three R's, as if that sort of teaching could ever be an end or a goal in itself. What we need to recognize is that the three R's can never be anything more than skills, techniques which are quite secondary to their main purpose, their main purpose being or should be the maximal realization of whatever potentials the individual is endowed with—self-fulfillment.

Our so-called educational institutions are instructional institutions, a very different thing from what goes on in a genuine educational experience. Education, as the very root meaning of the word implies, should be an experience in the growth and development of the capacity to relate creatively toward others, and this is what the self should be organized to be. Hence, a genuine educational institution would be organized to enable the child to grow and develop in his ability to relate warmly, lovingly, and creatively toward not alone other human beings but to the whole of nature, animate and inanimate—with the possible exception of such things as liver flukes, polio viruses, noxious bacteria, and the like.

Mental health, very briefly, may be defined as the ability to love and the ability to work. All of us who are engaged in the education of human beings should be dedicating our activities toward helping the individual achieve that end, mental health. Our educational institutions should be re-valued and reorganized toward that end in the light of the knowledge which is now abundantly available, which tells us not only what human beings are born as but also what they are born for: to realize their intrinsic nature and to fulfill themselves in terms of that nature. In other words, the function of the educator must be to enable the individual successfully to negotiate the journey in search of self, by giving him all the supports, sustenances, and stimulations that will enable him to carry on that journey as creatively as possible. This will require teachers who are themselves able to love, for it is by being loved that one learns to love; and those teachers will not only communicate the meaning of love to their pupils, but it will be their task also to communicate to them the facts and theory upon which education in human relations is based.

If we are told, "But that should be the job of the parents," the answer is, of course it should, but who is to create parents who will be capable of doing what they ought if their own parents have not been taught how to do so? The teacher must, in such cases, stand *in loco parentis* and, indeed, always in proximate relation to the parental role, for he will always need to amplify and correct the work of the parents. That is principally what a teacher's function should be. And if, once more, the teacher asks,"Am I to take over the parents' job when they have failed to do what they ought?" the answer is: If the teacher will not, who will? It should be the teacher's bounden duty to serve where parents have failed. For the one thing the developing human being must not be failed in is the sustenance and support he expects. The supreme treason is to fail the dependent human being when he is most in need of you. And when the parents fail, the child should know that his teachers will make up for the failure insofar as that is possible.

The teacher, in our culture, stands in a critical position in relation to the whole of humanity. This is a tremendous responsibility, and I have often been accused of placing too much responsibility on the shoulders of teachers. If any teacher thinks that, I do not believe he belongs in the teaching profession. No matter what the rest of the community may think about teachers, *I* believe that they are the most important members of the community and that it is not poets, as Shelley claimed, but teachers who are the true unacknowledged legislators of the world. And I think it is time that they began measuring themselves at their true worth, for no one will begin esteeming teachers at their true valuation until teachers themselves value themselves and their work for what they and what they should be doing are worth.

In the quest for self, teachers have a job of work to do on themselves before they begin working on others. They must begin the task of working themselves over in the desired direction—in the ability, in short, to love. Perfection in this, as in other matters, will almost certainly never be attained, but the very fact of the effort made will take the one who makes the effort a long way in the right direction and will be reward enough for everyone concerned. Furthermore, it is the moral obligation of every teacher to make himself acquainted with the best that has been said, thought, and done on the subject of man's intrinsic nature and the quest for self and then to apply in his classroom what he has learned. Teaching children to learn that effort is not only necessary in learning but can be pleasurable should be one of the purposes of education. No profit grows where no pleasure is taken.

Since the school is one of the principal agencies in the transmission of the culture's values to the child, it is of equally great importance that teachers shall revalue the values that they are called upon to inculcate into their children. The abstract inconsideration of good intentions is not enough. To be a teacher is to be responsible. The teacher's task is not an end in itself but a means of communicating humanity, joining loving-kindness to learning, and setting oneself in order as the basis for the practice of good human relations. It is personal influence which determines the size of a life, and in the quest for self it is the teacher's personal influence that will count as much as, and certainly in a large number of cases more than, anyone else's in helping the individual realize and fulfill himself.

The unattractive qualities of the philosopher-king brought up in Plato's Academy are the ideals at which some of our "best" educational institutions aim today. The resultant products, suffering from what has come to be known as the Ivy-League Syndrome, are unhappy examples of what an expensively organized educational institution can do. With a built-in design for success in terms of external validations, which includes the suppression of emotion, the denial of love, and a hypocritical appearance of rectitude, these tend to become the citizens at the top of the Establishment who constitute the leaders and cultural and moral arbiters of the community.

The values of a culture which produces such human beings are badly in need of revaluation, and I really do believe that it is the teachers of the land who must carry out that revaluation and the changes it dictates.

The present condition of Western man is not irremediable, even though politicians may think so. Of all classes of men and women, teachers are the best qualified, or should be, to remedy the ills to which man is subjected, so that he may live in dignity and enjoy the autonomy and power of his own personality, his own self.

REFERENCES

1. John Dewey, *The Quest For Certainty*. London, Allen & Unwin, 1929.
2. Felix Greene, *The Wall Has Two Sides*.
3. Francis L. K. Hsu, *Americans and Chinese: Two Ways of Life*. New York, Schuman, 1935.
4. Clark Moustakas, "True Experience and the Self," in Clark Moustakas, ed., *The Self*. New York, Harper & Bros., 1956, pp. 3–14.

11. *Psychiatry and happiness*

Freud, when asked what he thought a normal person should be able to do well, answered: "to love and to work." I would enlarge this to "to love, to work, and to serve." The ability to perform well in each of these respects is, I believe, the criterion by which mental health must be judged. These I regard as essentially the basic *human* abilities, as fundamentally necessary for the healthy functioning of the person and of the society of which he is a member as is the individual's proper metabolic activities for the healthy functioning of his body.

But what has this to do with psychiatry and happiness? Virtually everything, I should think.

Patients are seen by the psychiatrist because they are mentally ill; that is to say, because they are unable to function satisfactorily in relation both to themselves and to other human beings. Where they generally suffer most is in their inability to love, and this affects all their other functions and relationships, and they are "unhappy." Being "unhappy" generally means a state of dissatisfaction with oneself or with others or both and with particular conditions or conditions in general, with consequences that tend to be depressing. The anger of accumulated frustrations is turned against oneself with more or less serious self-disorganizing effects. From this "unhappy" state the psychiatrist is supposed to rescue the patient and restore him to a state of "happiness," to a state of mental health.

This notion of the psychiatrist's function is widespread, understandable, and unsound. Those who are ill very properly look forward to the time when they will be better, and this is as true of the mentally as of the physically ill. Certainly the state of health is a far happier one than the state of ill health, but good health is not the equivalent of "happiness"—whatever that may mean.

I sometimes think that the Western concept of "happiness" has contributed more than its share to the mental and physical ill health of millions of human beings. Happiness is the Golden Grail, the pot of gold at the end of the rainbow, a goal to be achieved, the reward of virtue, success, getting what one wants, having what one needs.

Clearly, millions of human beings who have been taught that these or something resembling them are the conditions of happiness are going to fail more or less in achieving those conditions, and because they have "failed" they are, by definition, therefore going to be "unhappy." But it is more than by definition: They are going to *feel* unhappy.

We have here a striking example of the self-fulfilling prophecy: predicting the consequences that will follow upon certain conditions and then causing them to be realized.

But "happiness" is a myth, an anomic myth, perhaps the most misconceived of human endeavors. Life and liberty are, indeed, necessities, but the pursuit of happiness is a fool's game, a will o' the wisp that eludes all who believe that by making it a goal they can, by the prescribed or by other means, achieve it. The truth is that happiness cannot be pursued and caught like a beautiful butterfly in the collector's net. Happiness defines pursuit, and all attempts to capture it are in vain.

Is the purpose of a human being's life to be happy? I believe not.

What is happiness? What do most people understand by happiness? What is it that they desire for themselves and for others when they think of happiness? Apart from the obvious requirements of health, money, an attractive congenial spouse, gratifying children, a beautiful abode, esteem, prestige, recognition, wit, talent, wisdom, valor, love, the attainment of whatever one has set one's heart on—what other ingredients should go into this cake?

My own view is that not one of these conditions is either a necessary or sufficient requirement of happiness, although one of them or all of them together may give some people for a time a feeling of whatever they consider happiness to be. But such a feeling soon loses its power to please as, in time, one returns to the steadying level of everyday life.

It is when one is least conscious of oneself that one is likely to be at one's "happiest." What folly it is to believe otherwise! To believe that those occasional peak experiences—those thrilling moments when the goal one has set oneself has been achieved or it just feels good to be alive, or when one receives an unexpected windfall or one's work is highly praised—are likely to be prolonged experiences that will maintain one in a constantly euphoric state, is silly. Such occasions are, indeed, memorable, but the feelings they generate do not endure, nor should they. How unpleasant it would be to be in a constant state of high spirits! Madmen are often so! But, then, was it not Dryden who wrote:

> There is a pleasure sure
> In being mad which none but madmen know.

The healthy-minded are content with occasional elevations of spirit. It is the weak-minded who seek to buoy their flagging spirits with drugs and "experiences" that will make them "high."

There is a Kentucky hillbilly response to the greeting, "How are you?" It is, "So's t' git along." It is enough. Perhaps more than enough, but enough. Lord Morley put it beautifully many years ago. He said, the great business of life is to be, to do, to do without, and to depart. How ridiculous this cult of happiness is! "So's t' git along." That is what the majority of human beings who live at a subsistence level would be willing to settle for. It is only when the standard of living rises that the interest in happiness seems to develop. Not, it would seem, because life has in other ways become happier but largely because under the improved conditions of life the new problems that are created produce the pressures, the need, for their reduction. And one way, it comes to be believed, of counterbalancing the weight of these new problems is the pursuit of happiness. It sounds silly put that way, but it is no less than the truth. And what is no less than the truth is that life will always be difficult. "Life," as E. M. Forster put it, "is a public performance on the violin, in which you must learn the instrument as you go along." It takes a lot of stress and strain to bring off such a performance, and if sometimes we manage to bring off a few creditable phrases, it is as pleasant as it is unexpected. And so it is. The moments of happiness we enjoy take us by surprise. It is not that we seize them, but that they seize us.

It is not so much the pursuit of happiness as the happiness of pursuit that is most likely to yield gratification, and then only occasionally. Ask yourself whether you are happy, said John Stuart Mill, and you cease to be so. Seek happiness and it will elude you. Happiness is a by-product, principally of work, and if it is work that one delights in, so much the better.

It is not the task of anyone, least of all the psychiatrist, to make people happy. What *is* the psychiatrist's task is to help those in need of help to see themselves as they are, to understand something of the history of how they came to be the way they now are, to accept themselves for what they are and not to condemn themselves at the bar of the judgment of what they think they ought to be, but, having accepted themselves for what they are, not to rest there but to go on, with the psychiatrist's help, to come to some sort of practicable understanding with themselves and with the world in which they live.

The mentally ill stand most in need of the assurance that there is someone who cares. And in spite of what Freud may or may not have said on the subject, the care of the patient begins with caring for the patient. As every general practitioner knows, well over eighty percent of the patients whom he sees in his consulting room are there for no other reason than that they want someone to talk to, who will listen, who will care, and be reassuring. This is what the patient expects from his psychiatrist: The reassurance that someone cares. He wants, in short, to be loved. It is my belief that this is the only demonstrative means through which the psychiatrist can ever successfully reach the patient and restore him, not to a state of happiness, but to a state in which he is actively capable again of participating in the human enterprise.

12. *Cultural development and religion*

Religion is that aspect of human conduct which is concerned with the fundamental relation of man to his fellows, to the great issues of life and death, salvation, immortality, and to the universe in which he lives. For the greater part of man's history, and for most human beings up to the present moment, religion has provided a moral system, an explanation of the sources both of life and morality and of the goals of human life, and the meaning of existence. In the service of this task most religions have called upon supernatural devices to assist them. From the earliest times it would appear that a principal industry of man has been the creation of supernaturals.

The emotional need of human beings to relate themselves not only to other human beings but to virtually everything to which they can possibly relate themselves, whether present to sense or not, is quite as powerful as the pressures which cause human beings to seek the satisfaction of their most basic needs. And this is the fundamental meaning of the truth that man cannot live by bread alone. Being beyond all other things the symbol-using animal, and being man by virtue of his symbol-using abilities, man has always sought and will always seek to relate himself through symbolic means to whatever it is that he cannot otherwise relate himself.

Clearly the world is for most human beings a mystery, and quite as clearly religion has provided, if not always a satisfactory solution, at any rate a more or less satisfying explanation of that mystery. At the same time it has supplied mankind with the sanctions for the conduct it has prescribed, and by ritual and ceremonial, prayer and worship, has assisted the individual to feel part of a fellowship the bonds of which would sustain him not only through life but also through death and afterward.

Thus religion has played probably the most important of all the roles as the great integrating, the great binding force in the history of humanity. To dismiss religion as an "obsessional neurosis," as Freud has done, in the light of that fact, seems to me an extraordinary misunderstanding of the nature of religion. It seems to me, on the other hand, that religion is as natural a development as any other of man's cultural activities, his social organization, his tools, his legal and educational institutions, and so on. Man's religion is as natural a response to his emotional and intellectual needs as are his responses to his need for tools, for the regulation of marriage, the conduct of children in relation to their elders, the relations of different families to one another, and the like.

Just as man's tools or his social institutions in the early phases of their development are primitive and in the course of time and with the accumulation of experience undergo further development, so it is with man's religious beliefs. At the present time there exist many peoples who are still living in a Stone Age technological culture; in many cases their religious beliefs are in a parallel state of development. At the same time there exist numerous peoples who are technologically highly developed but whose religious beliefs are probably more closely related to those of the Stone Age than they are to the Age of Science.

It has, indeed, often been remarked of late years that our scientific development has far outstripped our moral development. This can hardly be doubted. Possibly the human brain is a malignant tumor that is gradually destroying the human soul. But this *may* be doubted. In any event, there seems good reason to believe that religious development has not kept abreast of development in other fields. And when one inquires into the reason for this, one soon discovers the answer. It is that religion generally has built into its very structure the factors that inhibit development. Demanding implicit belief while at the same time claiming to have *the* answers, religion closes the minds of its adherents instead of opening them. In this lies the fundamental difference between religion and science, for the method of science is that of free and open inquiry. In the very method of science there is implicit the knowledge that there are no such things as final answers and that knowledge is infinitely perfectible. It is not, therefore, surprising that in the last hundred years the advance of science has proceeded at an incomparably more rapid rate than has the development of religion. But this need not continue to be so. And it is here, I believe, that science can be of the greatest help.

Comparing, as an anthropologist, the religious systems of so-called primitive peoples with those of the so-called civilized peoples, I cannot help but think that in many cases the religious systems of nonliterate peoples are in every way superior to those of most civilized peoples. I mean in the sense that those religious systems enable the individual to realize himself more fully as a human being than do the religious systems of the civilized world. Religion is not the whole of the life of nonliterate man, but it constitutes a far greater and a far more important part of his life than is true of civilized man. Nonliterate man is truly more religious than civilized man. The religious beliefs of civilized man are not more complex or really more advanced than those of nonliterate men—they are merely different, and often overlaid with the thoughts and coda and practices of accumulated generations, like so many strata superimposed upon one another. Accumulation and accretion do not constitute development. This is not to deny for one moment that there has not been some development in the religious systems of the West, but it is to suggest that the sheer weight of accumulated and often conflicting traditions claiming supernatural sanctions has served to retard rather than to advance the development of religion in the Western world. Probably because nonliterate peoples have not undergone a similar historical experience, their religions have often remained nearer the true purpose that religion exists to serve—and this I have already said is to help man realize himself more fully as a human being.

But "human being" is the operative term. What is a human being? How many of us know the answer to that question? I suppose all of us do. But our answers will be numerous and various. We know that no two human beings are either physically or mentally identical, not even so-called or rather miscalled "identical twins"; variability is the rule, and there are no exceptions to this rule. We know that man takes different forms in the varieties he presents in adaptation to the environments in which he has undergone long-term development, and we know that his behavioral responses to the environment are capable of being organized in an immense variety of different ways: his cultures. And up to very recently we have tended to attribute all these differences to differences inherent in the very nature of different groups of mankind. It is really only in this century that we have come to suspect that while the physical differences are mostly due to inherent differences, the psychical differences are almost certainly mostly not. That even the physical differences are superficial, minor, and quantitatively very small, while the behavioral differences represent largely a matter of difference in cultural experience. Finally, that the likenesses between all members of the species *Homo sapiens* are far greater than the differences. These likenesses are fundamental to the species as a whole, for they constitute the precipitate of a long evolutionary history. And I would suggest that it is not possible to understand the nature of man very profoundly unless one understands the nature of this peculiar evolutionary process which mankind has undergone and of which human beings are the culmination. If religion is a path, a road, rather than an end, then it were well for those who would wish to know where that path should really lead to acquaint themselves with the route which man has taken to reach his present estate. It is these evolutionary matters that I propose to consider in what follows. And, of course, I shall discuss their significance for what I believe is the future developmental direction of religion.

The principal evolutionary changes which led to the ultimate appearance of man took place during the Pliocene epoch, which began some 13 million years ago and came to an end about 2 million years ago. During the Pliocene vast areas of the land in which the precursors of man are believed to have evolved were deforested and turned into open savannahs. The manlike apes who were man's precursors were thus called upon, during this long secular period of time—that is, the Pliocene, which lasted for about 11 million years—to adapt themselves to the new way of life which the demands of the savannah called for as compared to the different kinds of challenges presented in the forest. With few exceptions all the members of the primates, the order of mammals to which man, in company with the lemurs, tarsiers, monkeys, and apes, belongs, are forest dwellers. They are all herbivorous and frugivorous, and all quadrupedal.

In the forest environment, in which the primates as a whole have probably spent some 60 million years, or perhaps it would be more accurate to say that the primates began their life in the forest some 60 million years ago, in the forest environment these primates had become perfectly adapted to its challenges. On the savannahs, in the new environment, those primates who found themselves forced to live in it had to adjust in a variety of ways very different from the modes of adaptation of their forest-dwelling relatives. Since vegetation is sparse on the tree-poor plains of the savannah, the first change one would be called upon to make would be in the manner of earning a living. Instead of living off vegetation, fruits, and nuts, one would now be called upon to live off other animals, small game, birds and their eggs, small animals that one could catch with the exercise of a little ingenuity and cooperation. To make a long and fascinating story short, those primates that were able to negotiate their way in the new environment more effectively than those who were not left a larger progeny behind them than the others, a progeny that would increasingly be capable of making further necessary adjustments to the environment. The others did not necessarily die out; they simply went off in other directions to occupy different niches in the environment.

What were the changes which occurred in the precursors of man? They were first of all the gradual development of the upright posture, for if one could free the forelimbs for the use of stones and implements during the chase while running after small game, one would be at so much greater an advantage compared with those who remained quadrupedal. A second change would be the development of the capacity to make rapidly successful responses to the challenges of the environment. This is intelligence. Those animals would have been most favored who increasingly exhibited this capacity and concomitantly lost those instinctive responses which predetermine much of the behavior of the nonhuman animal. With the increasing development of the capacity for intelligent behavior and the loss of instincts, the dependency period of the young must be greatly increased, for this is the period during which the young of such a species will have to learn how to be a functioning being in the new dimension of a culture that is principally a symbol-using society. In adaptation to the new way of life the precursors of man would be called upon to exhibit increasingly more complex forms of cooperative behavior. Hunting game, setting snares, digging pits are activities which call for cooperative behavior of a highly organized kind, as does the subsequent distribution of the food derived from the hunt. Furthermore, with the increase in the length of the dependency period of the young, there would be a high premium placed upon the possession of those qualities in the female which would enable her to minister most efficiently to her dependent child, for such women would be likely to confer higher survival benefits upon their children than females not so well endowed with the necessary sustaining qualities. Natural selection would favor both males and females who possessed the qualities of cooperation as against those who did not. Just as man is a fetalized animal in so many of his physical traits, he is also, as it were, fetalized in his psychical potentialities, in the sense that he exhibits a tremendous capacity for growth and development for a much longer period of time than any other creature.

The evolution of man is characterized by increasing plasticity or educability, with which is concomitantly associated increasing dependency and interdependency and cooperation. This triad—plasticity, dependency, and cooperation—are the three great qualities which led to the evolution of man as a human being, and which in man's own evolution as a human being, have played a dominant role. It should surely be obvious that if man is the most dependent and the most plastic or educable of creatures he must also be, if he is to survive, the most cooperative, for unless he receives a maximum amount of cooperation he cannot survive for any durable period of time during his first half dozen years, nor can he learn to be a functioning human being. While all these elements are present to some extent in all animals, that is, plasticity, dependency, and cooperation, they have attained their highest development in man. Most of us understand that man is the most educable and the most dependent of creatures, but what we do not seem to understand is that he is also the most cooperative, that, indeed, if we separate the necessity for cooperation from the plasticity and dependency requirements of man we do the greatest violence possible to his development as a human being. Indeed, without cooperation neither the dependency nor plasticity needs of the individual can be satisfied, and if under such a deficiency experience he manages somehow to survive, it is as a crippled human being rather than as a healthy human being, as a creature who has been deprived of his birthright, which is development—development as a healthy human being. The whole of human experience bears testimony to the importance of cooperation for the development of man, but it is only within the last few decades that science has been bringing the support of its discoveries to that testimony.

In studying the mother-child relationship in relation to the subsequent development of both the mother and her child, we discover that the cooperative organization of humanity is best seen in its most highly developed form in the relationship of the mother to her child, the relationship we call love. It is in the maternal-child relationship that is to be perceived the hearth and the home of the Golden Rule to do unto others as

155]

you would have them do unto you. The relationship between mother and child is symbiotic. It is not terminated at birth, as some of our medicine men have tried to persuade us, but becomes increasingly more complex at birth, for at this juncture the symbiotic relationship ceases to be principally biological, physical, and now becomes largely psychical. From the womb the child passes into the family, which is but an extension of the womb, and from the family the individual must be prepared to pass into the community, and from the community into the nation, and from the nation into the community of nations, and from the community of nations into the universe of which he is the very selfsame stuff.

These transitions from the womb to the family and its extensions can be made only through the love which every mother is normally equipped, as a long result of the evolutionary process, to give her child. This fact is recognized in the sayings of many peoples, and perhaps most succinctly in the ancient Eastern saying that since God could not be everywhere he created mothers. The mother of the human species is endowed with the kind of capacities for love which so conspicuously characterize her because the young of humankind needs that love more than anything else in the world in order to grow and develop his capacities for being human. This is not rhetoric but demonstrable and verifiable psychophysical fact.[1] The member of the species *Homo sapiens* who is not adequately loved during his first half dozen years is severely handicapped in his development as a human being for the rest of his life, for he has failed to receive those stimulations to development which are so necessary if he is to become what he is capable of becoming, namely one who confers survival benefits upon others in a creatively enlarging manner.

This, it seems to me, is what the whole course of human evolution has led to, namely, that human beings shall relate to each other as a loving mother relates to her dependent child. Such relatedness has had the highest selective value for the human species in all societies and in all times, and if men fail to recognize this or once having learned this truth ever forget it they will from that moment on be in imminent danger of destroying themselves. Just as the mother's love is physiologically and psychologically necessary for the survival and development of the child, so love is necessary to the survival and development of human beings all the days of their lives, for, as George Chapman put it,

> I tell thee Love is Nature's second sun,
> Causing a spring of virtues where he shines.

Every human being is born with an inbuilt system of values, the basic needs, all of which are oriented in the direction of love. The infant is born wanting to love and to be loved. He is born with the ability to confer survival benefits in a creatively enlarging manner upon his mother and reciprocally to receive similar benefits from her. His first act in this life is to give, to give to his mother those benefits of which she stands so much in need immediately after the birth of her child, and it is only second to his giving that he receives from her from whom all blessings flow that first savor of the milk of human kindness. And it is through the stimulus of this interchange that the young of humankind is stimulated to grow and develop in his own capacities for love.

It is in this maternal-child relationship that I see the workshop of future religion and the *fons et origo* of all morality, for in that relationship is inherent as a clear precipitate the whole of human psychical evolution and the crystal-clear indications of the direction in which human beings must proceed if they are to realize their evolutionary destiny, which is to live as if to live and love were one.

It is a perverse view of human nature, which too many of our Western religious systems have foisted upon an only too guilt-laden and anxiously pietistic branch of humanity, that human nature is originally sinful and nasty "in the flesh," that innate depravity is indissolubly part of man's heritage, and that in Adam's fall we sinned all. This is, of course, an easy explanation of man's naughtiness, and it is a very common way of explaining almost anything about man to fall back upon the device of its being innate. To attribute the obscurely understood to the even more obscurely understood is one of the most ancient of man's artful dodges. The truth is that when we inquire as scientists into the nature of human nature we find no evidences whatever of any innate nastiness or hostility or aggressiveness or sinfulness or any other of the whole calendar of evils that have been attributed to the defenseless human babe.

Nor is it true, as some putatively more enlightened thinkers have come to hold, that man is born neither good nor evil, but that he is born a kind of *tabula rasa* upon which we can inscribe whatsoever we will by way of good and evil. On the other hand, as I see the evidence man is born with all his drives oriented in the direction of goodness and growth and development in goodness. The evidence for this statement is now, I believe, bombproof and it is available to anyone who cares to take the trouble to verify it for himself.

By goodness I mean the process of conferring survival benefits upon others in a creatively enlarging manner. And I use the words "goodness" "love" and "cooperation" as essentially meaning this. In short, what I am saying is that man has evolved as a creature in whom goodness has been his most valuable adaptive quality, that he is born with this quality as the central sun of his being around which all the other needs revolve like the planets of the solar system revolve in their orbits around the sun, that he is born to love and be loved, and that all else that he is born with and develops is secondary to this. That to be a warm loving human being who relates himself in a creatively enlarging manner to himself and to others is beyond everything else the first and most important realization of the self. The self grows and develops in its relatedness to others, and by being loved by others develops in its capacity to love. This growth in goodness I see as the only real personal salvation and the basis and focus of what I should consider the only genuine religion, namely, the religion of goodness. Those who are interested and are capable of doing so will have to decide, upon the evidence, for themselves whether their goodness is to be their religion or whether their religion is to be their goodness. Whether God is love, or whether love is God. Whether we will continue to suspend our gods in the heavens or whether we shall be willing to bring them down to earth.

I foresee the development of religion in the future as a consistent part of the cultural development of the person based on a more accurate and more thorough understanding of the nature of human nature than humanity has enjoyed in the past, when a man's religion will be the development of his goodness and not the subscription to a traditionally organized system of superstitions which, like so many bunions, have impeded the pilgrim's progress.

When we have understood the meaning of the value system which is built into the very nature of man and with which he is born, the value system which is constituted by his basic needs, and when we have understood that all these needs are, in terms of development oriented in the direction of love, we shall perhaps for the first time understand that in this view of the nature of man's needs we have a unifying principle, which, like the principle of gravitation, brings together so much that is at present not clearly understood as related. Education, ethics, law, and religion all become different aspects of one and the same thing, namely, the ordering of man's growth and development in goodness.

From my point of view, it will be evident, that I do not think we have much in the Western world today that resembles education. We have a great deal of instruction. But instruction is not education. Instruction is training in the use of the three R's. Education is a causing to grow, a nourishing in the capacity to be a warm, loving human being, and the three R's are merely techniques in the service of that end, the end of goodness. I conceive of ethics and of law in precisely the same manner. The only relations between men that are good are loving, the only law that is just is love, and the only worship that is true is love. This is the law and the commandment of man's nature.

REFERENCES

1. The evidence will be found in some detail in my book *The Direction of Human Development*, Harper & Bros., New York, 1955. See also John Bowlby, *Maternal Care and Mental Health*, World Health Organization, Geneva, 1951.

13. *The role of the social sciences*

There are two novels, *Brave New World* by Aldous Huxley and *Nineteen Eighty-Four* by George Orwell, in each of which the gifted author attempted to give an account of the society of the 1980s as he foresaw it. The genius of each of these authors was such and their skill so great in depicting the social structures of the future that they succeeded in stirring the imagination of men everywhere. These two books at once established themselves as the classics they are likely to remain.

One of the remarkable things about these books is that in spite of the profound impression they made upon millions of readers, many of these readers have since failed to observe that they are already living in the midst of the conditions forecast by Huxley and Orwell. In his book *Brave New World Revisited*, published in 1958, some twenty-seven years after *Brave New World*, Huxley states how surprised he is to find the prophecies made in 1931 coming true much sooner than he thought they would. The one thing that Huxley did not foresee was the great acceleration in the rate of innovation, limited largely in our own society to revolutionary scientific and technological changes, without corresponding revolutionary but nevertheless very real social changes. The danger for the future lies in the fact that we, most of us, clearly do not understand the significance of these scientific and technological changes and fail to perceive what effects they are having on human values.

Society is the collective conduct of human beings of the past acting upon the present to determine the future. If we would protect ourselves against the possibility of becoming the victims of the future, we must do everything we can to understand and control the present. If, as I assume we are, we are interested in the direction which our lives will take in the very near future, a direction which it is within the power of each of us to influence, it is very necessary for us to make ourselves acquainted with the relevant facts. It is here that the social sciences, anthropology and sociology, can increasingly be of the greatest help to us.

I am happy to see that anthropology, my own field of major interest, is beginning to appear as a regular course in some high schools and also in some elementary schools, and that there are very few colleges remaining in which the subject is not taught. I hope we shall see courses in both anthropology and sociology established throughout every branch of our so-called educational system, so that it may truly be turned into a genuine educational system.

What education is or rather should be the anthropological sciences will make increasingly clear. Within the next two decades we are likely to witness the beginning revaluation of some of our most deeply entrenched values concerning the meaning, aims, and purposes of education. There will be an increase in the diffusion of knowledge concerning the evolution and the nature of human nature, so that for the first time increasingly large numbers of persons will begin to understand both what human beings are born *as* and what they are born *for*. Here the social and behavioral sciences will continue to make fundamentally important contributions, and as a consequence we shall witness the continuing dissolution of age-old myths concerning human nature and what human beings are born as. In short, the image of man we now have will undergo radical change, and this in itself will have the most far-reaching consequences for every area of human relations. In the warlike world in which we shall continue to live, we shall have won through to the knowledge that man is not born a warlike creature, hostile, aggressive, nasty, brutish, and innately depraved, but we shall come to understand that human beings are taught to be all these things by the violence that is done in the socialization process to their needs for development in the discipline of love, and that the most powerful need of the organism, the human organism, is to love and be loved.

The wider understanding of this view of nature in a world of conflict will present the informed citizens of that world with some profoundly challenging problems. These problems will all revolve around the central problem of how to lead a world dedicated to the solution of international problems by violence to understand that such solutions are not solutions at all but constitute a compounding of the felony which only serves to ensure the further destruction of human life and values and the recurrence of further wars; that war is a madness that no one can possibly justify, standing in opposition to everything that is decently and essentially humane. And to be human should mean to be humane.

The understanding of the true nature of man should at least encourage us to believe that it is not human nature that is responsible for crime and that most criminal of follies, war, but that it is human nurture that is responsible; that wars, indeed, begin in the minds of men not because of any innate propensity to war but because of the frustrations and reactive aggressiveness which human beings have been caused to accumulate, as so many armaments, during the socialization process.

Here, too, the social and behavioral sciences will play an important role in making both the knowledge and the means of its most effective utilization increasingly and more widely available. I would like to underscore here the fact which is already clearly evident, namely, that the social sciences will develop with an increasing emphasis upon the practical use of their findings, with the methods of practical use being the subject of research and publication. Because teachers in our elementary and high schools stand at the very center of the human situation, they will find themselves called upon to utilize the findings of the social and behavioral sciences and to apply those findings in the classroom. There will be a growing recognition of the crucial importance of the teacher to society, a recognition which will accrue principally because teachers themselves will have begun to lead the way, in the classroom, toward a sounder and a healthier valuation of human beings than is the case at the present time. With this growing recognition there will follow a rise in the prestige of teachers, soundly based upon the recognition of their true value as, next to parents, the most important members of the community. Whether teachers will continue to be rewarded on the principle that being a teacher is sufficient reward in itself * or whether there will be a substantial improvement in the salaries paid them, in recognition of their value to the community, is a question which can be answered only by the profession of teachers. If they will value themselves for what they are worth, there is a good chance that teachers may be freed from the economic anxieties which so often prevent them from devoting themselves wholeheartedly to what they should be encouraged to do: enriching themselves culturally so that they may be the sources of enrichment for their pupils.

The pace of social change will be accelerated. And here it is of importance to note that while social change may be proceeding before our very eyes, we will frequently fail to observe it or, what is quite as significant, refuse to acknowledge that such social changes are occurring. It is very desirable to be alive in oneself to this characteristic conservatism which tends to look upon the established mores as eternally enduring and unchanging. The truth is, of course, that every society grows by social change at whatever of its growing points social change is required. But not all social change, even at growing points, is healthy or desirable, so that it is important to be able to distinguish between the desirable and the undesirable kinds of social change. I believe there is a measure by which one can determine whether a social change is desirable or not. It is to put it to the test of whether or not it confers survival benefits upon the members of the community of man, individually and as a whole, in a creatively enlarging manner.

The increase in the expectation of life brought about by

---

* I must say that some of my contacts with the National Education Association lead me to believe that that interesting organization subscribes to this view.

medicine is, I think, an unqualified good, but the overpopulation in the many countries in which such advances have been made, and which constitutes a direct result of those advances, is an unmitigated evil. Survival benefits without the possibility of the creative enlargement of the life of the individual, whose existence has in so many cases merely been extended so that he might suffer more and bring suffering to others, is a ghastly disaster for everyone involved. Excess quantity where people are involved depresses the quality of humanity.

Longevity is not a good in itself; it is a good only when it is a life fulfilled, a life fulfilled in self-realization, and in the service, the realization of one's fellow man. It is not the quantity but the quality one puts into life that matters. In applying our measure to what is desirable in social change and what is not, we have touched upon one of the most serious, indeed *the* most serious, problem with which and the consequences of which we shall be faced for a long time to come. By becoming alive to the devastating effects of this problem and doing what requires to be done, we can solve that problem and greatly better the human condition. I refer, of course, to the population problem, the "population explosion."

The mindless and irresponsible reproduction now proceeding over the greater part of the civilized world will result in a doubling of the present world population of 3.5 billion by the end of the century. This is a tremendous rate of increase. It is iniquitous, a sin against the spirit and the flesh of man, for it both cheapens and reduces humanity to an uncontrolled cancerous proliferation of organisms which threatens, at the least, to reduce the quality of humanity if not to lead to its virtual destruction.

This is a problem which to some extent can be headed off if we take the necessary action now, but it is already later than most people are aware. Since most people will not do what they ought and take the necessary action by practicing birth control and inducing others to do likewise, we shall have to face up to the consequences of the deluge when it comes. It will not be pleasant. The consequences of crowding and overcrowding never are. In such a world we shall more than ever need people who, not having had the foresight to prevent the deluge, will at least have whatever it takes to see to it that birth control and induced abortion become legally and socially recognized as indispensably necessary controls for the greatest benefit of the greatest, that is optimum or healthiest, number of persons a society can support without sinking under its own weight.

Increasing respect and attention will have to be paid to parenthood as an art, in which the planning of parenthood and the spacing of children become matters far better understood than they are today. In which common sense, assisted by the social sciences, may enable so-called civilized human beings to understand that parenthood is the most important of all the professions, and that incurring obligations which one cannot meet, in the form of children whose rightful demands, whose birthright one is unable to honor, constitutes a crime against humanity. We must learn to understand that there is more than one way to genocide and that irresponsible conduct which threatens the very existence of humanity must be regarded as what it is, a crime against the human spirit by the irresponsible reduplication of the flesh.

Not unrelated to this matter of population control is the change in sexual mores which is proceeding at the present time but which many people refuse to acknowledge as occurring because they don't want it to occur and don't know how to deal with it when they are faced with the situation. This is especially true of the changing sexual mores among the young unmarried.

In most nonliterate societies, if not in all, premarital sexual relations are encouraged and regarded as a normal healthy expression of a strong and imperious drive. Promiscuity is strongly discouraged and is characteristic of no society. In the civilized world, with relatively few exceptions, premarital sex is strongly interdicted, and all the sanctions are against it. Nevertheless, sexual mores have been changing quite rapidly, as these things go, and premarital sex relations from a prohibited and sinful behavior will gradually come to be recognized, as it has long been in the Scandinavian countries, as a much healthier and individually and socially much less disruptive custom than the present unhealthy puritanical repressive custom of interdicting premarital sex and branding it as a personal, social, and religious sin.

A knowledge of the experience of other peoples in this connection, and what studies made by social scientists have already revealed, and what future studies will continue to illuminate, will be indispensably helpful in enabling us to see the problems with which we shall be confronted in sounder perspective than we do today. Sex will become much less of a motivation for marriage, and love—which is at present widely confused and identified with sex—may yet have a chance of reestablishing itself for what it is: a profound and creative involvement in the welfare of the other.

Involvement in the welfare of the other will be increasingly extended to all our fellow men, with the xenophobia and ethnocentrism which is characteristic of so many today replaced by the enriching concept of the community of man. Here the contributions of anthropology especially will have made more acceptable and prevalent the view of the unity without the uniformity of man, the view that all men are engaged in the common enterprise of humanity, playing their roles in that enterprise in a manner influenced largely by the differences in the history of their experience. The doctrine of racism will still, I am afraid, be with us in the world of the 1980s, but there will be more people who understand what is wrong with that doctrine and a greater inclination on the part of many to do something about it.

The doctrine of racism has it that there is a something called "race" which determines both the physical characteristics and the behavioral and cultural capacities of the individuals and the groups belonging to such "races." Anthropologists, social scientists, and geneticists have been able to find no evidence whatever for such claims as are made by the racists, and all the evidence indicates, as we learn more about the variety of man, that the facts will even more impressively reveal that the doctrine of racism has neither merit nor health in it.

As the facts of anthropological knowledge and discovery become increasingly known and the meaning of human variability is more fully comprehended, and allowing for the full and magnificent range of variability, we shall observe that all human groups once they have been afforded the adequate opportunities for development are capable of achieving behaviorally and culturally whatever any other human group has been and is capable of achieving. Peoples all over the world, formerly not enjoying the opportunities for development along the lines of Western civilization, with increasing opportunities will probably show that they are no less well endowed with the genetic potentials for meeting the challenges of those opportunities than the peoples of the Western world. With that demonstration in process of being finally made, we shall at last begin to understand the basic likeness of man's genetic behavioral potentialities. Not that they mean that all men are born biologically equal, which they are not, but that all men are born biologically unequal, and that therefore every man by his birthright has the right to be treated as the unique individual he is regardless of whatever ethnic group he may belong to.

By equality we shall more fully understand the acknowledgment of the view that not all men are born genetically alike but that they are born genetically unlike, and that therefore every human being has an equal right to the opportunity to develop his unlikenesses as well as his likenesses. We need to understand that we shall do well to cherish and encourage the unlikenesses in human beings as well as their likenesses. Mankind's greatest treasure does not lie buried in the imaginary islands of the buccaneer's dreams but in the uncultivated soil capable of yielding the genetic wealth which is the common heritage of humanity. The dark unfathomed caves of humanity have hardly begun to be explored. They bear untold riches, waiting to be brought into the light of day.

We shall, in the future, have to face the implications of the fact that man is not only a political animal but also a moral creature. Ethical concepts and considerations will have to play a far more vital role in our daily lives than they do today, so that, among other things, we come to understand that the solution to a great many human problems in no way depends upon the findings of the scientists, social or otherwise, but upon certain—one had thought self-evident—simple ethical principles.

167]

For example, it is or should be a universally understood principle that by virtue of the fact that an individual is a human being, it is his right to be treated as one, that he is entitled to the fullest opportunities for the realization of his birthright, which is the optimum development of his potentialities as a human being. It must be recognized that the greatest crime against the human spirit, against humanity, is the denial to any individual of the fullest possible opportunities for the development of whatever it is in him to develop. Anyone who denies humanity in this way by deliberately setting obstacles in the way of its realization in another must be regarded as ethically, socially, and legally reprehensible, and must be called to account for his crimes and helped to understand the error of his ways.

The social sciences can provide us with all the necessary facts which will support our ethical viewpoints and even provide us with a scientific validation for them. The decisions, however, we ultimately arrive at in our relations with our fellow men, on the manner in which we shall conduct ourselves in relation to them, will fundamentally be ethical ones. Assisted to a more profound understanding of the requirements of human beings by our increased knowledge of their nature, we shall be able to proceed with some degree of assurance that in our ethical aims we are advancing in the right direction.

The world of the 1980s will stand much in need of a revaluation of values, as the world, indeed, does at any time. Precisely as for the individual it should be a first principle that the unexamined life is not worth living, so too it should be in relation to the values by which a society lives. We shall need to make the discussion of ethics, the good life, and of ethical principles an indispensable part of the school curriculum, from the earliest ages of the child onward, so that ethical literacy becomes the rule rather than the exception. The good life is important for human beings because no other life is worth living. And by worth, of course, we mean value; that no life is as valuable to its possessor, to others, and to society as much as that which is lived in goodness, that the good man's religion is love, taking the view, with all due respect to the others, that a really practicably workable application of the highest embodiment of the

supreme moral principle is not so much that God is love, but
that love is God.

Religions are becoming less rigid than they were only a short
time ago, and as they develop with the times, there will be a
continuing meeting of the minds between reason and religion.
From this dialogue I see a great deal of good emerging, a hope
expressed in those germane and charming verses, "The Good
and the Clever," written by Dame Elizabeth Wordsworth
(1840–1932), first principal of Lady Margaret Hall at Oxford:

> If all good people were clever,
>   And all clever people were good,
> The world would be nicer than ever
>   We thought that it possibly could.
>
> But somehow 'tis seldom or never
>   The two hit it off as they should,
> The good are so harsh to the clever,
>   The clever so rude to the good!
>
> So friends, let it be our endeavour,
>   To make each by each understood;
> For few can be good like the clever,
>   Or clever, so well as the good.

The good and the clever are at long last already coming closer
together, and it is well to be aware of this, so that we may the
more intelligently and effectively be able to participate in the
dialogue and the rapprochement.

One of the institutions we most take for granted in the
Western world, the structure of our particular kind of family,
will come increasingly under critical examination. I regard the
family, for example, as it is at present structured in the Western
world, as something approximating a social disaster.

By the parents' exclusive concentration of their attention
upon the children in the drive toward making them a "success,"
a dissociation from other human beings is produced in a profoundly disturbing way. Our family values, in short, are devoted
to teaching the increasing development of self-interest and
interest in others only insofar as they are usable and instru-

mental in contributing to the further development of our own self-interest. The too-intense relationships so often developed between the members of the Western family lead to the development of much too intense emotional involvements of love and hate. In later life such persons only too often tend to react far too emotionally to all sorts of life situations, with the kind of violence and emotionality that is individually and socially damaging.

The Western family, alas, has also become an organization for the teaching of an incapacity to love. If mental health has one outstanding characteristic, it is the ability to love. By love I mean the communication of deep involvement in the welfare of the other, the giving of support and stimulation for the sustenance and development of the other, the satisfaction of the needs of the other. This is seldom adequately achieved in the Western family. Instead, there is a marketing approach to human relations and especially to "love." Love is made conditional, especially by mother, upon what she considers to be good behavior. The one thing in the world which should be freely, unconditionally given is dealt with as a commodity. "You do what I wish and I'll give you love. If you don't, I won't." The satisfaction of the need for love is made a crucial bargaining point, but the need to love others is subordinated to the need to be loved. And so the family produces individuals who crave love, but who are themselves crippled in their capacity to give it unconditionally and in any other context than one of commerce. The training in conditional love and in competition for success, with an occasional genuflection in the direction of the principles enshrined in the Sermon on the Mount, serves to produce the most ill-adjusted kinds of behavior which, characteristically, we attempt to deal with at the most superficial of levels. There is a great deal more to be said upon this important subject, but that cannot be done here. Here it must suffice to emphasize the necessity of continuous examination and evaluation of the values of the family and those of the society as a whole which the family transmits to its members.

The great danger which more than ever will continue to face

man is his increasing infatuation with things and his concomitant dehumanization. The pursuit of happiness in the form of the maximization of material comforts is a will o' the wisp. In any event, happiness pursued as such will always elude you, for it is not something that can be sought and found—the reason being that happiness is not a findable entity but the by-product of other things and principally, strange as it may seem, of work. It is not for nothing that mental health is defined as the ability to love and the ability to work. One of the discoveries that most people, it is to be hoped, will make during the coming years is that effort, work, can be pleasurable, not always, but a great deal more of the time than it is for most people at present. One achieves pleasure in work by working hard in one's early years, so that whatever one does later is comparatively easy. Thus, we shall have to cultivate habits of work in our young which at present go by default.

With work the concept of play will also have to be re-examined, so that we may yet make the curious discovery that the purpose of play is not to win but to have fun, to take pleasure in the game and in the development of one's skills, human and technical, in relation to others, and to rejoice in those skills in others as well as in oneself.

I think we shall have to reflect more deeply than we have done on the meaning of competition and of cooperation, on the meaning of competitive competition and cooperative competition, and revise our whole conception of work, games, sports, and the pursuit of creature comforts. We shall have to learn the lesson, from the many object lessons we already have before us if we would but look at them, that those who pursue creature comforts end up by belonging to the comforts, that the spoils do not belong to the victor but that the victor belongs to the spoils, the possessor to his possessions.

In a society in which the supreme value is Success, success in terms of external validations, the members of such a society will need more than ever to consider the only success that really matters: success in terms of internal validations. It is at this point that we are brought squarely to the issue of education.

Here, I believe, we are destined to witness some major changes in our conception of education. Not that these will have been brought about by the 1980s, but that they will at that time probably be more actively discussed than they are at present. As a consequence of the discoveries of the social and behavioral sciences, I believe we shall increasingly come to understand that the true purpose of education is to enable human beings to become proficient in the most important of all the sciences and the most important of all the arts, namely, the theory and practice of human relations. That all other education, instruction in the three "R's, must be secondary to this main purpose.

Educators will find themselves, as never before, in the forefront of a debate which will last a long time. Upon the outcome of the debate the very future of mankind will depend. It is therefore essential that those who are going to live and work in that time be as well prepared as possible to participate effectively in that debate. If, as I believe it is, education is the great American opportunity, it is the moral obligation of all of us to see to it that everyone has the chance to enjoy that opportunity, and for all of us to take full advantage of it. If we will do what we ought to do now, it will be much easier for us to do what we ought to do later. It is time we got down to the actual work of discovering what we ought to do. In an Atomic Age, it is necessary to point out that security is *not* a matter of weapons but of intelligence, and not intelligence of the I.Q. kind but the intelligence in which the ability to think critically is joined to the ability to love wholeheartedly.

I can conclude with no better words than those which I read in an obscure student journal when I was a student. They were written in 1925. I have never forgotten them, and they are more relevant today than they were when they were written, more than forty years ago. The writer, Alfred F. Pollard, was professor of history at University College, University of London. He wrote, "Whether mankind survives depends less on its science than on its humanity, upon whether we trust an increasing control over physical forces to men with a decreasing sense of responsibility for their use, and whether we regard as more 'natural' the war we think rooted in Nature or the peace we owe to our mind." [1]

REFERENCES

1. A. F. Pollard, "The War of Nature and a Peace of Mind." *Vincula* (University of London Students' Journal), 14 December 1925, p. 61.

14. *Great ideas of the*
social sciences

In considering the great ideas of any subject the first thing we ought to do is to determine what we mean by a great idea. What makes an idea great? This is a question which is worthy of discussion in its own right, and since a great part of the history of science could be written in terms of errors that have been fruitful, as well as in terms of the removal of great roadblocks of error which had served to impede the progress of thought, the discussion would obviously be a most interesting one. The idea of instincts in man was a fruitful error up to a point; beyond that point it became a hindrance to further progress. Psychology made a great advance when, in the 1920s, the idea of instincts in man was altogether dropped.[1] An erroneous idea may have great heuristic value; that is to say, in the course of doing something about it it may not only be discovered that the idea is an error but other important truths may be discovered in the process. This is not the fortuity of serendipity, but is not unrelated to it.

Obviously this is a subject deserving of separate treatment, but we cannot deal with that subject here. Let us, therefore, attempt to settle upon the definition of a great idea as being one which, in a major way, advances the cause of truth. That is a universal definition, that is to say, it will apply in all cases, including great ideas in the social sciences. Should we not, however, make the definition more particularly applicable to the social sciences? We might, perhaps, try. A great idea in the social sciences is one that has served to advance the understanding of man as a social creature. By "social," in the present context, we mean the process of interaction between two or more persons.

Without any further atempt at elaboration, then, let us proceed with our reflections upon great ideas in the social sciences.

It is perhaps necessary to mention the fact that while the term "social sciences" is only about thirty-five years old, the areas covered by that term have been rather desultorily the subject of systematic inquiry much longer. And here we must make a distinction between the "observer" who looks about him and sets down his thoughts on what he has seen, and the "inquirer" who is concerned to check and verify all observations, whether made by himself or by others, by the test of experience. The former are the "thinkers," the latter are the "scientists." Not that scientists don't think—they do, but there is a disciplined method to their thinking, which is usually wanting in the unadulterated thinkers. Social thinkers of this latter class should not be called social scientists, even though in some cases their contribution to the history of thought has been substantial. Perhaps we may call them "social philosophers." Because in a number of cases their contribution to social science has been very considerable, we shall consider the social philosophers with the social scientists.

I suppose we may regard Aristotle (384–322 B.C.) as the first social scientist, since we may regard him as the first universal man who took all knowledge for his province. His claim to being the first social scientist rests on many works, but the one which is of chief interest to us is the *Politics* because it is in this remarkable work that what is perhaps the fundamental idea of the social sciences makes its first appearance. This is the simple idea that man is by nature a political animal. Showing that man's natural tendency is toward association, and from association of individuals to the formation of communities, and thence to the formation of the *polis* or state, he concludes, "Hence, it is evident that the state is a creation of nature, and that man is by nature a political animal. And he who by nature and not by mere accident is without a state, is either above humanity, or below it; he is the

Tribeless, lawless, heartless one,

whom Homer denounces—the outcast who is a lover of war; he may be compared to a bird which flies alone." [2]

No social scientist has cared to dispute this conclusion.

What Aristotle is concerned to show is that man differs from all other creatures in that he alone is born with the capacity to realize the highest good in associations which are not merely associative but politically organized for that purpose. It is a great idea in itself. It is a great idea, also, because it is the forerunner of the idea developed some 2,200 years later that man is the culture-making animal and because, interestingly enough, it is in the direct line leading to the idea of world government.

It was Zeno (*c.* 350–*c.* 260 B.C.), the founder of Stoic philosophy, who developed Aristotle's notion of man's social nature to embrace all men, and we have in the teachings of the Stoics the appearance of the first cosmopolitan conception of a world society and world citizenship, as well as the beginnings of the idea of the brotherhood of mankind—a philosophy and an outlook that was ably represented in Rome by Epictetus (A.D. *c.* 90) and by the Emperor Marcus Aurelius (A.D. 121–180).

But to return to Aristotle, the greatness of his conception of man as a political animal lies in the fact that it represents the first explicit formulation of the fact that man is something more, or rather that he is not only an animal but also a social creature of a unique kind, distinguished from all other creatures by his capacity for speech, which enables him to recognize the difference between the advantageous from the reverse and to distinguish between the just and the unjust and other similar qualities, and it is association in these things which really makes a family and a state.

But we must leave Greece and Aristotle for Rome and the first great evolutionary sociologist of antiquity, Lucretius (*c.* 99–55 B.C.), whose great epic poem, *On the Nature of Things,* offers, among many other novelties, a virtually modern account of the social evolution of man. Lucretius actually presents the stages of social evolution through which man must have passed, much as a modern anthropologist would. Unfortunately, Lucretius' ideas do not seem to have been congenial to the world in which he lived, nor did those ideas find a place in the Western world until they were rediscovered independently nearly two millennia later.

With the advent of St. Paul's impact upon Rome with his vastly more influential idea, among others, of man's inherent sinfulness, so sharply set out in the *Epistle to the Romans,* Chapters 7–8, much more progress—in the wrong direction—was made. The Pauline view of human nature was that it is inherently sinful in the flesh. The doctrine of original sin, namely, the tendency to sin and depravity which is inherent in mankind as a direct result of Adam's sin of rebellion, is principally St. Paul's contribution, though the idea is already implicit in the story of the Fall. St. Paul's idea of original sin has had a tremendous influence upon the thought of Western humanity during the last nineteen centuries, and that influence is perhaps more widespread than and as profound as it ever was. I know of few ideas which have been more subtly influential upon the thought of social scientists than this, though in the latter part of the nineteenth century and in our own time there have been many for whom the attraction of the idea of the inherent naughtiness of man has lost something of its monstrous fascination. For there is not the least evidence that man is born, or is by innate nature determined, to be the nasty creature he is so often caused to become. Nevertheless, the belief that man is inherently a sinful, selfish creature is one of our most deeply entrenched orthodoxies.

Machiavelli (1469–1527) in *The Prince,* 1513, and in his *Discourses,* 1521, develops the sinful-selfish view of man's nature, as does Thomas Hobbes (1588–1679) in *Leviathan,* 1651. It was Hobbes who described the presocial state of nature as "a state of war of all men against all men" in which the life of man was "poor, nasty, brutish, and short." He flatly denied the social nature of man and asserted that all society is for either gain or glory, that mutual fear is the basis of all permanent social groupings. To circumvent the miseries of the unregulated and turbulent state of nature, men made a social contract to unite for their mutual protection. The contract was voluntary and not literally a formal one, but one that came about as a necessity of group life. Hobbes' is the classic statement of the social-contract theory of society. Its influence has been formidable.

It was Jean Jacques Rousseau (1712–1778) who gave the theory of the social contract its modern form. Instead of being a contract, as Hobbes eventually makes it, between the sovereign power and the people, Rousseau makes it a contract determined by the "general will" of the people. The difference is between power and will. Rousseau published *The Social Contract,* along with *Emile,* in 1762. His earlier writings—*A Discourse on the Moral Effects of the Arts and Sciences,* 1750, and *A Discourse on the Origin and Foundation of the Inequality of Mankind,* 1755—important as they are in their own right, both are propadeutic to *The Social Contract* and to *Emile,* Rousseau's notable contribution to educational theory.

It has been said that these works of Rousseau were the inspiration of the French Revolution. This is, of course, to claim too much. But most authorities are agreed that Rousseau's writings played a significant role in the comingabout—rather than in the bringingabout—of that holocaust. "Liberty, Equality, and Fraternity" were the principles of Rousseau's major interest. Rousseau is full of great ideas. Possibly more than any other social philosopher he has bequeathed us many ideas yet to be developed. The most important of these insofar as man's own nature is concerned is that nature is right. We have but to recognize that right, to recognize the principle of our own being, and encourage our children, assisted by art and reason, to achieve their growth in accordance with the requirements for development of their being, to learn in this way what human beings are born for. We can only know what human beings are born for—if they are born for anything—by discovering what they are born as. Reason is not enough because Reason can fly off into fantasy if she does not understand or forgets the nature of the creature she is attempting to guide and merely plies her art for instruction's sake, regardless of the true purposes of education. The good society will be free of tyranny, since it will fix as rights and duties all those things that are dictated by, and Reason finds appropriate to, our nature. To fulfill our nature is to be at liberty. Liberty does not consist in choosing our courses but in the freedom to grow in the ability to discern them. As Lord Acton (1834–1902) put it in a later day, "Liberty is not the power of doing what we like, but the right of being able to do what we ought." But the trick is, of course, to discover what we ought to do. What we ought to do, says Rousseau, is to follow nature, for man is born good, and we need but to attend to the requirements of his nature in order to perceive the direction in which we ought to go. Natural man, contrary to the misinterpreters and misrepresenters of Rousseau's views, is not the primitive man of the South Sea explorers, but the man we may in time become.

This is the idea that runs through all Rousseau's writings and gives them their essential unity: that man must be perfected by reason in accordance with his nature, and finally, that society can be brought to embody the highest morality of the individual. That was Rousseau's message. With the passage of the years it has gained, not lost, in urgency.

It is the tragedy of the Western world that its leaders have preferred to take the Hobbesian view of man's nature rather than that of Rousseau. But already the brilliant intuitive genius of Rousseau is being reenforced by the findings of the contemporary behavioral sciences. Possibly fifty years hence Rousseau will, at last, have come into his own.

Interestingly enough, it was a friend and executor of Rousseau, Daniel Malthus of Dorking, whose second-born son Thomas Robert Malthus (1766–1834) produced one of the most influential ideas in the whole history of social thought. This was contained in his *An Essay on the Principle of Population*, 1798. The idea was stated in that delightful novel, by Thomas

Love Peacock (1785–1866), *Melincourt,* 1817, where Mr. Fax, the character modeled on Malthus, is made to say, "Bachelors and spinsters I decidedly venerate. The world is overstocked with featherless bipeds. More men than corn is a fearful pre-eminence, the sole and fruitful cause of penury, disease and war, plague, pestilence and famine."

"I have read," writes Malthus in his *Essay,* "some of the speculations on the perfectability of man and of society, with great pleasure. I have been warmed and delighted with the enchanting picture which they hold forth. I ardently wish for such improvements. But I see great, and, to my understanding, unconquerable difficulties in the way to them. These difficulties it is my present purpose to state; declaring, at the same time, that far from exulting in them, as a cause of triumph over the friends of innovation, nothing would give me greater pleasure than to see them completely removed."

And what are these difficulties? They are, in Malthus' own words, "that the power of population is indefinitely greater than the power in the earth to produce subsistence for man.

"Population, when unchecked, increases in a geometrical ratio. Subsistence increases only in an arithmetical ratio.

"This natural inequality of the two powers of population, and of production in the earth, and that great law of our nature which must constantly keep their effects equal, form the great difficulty that to me appears insurmountable in the way to the perfectibility of society. All other arguments are of slight and subordinate consideration in comparison of this. I see no way by which man can escape from the weight of this law which pervades all animated nature."

The natural positive checks to population, Malthus stated, are disease, famine, and war, and there are also other artificial positive checks such as unwholesome occupations, too severe labor, bad nursing, and evils and distresses through excess.

From 1798 to the present time Malthus' ideas have been the subject of continuous and heated controversy. Already in his own day his publisher remarked that his book was more talked about than read, and this remains true today. Malthus deserves to be carefully read, for the population problem has become greatly more pressing since his day, and has resulted in every one of those disasters which Malthus predicted in the *Essay*.

It is often stated by critics of Malthus that his view are invalidated by the fact that the food supply could be indefinitely increased. Malthus was quite aware of this argument, and his answer was: "Yes; but that is no proof that it could keep pace with an *unlimited* increase of population." In any event, why compound the miseries of the greater part of humanity by encouraging the reproduction of human beings in societies in which such human beings are incapable of supporting themselves and their families by their labors, thus becoming a charge upon the rest of mankind?

That question is now more than ever critically before us, and Malthus's *Essay on the Principle of Population,* in its final sixth edition of 1826, is still the best discussion we have of it.

It was Malthus who provided Darwin with the idea of natural selection. As Darwin tells us in his *Autobiography,* "I happened to read for amusement 'Malthus on Population,' and being well prepared to appreciate the struggle for existence which everywhere goes on from long-continued observation of the habits of animals and plants, it at once struck me that under these circumstances favourable variations would tend to be preserved, and unfavorable ones destroyed. The result of this would be the formation of new species. Here then I had at last got a theory by which to work." As evidence of the fruitful effects of reading on the mind prepared is the fact that some twenty years later, upon reading Malthus, Alfred Russel Wallace (1823–1913) arrived at precisely the same conclusion and generalization as Darwin.

In the Introduction to *The Origin of Species,* 1859, Darwin writes, "In the next chapter [Chapter Three] the Struggle for Existence amongst all organic beings throughout the world, which inevitably follows from their high geometrical powers of increase, will be treated of. This is the doctrine of Malthus, applied to the whole animal and vegetable kingdoms. As many more individuals of each species are born than can possibly survive; and as, consequently, there is a frequently recurring struggle for existence, it follows that any being, if it vary however slightly in any manner profitable to itself, under the complex and sometimes varying conditions of life, will have a better chance of surviving, and thus be *naturally selected*. From the strong principle of inheritance, any selected variety will tend to propagate its new and modified form."

The idea of natural selection, which is Malthusianism on an extended scale, is the keystone of the theory of evolution. The principle of natural selection and the theory of evolution have exercised the most substantive of influences upon social theory and practice. Indeed, virtually every aspect of human thought and conduct has been influenced by these two concepts. These Darwinian ideas, as a rule, have had the most beneficial of effects, but in the misapplied form of Social Darwinism their effects have been unfortunate. Everything from imperialism to war, and Rugged American Individualism to ruthless competition in business has been justified by the appeal to Darwinian principles. Social Darwinism as a mode of thought is still very much with us, in spite of the writings of Espinas, Kropotkin, Novicow, Nasmyth, Allee, Emerson, and numerous others.[3]

What most Social Darwinists failed to understand is that man is something more than an animal, that he is a political animal, and that he has become this "something more" as a consequence of a unique evolutionary history which has increasingly freed him from dependence upon organic predispositions and caused him to become more and more dependent upon the accumulated ways of dealing with the environment of his group— namely, upon *culture*.

The concept of culture is one of the most significant and one of the youngest in the history of the social sciences. It has an interesting history. The concept of culture was first clearly stated by Gustav Klemm (1802–1867), German culture historian, in the first volume of his *Allgemeine Cultur-geschichte der Menschheit,* published in 1843, the whole work being completed in ten volumes in 1852. In the years 1854 and 1855 Klemm published his two-volume work *Allgemeine Cultur-wissenschaft.* The first of these works constitutes a history of culture, the second a science of culture. Klemm refers to culture as comprising "customs, information, and skills, domestic and public life in peace and war, religion, science, and art. . . . It is manifest in the branch of a tree if deliberately shaped; in the rubbing of sticks to make a fire; the cremation of a deceased father's corpse; the decorative painting of one's body; the transmission of past experience to the new generation." This is not quite a definition of culture—which Klemm does not seem to have attempted—but it is a fairly good description of what the contemporary anthropologist means by culture.

Klemm's work was read with close attention by a young Englishman named Edward Burnett Tylor (1832–1917), who was much influenced by it, as is apparent from his book *Researches into the Early History of Mankind and the Development of Civilization*, 1865, and in the two-volume work which followed, *Primitive Culture*, 1871. In the first volume of the latter work, which boldly emblazoned the word "culture," the word is defined as "that complex whole which includes knowledge, belief, art, law, morals, custom, and any other capabilities and habits acquired by man as a member of society."

Such is the inertia of cultural lag that it took fifty years for the word "culture" in this sense to find a place in a dictionary, and it is not until the twenties of this century that the term began to establish itself in anthropological thought and in the social sciences generally.

It is not the function of the historian of science to award prizes, but there can be no doubt that the merit for recognizing the meaning and significance of culture belongs to Tylor. However, the credit for preparing the way for the acceptance of the concept of culture belongs to the American anthropologist Alfred Louis Kroeber (1876–1960), who in 1917 published a now classic article in the *American Anthropologist* entitled "The Superorganic," in which the main point was that "the distinction between animal and man which counts is not that of the physical and mental, which is one of relative degree, but that of the organic and social [cultural], which is one of kind. . . . Mentality relates to the individual. The social or cultural, on the other hand, is in its essence non-individual. Civilization, as such, begins only where the individual ends."

It is of interest to note, as Kroeber recorded, that he was

afraid to use the term "culture" or "cultural" in his paper more than two or three times, for fear of being misunderstood, and so he wrote "social" where he would have wished to write "cultural."

The concept of culture has since been developed by many anthropologists and will long continue to be among the most fruitful of the ideas of social science.

The final great idea of the social sciences with which we shall deal here follows naturally upon this last: it is the application of the idea of culture to the concept of race which had developed during the nineteenth century.

Some astonishingly good, as well as some preternaturally bad, books were written on the subject of race during the first decade of this century. It was not until the first year of the second decade of the twentieth century that the first really scientific work on the subject of race made its appearance. This was *The Mind of Primitive Man,* published in 1911, the author being Franz Boas (1858–1942). Boas' *The Mind of Primitive Man* is notable for the fact that it presented, from the standpoint of science, the argument for the unity of man while broadly explaining the significance of its lack of uniformity. As a field anthropologist Boas had early made the discovery that beneath the difference in culture and skin color, head shape and size, there functioned a human being who was very much like every other human being everywhere else, uniquely and interestingly different yet fundamentally similar. It is in the making of the manner of these differences and likenesses clear to us that Boas made his great contribution, not only to science but also to humanity. For what he showed us was that so-called "racial" differences in the achievements of different peoples had no demonstrable connection with race but were to the most significant extent due to differences in the cultural history of those peoples. His demonstration, summed up in a few words, was that insofar as cultural achievement is concerned it is not race that determines culture but rather culture that determines the collective achievement of any group, whether a race or a social class. Boas demonstrated the nonsense of the concept of "racial purity" and the absurdities of the doctrine of "racial superiority." He showed that races were not static unchangeable entities but temporary dynamic eddies in a more or less continuous stream of cultural *and* physical change. The idea that culture rather than race is the significance determiner of the ways of life of a people as a scientifically demonstrable truth we owe to Franz Boas.

Boas concludes his book with the following words, and those words will serve well as a conclusion to this chapter: "I hope the discussions contained in these pages have shown that the data of anthropology teach us a greater tolerance of forms of civilization different from our own, and that we should learn to look upon foreign races with greater sympathy, and with the conviction that, as all races have contributed in the past to cultural progress in one way or another, so they will be capable of advancing the interests of mankind, if we are only willing to give them a fair opportunity."

REFERENCES

1. L. L. Bernard, *Instinct: A Study in Social Psychology.* New York, Holt, 1924.
2. Aristotle, *The Politics of Aristotle,* edited by Ernest Barker, New York, Oxford University Press, 1946.
3. Ashley Montagu, *Darwin, Competition, and Cooperation.* New York, Schuman, 1952.

15. *The new litany of "Innate Depravity"*

It is said that when the Bishop of Worcester returned from the Oxford meeting of the British Association in 1860 he informed his wife, at tea, that the horrid Professor Huxley had declared that man was descended from the apes. Whereupon the dear lady exclaimed, "Descended from the apes! Let us hope it is not true, but if it is, let us pray it will not become generally known."

It would seem that the last forty years of anthropological discovery and research in the behavioral sciences are in much the same situation, for while the findings of these disciplines are wholly opposed to the deeply entrenched view that man is an innately aggressive creature, most people either dismiss these findings out of hand or ridicule them as a rather eccentric idealistic heterodoxy which does not deserve to become generally known. In preference to examining the scientific findings they prefer to cast their lot with such "authorities" as William Golding who, in his novel *Lord of the Flies*, gives a colorful account of the allegedly innate nastiness of human nature, and Robert Ardrey who, in *African Genesis* and more recently in *The Territorial Imperative*, similarly seeks to show that man is an innately aggressive creature.

Golding's novel has steadily sold in the thousands each month

[186

since its publication in 1954, and Ardrey's *African Genesis,* published in 1961, has also enjoyed a popular success. Ardrey's *The Territorial Imperative,* published in August 1966, was a Book-of-the-Month selection and was declared by that distinguished naturalist, Clifton Fadiman, to be "a trail-blazing effort." Similar laudatory encomia by comparable "authorities" have been bestowed upon the book.

What is the explanation of the appeal such books have for so many people? Golding's novel is a rattling good story. Ardrey's books are, with his dramatist's skills, excitingly written and hold the reader spellbound. But these qualities are not the secret of their appeal. What, then, is?

Such books are both congenial to the temper of the times and comforting to the reader who is seeking some sort of absolution for his sins. It is gratifying to find father confessors who will relieve one of the burdensome load of guilt we stumble under, by shifting the responsibility for it to our "natural inheritance," our "inherited aggressiveness."

If it is our "nature" to be what we are, if we are the children of our "murderous" ancestors, we can hardly be blamed or blame ourselves for the sin of being little more than made-over apes. Our orneriness is explained, and so is the peccant behavior of children, juvenile delinquency, rape, murder, arson, and war, not to mention every other form of violence. It is all due to man's innate aggressiveness.

There is nothing new in all this. We have heard it all before. In the latter half of the nineteenth century and in the early part of the twentieth century this viewpoint formed the foundation for the doctrine of Social Darwinism. It was implied in such ideas as "the survival of the fittest" and "the struggle for existence," and in such phrases as "the weakest go to the wall," "competition is the life-blood of a nation," and the like.

Such ideas were not merely taken to explain, but were actually used to justify, violence and war. As General von Bernhardi put it in 1912, "War is a biological necessity . . . it is as necessary as the struggle of the elements in Nature . . . it gives a biologically just decision, since its decisions rest on the very nature of things." [1] One wonders what von Bernhardi would have said after the "biologically just" defeat of Germany in two world wars? No doubt the general would have had little difficulty in finding an "explanation."

The new liturgy of "innate aggression" as an explanation of man's proclivities to violent behavior does not seek to justify that behavior, but by thus explaining it to point the direction in which some measure of control may be exercised over it. In this Dr. Konrad Lorenz, one of the founders of the modern science of ethology, the study of behavior under natural conditions of life, has taken the lead. In his book *On Aggression*, published in April 1966, he has set out his views at length. In many respects they parallel those of Ardrey.

Ardrey's and Lorenz's views suffer from precisely the same fatal flaw, namely, extrapolation from other animals to man.

Ardrey argues that since the earliest manlike forms, indeed the earliest men, the australopithecines of Africa, made and used tools and employed some of them as weapons with which to bash in the brains of baboons, the australopithecines were therefore "killers," and *therefore* man is a killer by nature! Lorenz says exactly the same thing.[2]

Ardrey's views constitute a revealing example of the manner in which a man's prejudices may get in the way of his reason and distort his view of the evidence. He refers to some of his early experiences of violence which convinced him of the murderousness of human nature. Hence, when through the distorting glass of his prejudgments he looks at a tool, it becomes not simply a scraper but a weapon, a knife becomes a dagger, and even a large canine tooth becomes "the natural dagger that is the hallmark of all hunting mammals," while in "the armed hunting primate" it becomes "a redundant instrument. . . . With the advent of the lethal weapon natural selection turned from the armament of the jaw to the armament of the hand."

The teeth are no more an armament than is the hand, and it is entirely to beg the question to call them so. Virtually all the members of the order of primates, other than man, have large canine teeth, and these animals, with the exception of the baboons, are all vegetarians, and it is because they are so that they require large canine teeth. That such teeth may, on occasion, serve a protective purpose is entirely secondary to their main function, which is to rip and shred the hard outer coverings of plant foods. Defense against predators is a purely secondary function which such teeth may perform. As Professor Adolph Schultz has pointed out, protection is most efficiently provided by the combined alertness and keen vision of the organized social group. "The long canines of adult monkeys and apes are not very dependable weapons, since they become broken, abscessed, or even lost, especially after the enamel has partly worn off, far more frequently than they do in carnivores." [3]

"Man," Mr. Ardrey informs us, "is a predator whose natural instinct is to kill with a weapon." [4] Early man's hunting, according to him, was the result of instinctive belligerence, not of the hunger for food. But the fact is that early man did not hunt for pleasure, in order to satisfy his "predatory instincts." He hunted for food, to satisfy his hunger, and the hunger of those who were dependent upon him. He did not hunt because he was a killer, any more than contemporary man is a killer when he slaughters animals in abattoirs so that he and others may eat them. Early man was no more a killer than we are killers when we sit down at table to consume a steak or a chicken.

When Mr. Ardrey admiringly presents us with *West Side Story* as a "vivid portrait of natural man," in which "we watch our animal legacy unfold its awful power," in the form of juvenile delinquents in their "timeless struggle over territory, as lunatic in the New York streets as it is logical in our animal heritage," we can only remark that it is worthy of William Golding.

The evidence renders Mr. Ardrey's "personal interpretation" quite unacceptable. Everything we have learned about early man points to the nonviolent nature of his life, to the contribution made by cooperation to his physical and social evolution. The invention of speech, the social process of hunting, the development of food-getting and food-preparing tools, and the like—all these are highly cooperative activities, the survival benefits of which are never once mentioned by Mr. Ardrey.

189]

But, then, Mr. Ardrey is arguing a thesis. And the same is true of Lorenz.

Why do reasonable beings behave so unreasonably, asks Lorenz. And he answers, "undeniably, there must be superlatively strong factors which are able to overcome the commands of individual reason so completely and which are so obviously impervious to experience and learning. . . . All these amazing paradoxes, however, find an unconstrained explanation, falling into place like the pieces of a jigsaw puzzle, if one assumes that human behavior, far from being determined by reason and cultural tradition alone, is still subject to all the laws prevailing in all phylogentically adapted instinctive behavior. Of these laws we possess a fair amount of knowledge from studying the instincts of animals." [5]

It is in these sentences that the fatal errors committed by Lorenz are exhibited. First, he assumes that man's frequent irrational behavior is phylogentically based, and second, this enables him immediately to conclude that the "laws" derived from the "study of the instincts of animals" are applicable to man.

There is, in fact, not the slightest evidence or ground for assuming that the phylogenetically adapted instinctive behavior of other animals is in any way relevant to the discussion of the motive forces of human behavior. The fact is that, with the exceptions of the instinctoid reactions to a sudden withdrawal of support in the human infant and to a sudden loud noise, man is entirely instinctless.

Those who write of "innate aggression" in man appear to be entirely lacking in any understanding of the uniqueness of man's evolutionary history. Unacquainted with the facts or else undeterred by them, they insist on fitting whatever facts they are acquainted with to their theories. In doing so they commit the most awful excesses. But, as is well known, nothing succeeds like excess. Lorenz's assumptions and interpretations are typical.

"There is evidence," he writes, "that the first inventors of pebble tools, the African australopithecines, promptly used their new weapon to kill not only game, but fellow members of their species as well." [6] Is there? This is my special field, and I am unacquainted with the evidence. A fractured skull of a child and a broken jaw have been found among australopithecine remains, and these have been attributed by Leakey—as he fetchingly puts it, "in police parlance"—"to a blow from a blunt instrument." The truth is that no one can say what such fractures may have been due to. Leakey's "modern police parlance" refers, of course, to murder. As one who for more than thirty years has served as an expert witness in interpreting the manner in which various bones have come to be fractured, I can think of a score of causes wholly unconnected with "a blow from a blunt instrument." But the proponents of the doctrine of "innate aggressiveness" are uninterested in such alternative explanations.

Lorenz continues: "Peking Man, the Prometheus who learned to preserve fire, used it to roast his brothers: beside the first traces of the regular use of fire lie the mutilated and roasted bones of Sinanthropus pekinensis himself." [7]

This is Lorenz's interpretation of the evidence, and it is one he shares with many others, but it is gravely to be doubted whether it is a sound one. The cracked bones of Peking man may represent the remains of individuals who died during a famine, and who may well have been eaten by their surviving relatives or friends. This sort of thing has been known to occur among most peoples of whom we have any knowledge. There is, however, no record of any people ever having made a habit of killing their fellow men in order to make a meal of them. It is absurd to suggest that Peking man used fire "to roast his brothers." Does Lorenz seriously believe that Peking man made a practice of "roast brother"? Has it never occurred to Lorenz that, like some contemporary peoples, burning the corpse may have been Peking man's way of disposing of the dead?

Lorenz writes, "One shudders at the thought of a creature as irascible as all pre-human primates are, swinging a well-sharpened hand-ax." [8]

Really! For a serious student of animal behavior Dr. Lorenz seems to be singularly uninformed on the nature of the temperament of "pre-human primates," if we are to judge what

191]

their temperament may have been like from those exhibited by the living great apes in their natural habitats. The field studies of Schaller on the gorilla, of Goodall on the chimpanzee, of Harrisson on the orangutan, as well as those of others,[9] show these creatures to be anything but irascible, and there is not the least reason to believe that man's prehuman primate ancestors were any different. Imprisoned monkeys and apes in zoos or laboratories are not the best examples from which to deduce the behavior of such creatures under natural conditions.

Lorenz writes of early man faced with "the counter-pressures of hostile and neighboring hordes." [10]

Again, there exists not the slightest evidence of hostility between neighboring hordes of early man. The populations of early man were very small, a few score or few hundred individuals at the most. "Neighboring hordes" would have been few and far between, and when they met it is extremely unlikely that they would have been any less friendly than food-gathering hunting peoples are today.

"The hostile neighboring tribe," writes Lorenz, "once the target at which to discharge phylogenetically programmed aggression, has now withdrawn to an ideal distance, hidden behind a curtain, if possible of iron. Among the many phylogenetically adapted norms of human social behavior, there is hardly one that does not need to be controlled and kept on a leash by responsible morality." [11]

And there we have it! Man's aggressiveness is "phylogenetically programmed," and can be kept within bounds only by moral controls.

It has never occurred to Lorenz, who knows a great deal about greylag goslings but apparently very little else that is not in the realm of nineteenth-century speculative desk-anthropology, that far from being innate, man's aggressiveness is a learned form of behavior. There is absolutely no evidence whatever—indeed, the evidence is entirely in the opposite direction—that man is in any way "programmed" to behave aggressively.

Throughout the 2 million years of man's evolution, the highest premium has been placed on cooperation—not merely intragroup cooperation,[12] but upon intergroup cooperation,[13] else there would be no human beings today. Intra- or inter-group hostilities in small populations would have endangered the very existence of such populations, for any serious reduction in numbers would have made the maintenance of such populations virtually impossible. There is not in fact the slightest evidence nor is there the least reason to suppose that such conflicts ever occurred in human populations before the development of agricultural-pastoral communities, not much more than 12,000 years ago.

The myth of early man's aggressiveness belongs in the same class as the myth of "the beast," that is, the belief that most if not all "wild" animals are ferocious killers. In the same class belongs the myth of "the jungle," "the wild," "the warfare of nature," and, of course, the myth of "innate depravity" or "original sin." These myths represent the projection of our *acquired* human deplorabilities upon the screen of "nature." What we are unwilling to acknowledge as essentially of our own making, the consequences of our own man-made environment, we saddle upon "nature," upon "phylogenetically programmed" or "innate" factors. It is very comforting, and if somehow one can connect it all with one's findings on greylag goslings, studied for their "innate releaser mechanisms," it makes everything all the easier to understand and accept.

What, in fact, such writers do, in addition to their wholly erroneous interpretation of human nature, is to divert attention from the real sources of man's aggressiveness—namely, the unsound values by which in a highly competitive, overcrowded, threatening world, man so disoperatively attempts to live. It is not man's innate nature, but his external nurture that requires our attention.

REFERENCES

1. General von Bernhardi, *Germany and the Next War*. London and New York, 1912, pp. 16–37.
2. Konrad Lorenz, *On Aggression*. New York, Harcourt, 1966, p. 239.
3. A. H. Schultz, "Some Factors Influencing the Social Life of Primates in General and Early Man in Particular." In S. L. Washburn, ed., *Social Life in Early Man*, Chicago, Aldine, 1961, p. 73.

4. Robert Ardrey, *African Genesis*. New York, Atheneum, p. 316.
5. Lorenz, *op. cit.*, p. 237.
6. *Ibid.*, p. 239.
7. *Ibid.*, p. 239.
8. *Ibid.*, pp. 241–242.
9. See Irven DeVore, ed., *Primate Behavior: Field Studies of Monkeys and Apes*. New York, Holt, Rinehart & Winston, 1965.
10. Lorenz, *op. cit.*, p. 243.
11. *Ibid.*, p. 253.
12. Th. Dobzhansky and Ashley Montagu, "Natural Selection and the Mental Capacities of Mankind." *Science,* vol. 105 (1947), pp. 587–590.
13. Ashley Montagu, *Darwin, Competition and Cooperation*. New York, Schuman, 1952; Ashley Montagu, *The Direction of Human Development*. New York, Harper & Bros., 1955; Ashley Montagu, *The Human Revolution*. New York, Bantam Books, 1967; Ashley Montagu, *On Being Human,* 2nd ed. New York, Hawthorn Books, 1966.

16. *"Race" and humanity*

It is a common human failing to believe that if a word exists then there must exist something in reality which corresponds to it. Do "devils" exist, or "succubi" or "incubi" or "dragons" or a thousand and one other figments of our imagination? "Race" belongs in the same category with these words. It is an invented category, not a discovered one. As the tidy creature he is, man likes to inventory, classify, pigeonhole, and otherwise categorize his experience. His taxonomic activities represent an attempt to make some sort of order out of the bewilderingly variegated and intractable materials of the great big buzzing confusion of experience. It is a laudable response to the challenge of the environment and has yielded, on the whole, fruitful results. Sometimes, however, man's taxonomic activities have gone badly awry. The world of experience is often complex and is often not readily fitted into the arbitrarily created pigeonholes we have devised to receive it. When, with some manipulation and forcing, we wedge the data of experience into the devices we have created to receive them, our words and ideas, and then proceed to identify what we have thus factitiously compelled into our arbitrarily constructed frameworks with what we believe exists and goes on in "nature," we commit one of the oldest of human errors. Our minds become museums of the artifacts we have ourselves created, and we their most zealous caretakers. Seeing the world through the distorting-glass of our own predilections, we tend to identify our prejudices with the laws of nature, forgetting that the so-called laws of nature are also our own way of interpreting the world of experience.

Classifications of races exist; races do not. There have been innumerable classifications of the "races" of mankind, some recognizing a few "races," others claiming to distinguish scores of them.

The difficulty with such classifications has always been that they arbitrarily set boundaries between populations where no such boundaries exist, for the truth of the matter is that populations grade so imperceptibly into one another that it is, in most cases, not possible to determine where one ends and the other begins. Such gradients are called *clines,* and clinal phenomena are encountered everywhere within the human species. The arbitrariness of the customary exercises in the classification of human populations has been so obfuscating and stultifying that this alone would constitute sufficient ground for dropping the concept of "race," insofar as it has any reference to man. But there is a more cogent reason for abandoning this chimerical concept. It is simply that the fallacies which are inherent in the concept of "race," to which so many people subscribe, not only have no counterpart in reality but constitute myths which have been and continue to be extremely destructive.

The myth of "race," in which most people of the Western world believe as if it were a demonstrable truth, takes the following form: There is a something called "race" which is responsible for the physical characteristics, the behavioral traits, and the cultural achievements of different peoples. These three traits are believed to be indissolubly linked with one another. Hence, in accordance with this myth, physical traits that distinguish various "races" from each other may be taken as indicators of the behavioral and cultural capacities of the individuals exhibiting such physical traits.

What is unsound in this widespread belief is its basic assumption that there exists a linkage between physical, behavioral and cultural traits. No such linkage, in fact, exists.

The genes subserving the development of each of these categories of traits are inherited quite independently of one another. Genes do largely determine the physical traits of the individual and of populations, but it is quite another thing to extrapolate from this the view that genes determine behavior and the capacity for cultural achievement. They do not. While there can be very little question that genes influence the development of behavior, there can be equally little question that they do not determine it. The major factor influencing the development of human behavior is the human environment, the man-made part of the environment, that is, culture.

Man's adaptive dimension is culture, and man learns how to adapt himself to that environment from other men. What an individual learns and what he will achieve is determined by two principal factors: (1) the cultural environment in which he learns to be a human being, and (2) the quality of his genetic endowment. No matter how superior the genetic endowment of the individual may be, if the cultural environment is such as not to make any demands upon it for outstanding achievement, or for the matter of that any special kind of achievement, there will be no outstanding or any other kind of achievement. Achievement in any field or in any respect requires opportunities. Where opportunities are wanting, there will be no achievement. Where opportunities and encouragements are present, achievement will vary according to the limits set by the requirements of the culture. Nonliterate peoples have never built and will never build a submarine or a skyscraper, not because their genes render them incapable of doing so but because they have culturally never experienced the slightest need for such structures and have therefore never developed the technologies necessary for their envisagement or construction. Cultural needs, not genes, determine cultural achievement; genes as potentialities make that achievement possible, but they neither encourage it nor determine it.

It is highly probable that the genes that render cultural achievement possible *are fundamentally similar* in all the populations of humanity. The reason why it is possible to say this with a high degree of probability is that during the 2 million years or so of man's evolution the selective processes which have been at work upon him must have been much the same in all populations.

Throughout the evolutionary history of man he has been a food-gatherer and hunter. It is only during the last 12,000 years of his history that some populations developed agriculture and some went on to develop an urban way of life. All of man's basic traits were developed long before that. Under food-gathering and hunting conditions of life, populations are small and the challenges of the environment, differing as they may from the jungles of central Africa to the icy wastes of the Arctic, remain fundamentally alike. What is required under such conditions of life is the ability to meet the daily demands of life with the necessary adaptive responses. The traits having the highest adaptive value under such conditions are plasticity, malleability, cooperativeness, and the generalized intelligence which enables one to make the appropriately successful responses to the challenges of the environment. In the course of man's evolution the selective pressures acted not toward the development of any particular ability but toward the generalized ability of adaptability. Hence, there would have been no development of genetically based special abilities in one population differing from those developed in other groups. Since there was no particular premium placed upon the development of such abilities, there would have been no selection for them in any group.

It is man's generalized ability to adapt himself to all environmental conditions and challenges, *not* a fitness in one special ability or another, which has been at the highest premium in the course of his evolution. It is from such considerations that most anthropologists reason that there exist no significant differences in the genetic constitution for behavior and intelligence as well as for cultural achievement among the various populations of man. Possibly some genetic variability exists for the substrata of behavior as between different populations, but if such genetic variability does exist it cannot be large. The variability within populations is almost certainly much greater than that which exists between populations.

To what, then, are due the differences in behavior and cultural achievement that exist among populations? The racist chooses to believe that these differences are due to genes. Anthropologists choose not to believe anything unless there is good evidence for it, and the evidence indicates that, allowing for such genetic variability and its influence which we have already referred to, the behavioral and cultural differences among the populations of mankind are principally, if not wholly, due to the differences in the history of experience of each population. For example, the peoples of Europe are technologically and in many other respects more advanced than the nonliterate peoples of the world because they have for long enjoyed the cross-fertilizing effects of contacts and relations with innumerable peoples of the greatest diversity of cultural background, whereas the nonliterate peoples have been virtually isolated and have not experienced anything remotely resembling the European experience. When Caesar landed on the shores of Britain in 55 B.C. he found the Britons in a Bronze Age stage of cultural development. The Romans occupied Britain for more than 500 years, then followed the Jutes, the Angles, the Saxons, and the Normans, but it was not before the end of the fifteenth century that the English began to blossom culturally. It took 1,500 years of such cultural cross-fertilization before the English began breaking out like a glorious shower of stars dazzlingly beautiful through the clouds which had hidden them for so long. Who, during these earlier centuries, would have predicted that these rude barbarians would produce a Shakespeare, a John Donne, an Isaac Newton, and a John Keats? With a similar history behind them, it is probable that every people would have developed along similar lines.

The conditions necessary for the development of a high civilization are very special, and genes or not, there can be no such civilization unless the necessary conditions are present. The same holds true for individual achievement; no matter whether the necessary genes are present or not, there will be no achievement unless the appropriate conditions are present.

On a population basis genius in any high civilization is a rare event, while the ability for high achievement is only a little less rare. We cannot speak with certainty of genes for genius in nonliterate populations. It must be remembered that such populations are very small, hence the range of variability is likely to be somewhat less for such genes than in a large population. On a population basis one would hardly expect to find genius, although one would expect to find genetic constitutions which, under the appropriate conditions, would be expressed in extraordinarily high achievement. Sequoyah, the Cherokee Indian who from completely nonliterate beginnings invented the Cherokee alphabet and syllabary, represents perhaps the best-known example of such a genius, and there have been others. However, one would not expect many geniuses. If there have been such genetic constitutions for genius in nonliterate societies, there has been little call upon them, because there has been no need, and so it is quite possible, even probable, that many geniuses in nonliterate societies have died as mute inglorious Miltons, who were never called upon to pluck the poet's lyre or solve a differential equation. Genius, like high achievement, requires the proper soil in which to flourish. Nor is genius always recognized when it occurs. However, in every society there is no difficulty in recognizing the man of courage, of ability, even though the genes may be there for a great deal more.

Indeed, every bit of evidence available to us indicates that what the average man of any society has done the average man of every other human population can also do. When all the peoples of the world shall have enjoyed all the requisite opportunities and a sufficient amount of time in which to have taken advantage of them, it will be time enough then to take a census of the distribution of the genes for genius and those for high achievement. At that time, it is to be hoped, such a question will be of merely academic interest, for the really basic question is not a matter of genes at all.

The basic question concerning human beings is not whether they belong to some classifactory group or "race" or not, fascinating as the physical and cultural differences are that exist among them, but whether they are human beings. And that is the long and short of it. If an individual is a human being, then he should enjoy all the rights and privileges of being human and should be afforded all the necessary opportunities for fulfillment, whatever his genetic constitution may be. The birthright of every human being is fulfillment of his unique capacities as a human being.

In this connection science is utterly irrelevant and always will be, for the problem, the question, is not a scientific one but an ethical one—and when science has said everything it has to say on the subject, the final word will have been spoken by ethics. One's relation to one's fellow man is not a matter of science, skin color or sociology, but plainly and simply a matter of humanity.

17. *What is science for?*

When the members of "the invisible college," which in 1662 was to become the Royal Society, talked about science they were in no doubt as to what science was for. It was for practical use. As early as 1646, in a letter to a friend, Robert Boyle wrote, "Our new philosophical college . . . values no knowledge, but as it hath a tendency to use." [1] From the very first the technological requirements of a burgeoning economy played an important role in determining the choice of problems which the "virtuosi" set themselves, as were later set for them, to solve. [2]

During the eighteenth century the purposes which science was conceived to serve underwent something of a change. Science was aristocratized. It was taken up by the leisured classes, and the *Philosophical Transactions* was read largely by very much the same people who subscribed to the *Gentleman's Magazine*. Country gentlemen and clerics submitted their observations and the results of their experiments to the *Philosophical Transactions* in much the same spirit as they later wrote letters to *The Times*.

The eighteenth century was an expansive age, the age of the great voyages of discovery of Captain Cook and Bougainville, and above all the age of ideas, of freshets of daring new thoughts which were soon to overflow into the great revolutions, industrial, political, social, and scientific, of which we are all the direct heirs. The leisure of the theoried classes of the eighteenth century constituted a happy medium in which to cultivate science, and it became largely a science for science's sake. It was a delightful diversion. This aristocratic view of science is a principal reason why the eighteenth century was, on the whole, a very sterile period in the history of science.

It was the eighteenth-century attitude toward science as being largely a leisured-class diversion to be pursued for its own sake that determined the view of the purpose of science which came to be generally held and which still persists in some quarters into the second half of the twentieth century. It is the view that the purpose of science is to discover the laws of nature, and whether or not the discoveries of the scientist have any practical use should be of no more concern to him than the uses to which those discoveries may be put. Those scientists who are of middle age will recall that this was the attitude of many of their professors, who took something very like spiritual pride in their avowal of disinterest in any practical uses to which their work might be put.

There were men who called themselves "pure scientists"; like the "pure mathematician" Hardy, who offered the toast, "Here's to pure mathematics. May it never have any use," they pretended to be offended when anyone suggested that their work might be put to practical use.

A factor contributing to this mandarin attitude was undoubtedly the passionate devotion of many scientists to their work. One does not make a trade of a devotion. It is freely given and unconditional. A scientist, in any event, is not in business. He burns no incense before empty shrines. He is a man of integrity. Practical scientists are technologists, but the "real" scientist sticks to his last—which is science.

This is a viewpoint which requires, I believe, modification. What is science for? Before we can return any useful answer to that question it is necessary to agree upon what science is.

What science is is what the scientist does, and what the scientist does is, I think, best described in terms of the attitude of mind which the scientist brings to his work. The scientific attitude of mind is characterized neither by a willingness to believe nor by a willingness to disbelieve, nor is it characterized by a desire to prove a theory to be one way or the other. The scientist is characterized by one attitude of mind only, and that is the desire to discover what *is*. As a scientist the method he most relies on is verification. Having done all that is necessary to verify his own findings, he publishes them in the hope and expectation that other independent scientists will check his findings and either confirm them or not. He is as ready to accept the proof of the errors he has committed in arriving at his results as he is to accept the confirmation of his findings.

While a scientist's motivations for his work may be interesting, they have no relevance whatever to the processes he uses in his scientific work. Whether he is a Moslem, Jew, or Christian, a Mongoloid, Negroid, or Caucasoid, and whatever his political creed, there is only one scientific method and it transcends all such boundaries. Science is the discovery and ordering of the relations between conditions in a systematic and verifiable manner—in a manner such that scientists anywhere can verify the findings.

If this is what science is, that is, a method *of* rather than an activity *for,* we may go on to the next step. If science or scientific pursuits have a purpose, and we must assume that all scientific activities are purposive, then that purpose is not the discovery of anything *for* but the discovery *of,* the discovery *of* the relations between conditions, the ordering *of* those relations, and the understanding *of* their significance. The purposes for which scientific activities are engaged in, as I have already said, are something quite apart from the purposive behavior involved in the sciencing of the scientist. Attempting to find a safe and effective agent to combat the cause or causes of the common cold is a purposive activity in which many scientists are engaged. The hope of these scientists is that when such an agent is discovered it will either help to prevent the development of or reduce the incidence of colds, much as the polio vaccines have served to prevent the development and reduce the incidence of poliomyelitis. But the motivation for their work and the carrying out of the work itself are two very different and separate processes. Not only must these two different and separate processes be critically distinguished, they must also be kept separate. Never must the scientist permit either what he would wish to be or not to be to affect the conduct or the outcome of his work. The moment he falls short of that avoidance of bias, he ceases to be a scientist and becomes a special pleader. Not that the scientist, once his findings have been established, does not sometimes have to explain them to those who are unacquainted with either the methods he has used or their significance, but this is a very different thing from bringing his personal bias to bear upon the processes he pursues in his scientific work. Scientists are human and often do have biases of various sorts. The important thing is to recognize the biases one has, acknowledge their existence to oneself, and to take all the necessary precautions to be on one's guard against them.

Science, like any other human activity, is pursued by human beings within a social matrix and is therefore of social relevance. Now that science has reached, as it were, the social critical mass and the practical applications of science threaten the very existence of the species, the "of-ness" of science has been greatly overshadowed in importance by its "for-ness." For there can surely be no doubt that survival as such is more important than scientific discovery. These are far from being incompatibles. Science properly used and controlled can be for man a means of enlarging his experience and of maximizing his happiness. Science as a human activity must always be free. It must never be subjected to political or social pressures. But these uses to which scientific discoveries are put must be controlled in the interests and for the benefit of mankind. And this brings me to the answer to the question, "What is science for?"

Science as a social activity should be for the benefit of mankind. Certainly, as science, science may be pursued for the sheer joy of it or for any other related reason, but in its practical applications it most certainly should be controlled. *The control, however, should be left to the scientist.* The scientist should be as responsible for the uses to which his ideas and findings are put as he is responsible for the integrity of his work as a scientist. The scientist can no longer dissociate himself from the consequences of his scientific activities. He must hold himself as responsible for them as the engineer must who builds a bridge over which his fellow men will pass. In more than a metaphoric sense the scientist builds bridges over which his fellow men will pass. He must be responsible for them.

The scientist must learn to consider himself as more deeply involved in the community of mankind than any other class of man, for the very cogent reason that the consequences of his scientific activities are more likely to affect the welfare of his fellow men. For that reason also, he can no longer take the view that his scientific work is ethically and socially neutral, for the truth is that the effects of science have the profoundest and most direct repercussions upon the pursuit of the good life within the framework of society. No one, surely, can any longer entertain any doubts on that score. It is impossible to think of a single science which has not either directly or indirectly contributed, in one way or another, to the increase and enlargement of man's biological capacities, in the sense of contributing to his better health, greater comfort, increased longevity, and superior mastery of his environment. Insofar as science has done so, it has, among other things, altered man's way of life and changed his conceptions of his relations to his fellow men. Science has, indeed, not only prolonged the life of man but has enlarged his capacity to fulfill himself and live more completely. The promise of science in this direction is virtually unlimited, and it seems to me that the fulfillment of this promise is what science is *for:* for the increase of the welfare and happiness of all mankind.

While the layman has often realized the value of scientific work and understood that the scientist was in fact working for the benefit of mankind, whatever the scientist himself might think of his own motivations he has usually deprecated all attempts to endow his activities with "higher purposes." He has usually been most unwilling to be associated with any idea that he was working for the benefit of mankind. A scientist must above all abjure all sentimentality, for sentimentality is essentially the conferral of nobility upon ignoble things, and it is—or was until recently—ignoble for a scientist to confess an interest in the welfare of mankind as a prime motivation, or any part of his motivation, for his scientific labors.

I believe that this attitude of mind has been damaging to everyone concerned and is largely responsible for the uncontrolled misuses to which scientific discoveries have often been put. The scientist must freely acknowledge to himself that he is engaged in activities which are capable of having the most profound social consequences and that therefore it is his moral obligation to see to it that his work is constructively and not destructively utilized. If he takes this view then he is directly involved in the welfare of mankind. He need no longer hesitate to acknowledge to himself that he is working in the hope that what he does may have some value for his fellow men.

If science as a social activity is *for* anything, it is not to rest satisfied with the discovery and demonstration of what *is* but rather to continue with the discovery to its application to the advancement of the welfare of mankind. Associations for the advancement of science are essentially associations for the advancement of the welfare of mankind. It is interesting that such associations have come closer to the recognition of that fact than have the individual scientists who together constitute the membership of such associations.

REFERENCES

1. Thomas Birch, *The Works of the Honourable Robert Boyle in Five Volumes,* vol. 1. London, 1744, p. 20.
2. Robert K. Merton, "Science, Technology and Society in Seventeenth Century England." *Osiris,* vol. 4, pt. 2 (1938), pp. 360–632.

18. *The history of medicine*

It has been remarked that the longer you can look back, the farther you can look forward. In a world so rapidly shrinking in size and increasing in numbers as ours, in which social and technological change is proceeding at an ever-accelerating rate, it is imperative for every professional group to look to the future with the vision that has grown of experience and understanding. Of no profession is this more true than that of medicine, for here the changes are likely to come very rapidly, and those changes are likely to be fundamental. A good look at the evolution of medicine will be helpful in enabling us to perceive the direction in which medicine is still evolving.

History, it should be remembered, refers to events which have been recorded. Of the prehistory of medicine we know very little indeed. Man as man has had a history extending over some two million years. During a considerable part of that period, medical practices were almost certainly in vogue, but what they may have been we can only partially reconstruct from archeological remains and partly from the study of the nonliterate cultures of our own time, which are so rapidly vanishing.

Perhaps the oldest representation of a medicine man is the figure on the wall of the cave of Les Trois Frères in the Pyrenees. This shows the figure of a man adorned in the skin of an animal with antlers, obviously engaged in causing the

forces to which he is appealing to do his bidding. In this respect he is in the direct line of ancestry of the modern medical
man. The representation is almost certainly of Aurignacian
age, that is to say, about 15,000 years B.C. From the study of
contemporary nonliterate cultures we may reasonably infer that
the medicine man of Les Trois Frères was engaged in a magico-
religious ritual calculated to compel the attention of the supernaturals. In nonliterate cultures both disease and death are
viewed as due not to natural causes, but invariably to the influence of some malevolent power. That power may be the
work of an enemy either directly or through the agency of a
sorcerer, it may be the work of the spirit of the dead, or it may
be directly due to the supernaturals. In most nonliterate
societies disease is regarded as of magical origin.

In such societies disease is ascribed to two possible causes:
(1) the projection of some dangerous material or influence into
the victim's body, and (2) the abstraction of a part of the victim's body or of his soul. The function of the medicine man is
in the one case to remove the projected material from the body
of the patient and in the other case to restore what has been
abstracted.

The nonliterate medicine man is a highly efficient practitioner and in his own world is able to bring about cures in
cases which have utterly defeated the best efforts of the most
highly skilled physicians trained in the Western world. Where
the nonliterate practitioner is most successful is in those cases
in which the culturally conditioned beliefs of the individual
have, under the appropriate conditions, produced in him the
conviction that he has been the victim of magico-religious
forces. The medicine man can generally suck these out of the
victim's body and show the noxious material to the patient in
the form of a small stone which he spits from his mouth into the
palm of his hand. Returning the part of the body or soul which
has been abstracted from the victim's body is somewhat more
difficult, but by the proper ritual and incantation this can often
be achieved.

It is of interest to note that in some nonliterate societies the
medicine man is perfectly aware of the fact that he is a faker,

but that very same man will believe that while he is so, the other medicine men are the genuine articles. This is a state of affairs which is not limited to nonliterate societies.

In prehistoric times, among Neanderthal peoples, we have evidence of surgical procedures of some complexity being practiced with skill. Thus, among the Shanidar Neanderthalers of Iraq, going back some 50,000 years, orthopedic surgery was not unknown, while among Neolithic and Bronze Age peoples the difficult operation of trephination was quite widely practiced. Among some existing nonliterate peoples the operation is performed not only to relieve the patient of spirits that are disturbing him, as in mental illness, but also to produce cerebral decompression as a result of injury, to relieve headaches, and as a cure for epileptiform seizures. The evidences of healing indicate that the operations are highly successful.

From nonliterate medicine to folk medicine is but a step, for though with folk medicine we pass into the historic period, the prevalent motif still remains magico-religious. A book published a few years ago by an M.D. which consisted of nothing but folk medicine should make it clear that folk medicine is very much still with us, especially since that book has sold several million copies. I have myself no doubt as to the efficacy of Vermont vinegar, but not for the reasons claimed. And I have myself witnessed the practice of folk medicine in the twentieth century among the illiterate parents of university graduates. I could not have been afforded a more vivid demonstration of the continuity of contemporary scientific medicine with the magico-religious medicine of prehistoric man. In the case I witnessed, the aunt of the woman who was the patient exorcised the demons, or whatever she conceived the causative agents of the disease from which her niece was suffering, by incantation and the ritual of putting a burning coal into a glass of water and pronouncing the proper spell. The patient recovered—and that, of course, proved the value of her aunt's expertise.

I do not for a moment suggest that all folk medicine is worthless. On the contrary, some of the best remedies of folk medicine form the basis of many modern medical remedies. I am merely saying that much in folk medicine represents a continuation of the belief in the magico-religious causation of disease, and that as time passed experience with different plants yielded the knowledge that in certain diseases they had a remedial effect.

The first genuine medical men came into being with the birth of civilization, and that almost certainly occurred in Mesopotamia, that is, the region between the Euphrates and Tigris rivers, at Sumer some 6,000 years ago. There exists a Sumerian seal which belonged to a physician who lived about 3000 B.C. There is a similar seal which belonged to a Babylonian physician dating back to about 2300 B.C. The code of King Hammurabi (second century B.C.) of Babylon has many references to the laws applying to physicians. For example, "If the doctor shall treat a gentleman and shall open an abscess with a bronze knife and shall preserve the eye of the patient, he shall receive ten shekels of silver. If the patient is a slave, his master shall pay two shekels of silver." But if the gentleman dies the doctor's "hands shall be cut off." In the case of the slave, "he shall replace the slave with another slave."

Evidently in Babylon the practice of medicine was regulated by the state even down to the payment of fees and the penalties prescribed for what was considered incompetence. We see then that socialized medicine has an extreme antiquity. Medicine in Babylonia was still dominated by magical and religious ideas, as we know from clay tablets of the time which contain, among other things, a good many incantations and charms. Divination was widely practiced, the clay model of the sheep's liver, mapped out in squares each with a hole for a peg, providing a principal diagnostic tool. Compared with the fresh liver of a sacrificed animal, any departure from the fresh specimen was carefully pegged out on the model and the proper diagnosis drawn from the configuration thus presented. It is probable that physicians in Egypt belonged to the priestly class.

In the fifth century B.C. Egypt was already a highly developed kingdom with several million inhabitants. The Ebers Papyrus, one of the oldest books of any kind, is the best-known medical book of antiquity. It dates to about 1500 B.C. and contains some 900 recipes or prescriptions. Blind empiricism is mixed

211]

with sound observation, spells and incantation, and the driving out of devils is still the keystone of Egyptian medicine. In taking the prescribed medicine one was to repeat such a magical spell as "Welcome remedy! Welcome! that dost drive away that which is in this my heart and in these my limbs." The modern patient may not utter such spells when he takes his medicine, but for the most part he has a scarcely less magical belief in the efficacy of the medicine he is prescribed than his Egyptian relative of 4,000 or more years ago.

It is of interest that the Old and New Testaments have practically no references to the physician, and indeed the Hebrew word so translated could more justly be rendered as "healer." God alone was regarded as the healer, and it was he who sent disease as a punishment to men for their transgressions against Him. This is not to say that the Jews were without medical knowledge. On the contrary, they appear to have made great advances in medical knowledge during this period. This is especially true in the realm of prophylaxis, individual and public health. Indeed, the Jews were the pioneers of public health, as they were of a social conscience, of the doctrine of the brotherhood of man, and of the subordination of the individual to the community. The good of the greatest number must be sacrificed to personal comfort or convenience. Physical purity was the complement of moral purity, and cleanliness was literally next to godliness.

Medicine in the East as presented through the four *Vedas,* written in Sanskrit about 1500 B.C. indicates that Hindu medicine at this time consisted mainly of incantations and spells. But by the beginning of the Christian era the Hindu physician Charaka (first century A.D.) and Susruta (about the fifth century A.D.) make their appearances. Susruta, the more noteworthy of the two, was aware that malaria was caused by mosquitoes, that there was a relation between rats and plague, that it is not for some years after puberty that the female is physiologically ready for reproduction, and much else of the same remarkable caliber. "He who knows only one branch of his art is like a bird with one wing," remarked Susruta. This physician mentions some 760 medicinal plants, and more than

100 surgical instruments. The ancient Hindus performed operations such as Caesarian section, excision of tumors, lithotomy, and rhinoplasty, the latter operation almost certainly having originated in India. Thus the Hindus were the pioneers of plastic surgery.

Going farther east to China, the father of Chinese medicine was the mythical Emperor Shên Nung, who lived about 2735 B.C. He was a man of great ability and learning. His "Great Herbal," the *Pen Ts'ao*, contains descriptions of more than 1,000 drugs and is still in use in China. Thus, the *Pen Ts'ao* has the longest continuous record of use, 5,000 years, of any medical book in history. Many of the drugs and compounds listed are in use to this day, such as opium, rhubarb, aconite, croton, iron, arsenic, and sulphur. Ephedrine was isolated from the Chinese herb *Ma Huang*.

Another noteworthy medical work was written by Emperor Huang Ti about 2650 B.C. This is the *Nei Ching* or "Book of Internal Medicine," a work upon which all Chinese medicine rests. Written 4,000 years before William Harvey, this work gives a thoroughly Harveian description of the circulation of the blood.

It is impossible here to enter any further into a discussion of the very remarkable achievements of Chinese medicine and surgery which came to full fruition in later times.

Skipping over the early pre-Helladic Greeks, to Greek medicine, Hippocrates, born on the island of Cos in 460 B.C., is the outstanding figure. Of the 100 or more books which make up the *Hippocratic Collection,* he was not the author, but he was almost certainly the inspiration of them all. The Hippocratic Oath is familiar to all medical men, and exemplifies Hippocrates' high conception of the conduct required of the physician. Hippocrates' greatest contributions to the development of medicine were his natural conception of the causation of disease and his awareness of the importance of environmental factors in disease. In treatment Hippocrates made little use of drugs. He knew that there was in most diseases a tendency to natural recovery. "Our natures," he said, "are the physicians of our diseases." It is best to allow many conditions to take a natural course, without our meddlesome interference.

Among the great contributors to Roman medicine stands Soranus (A.D. 98–138). Soranus was the leading authority on obstetrics, gynecology, and pediatrics among the ancients. Celsus' *De Re Medicina,* written about A.D. 30, represents the only surviving part of an encyclopedic work dealing with philosophy, military strategy, law, medicine, and probably other subjects. Celsus was a member of the noble family of Cornelli, and was almost certainly not himself a physician. *De Re Medicina,* rediscovered during the Renaissance, was printed at Florence in 1478 and thereafter enjoyed a long and well-merited fame, for it gave a clear and most elegantly presented account of Roman medicine of the first century A.D.

The most influential figure of the Graeco-Roman tradition in medicine was Galen of Pergamum (A.D. *c.* 130–200). Galen's influence in medicine dominated the next 1,200 years. He became an orthodoxy, and to depart in any way from his canon was considered a heresy. No wonder, since Galen regarded the body as the husk of the soul—a doctrine which Christian and Moslem alike found congenial in an Age of Religion.

Galen recognized the value of anatomy for the physician, but his own knowledge of anatomy was based upon that of the pig and the Barbary ape. Galen followed Hippocrates as a practitioner of medicine, and the simple vegetable products he prescribed are still known as "galenicals." Galen was a remarkable animal experimenter, demonstrating and being the first to distinguish between motor and sensory nerves, the sympathetic and central nervous systems. Among other things he also showed that loss of voice was due to division of the recurrent laryngeal nerve, and much else.

The Romans' contribution to medicine in terms of diagnosis and treatment was negligible, but in terms of public health their contribution was of major dimensions. Sewerage, sanitation, plumbing, drainage, and water supply, gymnasia, swimming pools, public baths, hot and cold baths, and the use of natural healing springs, are all Roman contributions.

The Roman state medical service was a model of what such

services should be. The state financed the teaching of physicians, appointed them to the armed services, and instituted the *archiatri* or public physicians appointed to attend the poor and to supervise medical practice within their area. The court physicians were invested with special privileges and dignity and had a voice in the government. *Valetudinaria,* private hospitals or nursing homes, appeared during the first and second centuries A.D. A Roman army hospital constructed on the corridor system has been excavated at Novaesium (modern Neuss) near Düsseldorf, and represents one of the most perfect examples of such structures.

Arabian medicine in its best form is represented by the works of the Moslem physicians Abú Bakr Muhammad ibn Zakariyýa, known as Rhazes (A.D. *c.* 860–932), and Abu Ali al Hussein ibn Abdallah ibn Sina, or Avicenna (A.D. 980–1037). Rhazes was originally a philosopher and musician and did not begin the study of medicine till he was forty. His work *A Treatise on Smallpox and Measles* clearly distinguishes between these diseases, the two most frequent in Persia, where he was born and lived. He was strongly opposed to every form of quackery and magic and was a zealous proponent of the Hippocratic method.

Avicenna was the outstanding figure of Arabian medicine and a most powerful influence throughout Europe for six centuries. He has been called the Prince of Physicians. He was an infant prodigy and at the age of eighteen became court physician at Bokhara. He is identified by some with the poet Omár Kháyyám. His work *The Canon of Medicine* is still studied in the East. In this work pulmonary tuberculosis was for the first time regarded as a contagious disease, and in it he makes many interesting observations which only now are beginning to re-receive the attention for which they have so long been waiting. He notes the effect upon health of emotional disturbances and the therapeutic value of music, of climate, the seasons, bathing, and sleeping.

The medieval period witnessed slow but steady progress in medicine and surgery. Mondino de' Luzzi or Mondinus (*c.* 1275–1326), who was born and taught at Bologna, instituted anatomy as the basic foundation of the medical curriculum, and his

Anathomia, written in 1316, represents the first practical manual of anatomy. He was the first professor to descend from his *cathedra* and carry out the dissection with his own hand, assisted by his brilliant girl pupil, Alexandra Galiani.

In London St. Bartholomew's Hospital was founded in 1123 and St. Thomas's in 1215, under the control of the church. By the fourteenth century most such hospitals had become lay institutions.

The work which revolutionized the study of medicine was published in June 1543, six days after the work which revolutionized our view of the world. The former was Vesalius' *De Humani Corporis Fabrica,* and the latter was Copernicus' *De Revolutionibus Orbium Coelestium.* Vesalius, a Belgian (1514–1564), had studied at Louvain, Paris, and at Padua. In the university of Padua he was appointed professor of anatomy and surgery in 1537. Six years later, at the age of twenty-eight, Vesalius published his magnificent folio *De Humani Corporis Fabrica,* with numerous original wood engravings attributed to another Belgian, a pupil of Titian, Jan Stephan van Calcar. This work was a masterpiece in every way, and although not entirely free of galenical anatomy, it was an account of the structure and mechanism of the human body which was for the first time based virtually entirely on dissections of the human body. In this work Vesalius severely criticized his predecessors, and with the zeal of a young man who has not learned the tact necessary, let us say, to become the president of his university, he laid about him in a hearty and unrespecting manner. The old men were wounded, but everyone else took to Vesalius' great book as they should have done. It became a classic in its own day, and has remained so since—the definition of a classic being that it is either unread or out of print. In the case of Vesalius' great book, it is both, and the English translation goes a-begging for a publisher to this day.

From the middle of the sixteenth century onward, the history of medicine is the story of enlarging and continuous progress. In addition to being perhaps the most dramatic story of progress in any field, it is one of the most interesting, and in what remains I should like to turn to a discussion of the significance of all this progress for man.

What medicine has meant for man can be quickly understood from the fact that up to the year 1861 the average age at death of human beings was 33.3 years, and this held true for the United States as well as for other lands. One hundred years later this figure had been more than doubled. This increase in longevity is principally, if not entirely, due to the contributions which medicine has made to virtually every possible aspect of man's physical and mental wellbeing. Indeed, it may truly be said that there are very few persons alive today, wherever modern medicine has flourished, who do not owe their wellbeing to the benisons which medicine has bestowed upon them.

Where, then, does medicine go from here? I think we can clearly see where the future development of medicine will lead. For one thing it will lead to an increasing concentration on the maintenance of health rather than upon the concentration on illness, which largely characterized the earlier history of medicine. This concentration on illness was inevitable in periods when the causation of disease was not understood and in which the problems of epidemiology were formidable. Disease will always have to be cured, but the achievable end to which medicine will increasingly strive in the future will be the prevention of disease. And this will increasingly become a social activity. The health of the individual, and therefore of the community, is the community's most precious possession, and with the growing consciousness of this the community, the state, will increasingly become more actively involved in the health of the people. Wherever the community or the state has made movements in this direction, the greatest opposition to such proposed assumption of its obligations by the local or state government has come from the medical profession. The profession has considered that its rights were being threatened, and so the opposition has been considerable. But the interesting thing about this piece of history is that wherever such measures have been passed into law and have been established as going concerns, and I refer particularly to the health-insurance schemes in Europe of the last and this century, it is the medical

217]

profession that has eventually become the staunchest defender of such public medicine.

In England the National Health Service is the latest of these governmental enterprises to be developed. The service has many faults: no one in the service is adequately recompensed, there are too few persons staffing the service, there are too few hospitals and too many antiquated hospitals, there are long waiting lists of persons awaiting the services of a surgical staff, and so on. But these are all remediable faults, and it seems to me that with the examples of the national health services of the Scandinavian countries and the United Kingdom before us, we could do even better in the United States. Since the greater participation of the federal government in protecting the health of the people is inevitable, the public rather than private interest will increasingly have to be put first. Medicare, established in 1967, is a step in the right direction, but it is only a first step. The wise anticipation of the inevitable is not incompatible with an even fuller and more fruitful life, both private and public, for the medical man than he at present enjoys.

The history of medicine is the history of the triumph of science over superstition and of conscience over cupidity. It is in the direction of that long and noble tradition that medicine is, I am convinced, destined to advance.

19. *Culture and the evolution of man*

It is an interesting fact that discussions of the evolution of man have almost always been devoted to the evolution of his physical traits within an environment virtually exclusively physical. Almost every possible environmental factor that could have been involved in man's physical evolution has been considered, but until the very recent present the role played by cultural factors in the physical evolution of man has received practically no attention. This is all the more surprising in view of the fact that, with the publication in 1871 of *The Descent of Man,* Darwin placed the problem squarely before his contemporaries. He did more than that. Darwin devoted a great part of his book to the consideration of the evolution of man's intelligence, the effects of sexual selection, the evolution of man's moral faculties, and the consequences of the action of these factors upon man's physical evolution. Darwin presented his arguments with his usual combination of clarity and cogency. His book was persuasive without being proselytizing. It was widely read and discussed. Nevertheless, the stimulus it provided appears to have evoked little response, at least with respect to further inquiry into the relation between cultural and physical factors in the evolution of man.

This failure to follow the lead so ably provided by Darwin

constitutes a puzzling chapter in the history of science. It is quite evident to anyone acquainted with the history of the literature, both secular and scientific, of the period that Darwin was not thinking and writing in splendid isolation. The ideas he developed were of considerable interest to his contemporaries. Darwin was not, in fact, thinking ahead of them. Indeed, many of the ideas developed by Darwin in *The Descent of Man* relating cultural factors to man's physical evolution had, in one way or another, already been discussed by such writers as Lord Monboddo in his *Antient Metaphysics,* published in six volumes between 1779 and 1799, by Johann Gottfried Herder in his *Ideen zur Philosophie der Geschichte der Menschheit,* four volumes, 1784–1791, by Lord Kames in his *Sketches of the History of Man,* published in 1774 in two volumes and in 1791 in an enlarged edition of four volumes, and by Thomas Love Peacock in his *Melincourt,* published in 1817, an enchanting anthropological novel which no reader of this book should do himself the disservice of failing to read, and in a fair number of similar works which appeared prior to and after the publication of *The Origin of Species* in 1859. No one, however, before Darwin, had discussed the relation between cultural factors and the physical evolution of man at such great length and as cogently as he. The times were not, apparently, propitious for the further development of Darwin's ideas by others. The concentration of interest was largely focused upon man's physical evolution, while those who pursued their interest in man's cultural evolution did so as if what they were concerned with were entirely unrelated to that other world of the student of man's physical evolution.

Physical and cultural anthropology developed as two separate disciplines; a specialist in one of these disciplines, in most cases, could not unfairly be described as one who agreed not to know what was going on in the other. In such circumstances it was not surprising that the two seldom met. Historically, physical anthropology grew out of the medical and zoological sciences. For many years its principal representatives were medical men working within the medical or zoological forum. Cultural anthropology, on the other hand, developed largely from the side of the humanities, so that when it became a university subject it was usually pursued in a department which was far removed from that in which the physical evolution of man was being studied. Even when the physical and cultural anthropologists were brought together under the same roof and were subsequently joined by the archaeologists, it took years before some evidences of cross-fertilization were to be observed. But that this was occurring even when it was least obvious should be clear to all who participated in the process. A great deal more was going on in the minds of some of those who were exposed to this triple intellectual climate than, for a time, appeared upon the surface. The latency period lasted about a generation, during which time a great many novel ideas were being received and more or less passively allowed to find their proper relations in the heads of those undergoing the experience. It is literally only within the last two decades that these ideas have begun to spark.

In the Introduction to *The Origin of Species,* 1859, page 5, Darwin had described the process by which evolutionary change comes about in the principle of natural selection, as follows:

> As many more individuals of each species are born than can possibly survive; and as, consequently, there is a frequently recurring struggle for existence, it follows that any being, if it vary however slightly in any manner profitable to itself, under the complex and sometimes varying conditions of life, will have a better chance of surviving, and thus be *naturally selected.* From the strong principle of inheritance, any selected variety will tend to propagate its new and modified form.

It is the demonstration of the validity of this principle that will always remain Darwin's greatest contribution to our understanding of the evolutionary process. Since Darwin's demonstration was, at first, based entirely on physical changes, it was the latter that drew and remained the focus of attention of virtually all evolutionists.

Until very recently physical anthropologists had been busy attempting to relate man's physical traits to the pressures of the

221]

physical environment. Every physical trait, it was assumed, must in some manner represent an adaptation to the physical environment, an adaptive trait. What was almost wholly overlooked is that man's principal means of adapting himself to the physical environment is culture.

Culture is an agency not only for controlling but for changing the pressures of natural selection and thus for influencing the evolution of man both physically and culturally. The cultural processes through which such evolutionary changes are achieved are many, as for example, through the development of tools, marriage regulations, sexual selection, social selection, cooperativeness, economic development, migration, improved care of children, and the like. It is principally through cultural pressures that primate nature, in the case of man, has been changed into human nature. It must be emphasized that this change has been brought about not, among other things, by the suppression of primate instinctual drives, but by their gradual supplantation by an adaptively more effective means of meeting the challenges of the environment, namely, by enhancing the development of intelligence.

The development of intelligence increasingly freed man from the bondage of biologically predetermined response mechanisms and the limiting effects they exercise upon behavior. In the evolution of man the rewards have gone not to those who could *react* instinctively but to those who were able to make the best or most successful *response* to the conditions with which they were confronted. Those individuals who responded with intelligence were more likely to prosper and leave progeny than those who were not so able. If there is one thing of which we can be certain, it is of the high adaptive value of intelligence as a factor in both the mental and physical evolution of man. In the course of human evolution the power of instinctual drives has gradually withered away, until man has virtually lost all his instincts. If there remain any residues of instincts in man, they are, possibly, the automatic reaction to a sudden loud noise, and, in the remaining instance, to a sudden withdrawal of support; for the rest, man has no instincts.

Instinct has been described as "lapsed intelligence." But

instinct as such is no longer intelligence. Intelligence is a far superior instrument to instinct in meeting the requirements of a complex environment. Instinct does not permit of the emergence of novelty, of innovation, or of originality. Intelligence does. The development of high intelligence was conditional upon the liberation from the body-compulsion of instinct.

Instincts are organic; they rise from within the organism; they are parts of its bodily structure. They are somatized, narrowly limited, behavioral responses. It is a main difference between nonhuman animals and man that the former rely upon the body and its capacities as the means by which adaptation to the environment may be implemented, for example, by the development of structures which may be used for defensive or offensive purposes; whereas man has evolved by the opposite principle, namely, by escape from the restricting bondage of reliance upon organically determined predispositions to the freedom of what has been called "the superorganic," to culture. This was gradually achieved with the discovery and inventive development of tools.

It is known that some primates will defensively, and sometimes offensively, throw stones and other materials at intruders. It is probable that the precursors of early man used stones in this manner. This is an extracorporeal, an instrumental, use of an object. A stone used for such a purpose is the crudest of all tools—but it is a tool. The *use,* however, of an object as a tool and the *making* of a tool to a special design for a particular purpose are two quite different things. I have seen an orangutan make a tool out of the straw on the floor of its cage. It folded a sheaf of straw into a firm mass and with it reached food otherwise out of its reach.[1] That was tool-making. In order to qualify for hominidity, it is not enough to make a simple occasional tool; it is necessary to play variations upon the raw material from which the tool is made, to improve upon those variations and perpetuate them. The creature that can do such things differs from all others that cannot. Such a creature is a man. A creature that can create such tools must be capable of mental

223]

processes which also serve as tools, mental tools, concepts, ab
stractions, words.

The capacity for such mental tools was undoubtedly gradu
ally developed, and it seems highly probable that the develop
ment of physical tools went hand-in-hand with the developmen
of mental ones. Tools, physical or mental, open up a world o
unlimited possibilities for development; the advantages the
confer shift the direction of the selection pressure of tha
development from the body to the mind. The evolutionar
result of this is the development of a man-made extrasomati
environment, namely, *culture*—in Leslie White's excellent defi
nition, the class of things and events, dependent upon th
symbolic process, considered in an extrasomatic context.[2]

With the loss of his instinctual equipment and as a result o
the increasing enlargement of the brain, the human infant i
born in both a physically and behaviorally immature condition
In the course of evolution this has rendered him increasingl
more dependent upon others for all that he has had to learn a
a functioning human being. As such the human child mus
acquire from the world of human beings outside himself wha
other animals develop from within themselves. A long depen
dency period has considerable selective value, in that it favor
the prolonged maturation of the organism and affords the tim
necessary for learning.

It is quite erroneous to suggest, as is sometimes done, tha
natural selection is no longer at work in man, or that he is n
longer evolving, or both.

When the conditions among other animals are considered
it is found that the members of all species vary in the degree o
their adaptive fitness in relation to different aspects of th
environment. Among such animals lack of adaptive fitness in
single trait may prove of considerable disadvantage and, i
some cases, even lethal. Man, however, has created an environ
ment that is capable of meeting an ever-increasing range o
adaptive fitnesses—high or low. A trait of low adaptive fitnes
under earlier conditions of cultural development, which woul
have put an early end to its bearer, diabetes, for example, toda
elicits so much support from the man-made environment that i

is biologically no longer the extremely disadvantageous trait it once was.

Through cultural means, by the application of scientific discovery and technical advance, man provides an enormous amount of buffering against the impact of defects which in earlier times would have laid him low. Advances in medicine alone have made it possible literally for millions of individuals to survive to a ripe old age who would not otherwise have done so. Insulin and diabetes, liver and pernicious anemia, BCG and tuberculosis, antibiotics and many bacterial diseases, not to mention the successful treatment of many forms of inborn errors of metabolism—these are but a few examples.

Modern civilizations provide a great variety of niches for virtually every kind of physical and mental type, and as civilization advances those niches become ever more embracing in scope. With the exception of the individual who is in some way totally incapacitated, there increasingly tends to be a place for everyone in such a society. A wide range of niches is available.

The biologically low adaptive fitness of the individual in one or more traits is compensated for by the appropriate adjustive medical or social process or both. By this means biological damage is reduced or avoided.

It is on grounds such as these that it has been argued by some that natural selection is no longer operative in man, that it has been nullified or bypassed by man's taking his evolution into his own hands. This is to misunderstand what has in fact occurred and what is continuing to occur, namely, *not* that natural selection has ceased to operate in man but that, like a refreshing river, its course has simply been redirected to flow in deeper and newer channels. To abandon the metaphor for the reality, natural selection operates in relation to man in the new zone of adaptation into which he has moved, in the new environments which he has created. Fitness is a matter of fitness in relation to an environment, and not to someone's idea of natural selection. It is desirable to dispel the false idea that there is such a thing as absolute fitness. Fitness is always in relation to some part or parts of the environment. No one is ever equally fit in relation to every part of the environment.

Natural selection is fitness in relation to the environment as measured by fertility.

At this juncture I should like to raise a point of some contemporary urgency. If fertility is a measure of fitness, it may well be asked whether man is not perhaps becoming too fit for his own good. Is he not increasing at too rapid a rate? What has been called "the population explosion" does, indeed, constitute a threat to the welfare of mankind. But it is a threat which man can meet by precisely the same means with which he has met other and even more alarming dangers throughout his history—by the use of his intelligence. Even now agencies all over the world are at work seriously considering methods of controlling population increase. The Japanese have most effectively solved this problem in their own land. There is no reason why men in other lands cannot do likewise. The danger, however, is with us, and the threat to human welfare it constitutes speaks to us with an urgency that demands our most active attention. We are very good at controlling death. We need to be at least equally adept at controlling birth. It would be unthinkable that man should this way be hoist with his own petard.

Such matters are by no means a digression from the main theme of this book. On the contrary, they are in the direct tradition of Darwin's own discussion of them in *The Descent of Man*. In the matter of population increase Darwin wrote,

> Natural selection follows from the struggle for existence; and this from a rapid rate of increase. It is impossible not to regret bitterly, but whether wisely is another question, the rate at which man tends to increase; for this leads in barbarous tribes to infanticide and many other evils, and in civilized nations to abject poverty, celibacy, and to the late marriages of the prudent. But as man suffers from the same physical evils as the lower animals, he has no right to expect an immunity from the evils consequent on the struggle for existence.[3]

Darwin was, of course, quite sound in asserting that man had no right to expect immunity from the evils consequent on the struggle for existence, as long as—he might have added—he does nothing to control the rate of natural increase. It is clear that man has no right to expect immunity from smallpox and other diseases as long as he does nothing to protect himself against them. But man can, by controlling his own environment, confer upon himself a lasting immunity against smallpox and similar diseases, and what is more, it is his moral obligation, enforceable by the laws of most civilized states, to do so. Vaccination against smallpox has saved untold millions of lives. In bygone years scarcely anyone was spared, and the stamp of "the pox" was a familiar sight throughout Europe. Since that time man in the Western world has progressed so far in the control of this disease that there is today many a physician who has never seen a case of smallpox.

Man possesses the power to achieve a similar immunity from the socially and biologically deteriorative consequences of his own capacity for rapid multiplication. Within the last few years there have been growing indications that man may yet make himself master of his own numbers before it is too late.

The more clearly we understand the role that cultural factors have played in the evolution of man, the better we shall be able to control his future evolution. And if the lesson is learned that physical (genetic) and cultural evolution are not mutually exclusive processes, we shall be better prepared to understand the lines along which man's future development must proceed.

REFERENCES

1. M. F. Ashley Montagu, "A Note on the Behavior of an Orang-Utan," *J. Mammal.*, II: 231–2, 1930.
2. Leslie White, "The Concept of Culture," *The American Anthropologist*, 61: 227–251, 1959.
3. Second edition, 1874, Chapter 5; reprint 1901, p. 219.

20. *Man in the world of the future*

In the age of science fiction, of Superman, and space-ships traveling through intergalactic space with frictionless ease, the man of the future has, indeed, become a thing to conjure with—in every sense of the word.

Horizons are unlimited and so is the imagination. Our comic-book artists are enjoying a regular field day—anything goes. And the further it goes, the better. The comic books exist in order to amuse. They do not claim to serve any other function, certainly not to base their predictions as to the man of the future upon scientific findings. On the other hand, in creating their men of the future the comic-book artists do utilize some scientific data. Their tastes are nothing if not eclectic: a few facts from electronics, neurology, evolutionary theory, some H. G. Wells and Jules Verne thrown in, a good stirring of the lot, and out of this witch's broth emerges the man of the future in a thousand different forms.

The miracles of religion have given way to the miracles of science, and the age of faith has by almost inperceptible degrees advanced into the age of faith in the miracles of science. That is why anything goes not only in science fiction but also in the realm of belief in the possibilities of science. If science has become the secular religion of our day for so many people, it is no less a paradox that this age of science is perhaps the most credulous that Western civilization has known. In the name of science people can be persuaded to believe almost anything. Never is a long time, and who can say that man will "never" develop this or that extraordinary trait? No one. Certainly not the comic-book artists.

Several scientists have from time to time tried their hands at predicting what man would look like half a million years hence. On the whole, their predictions are on the conservative side, and in this I am inclined to agree with them, though I disagree with them on some essential details.

Provided there are no major natural environmental changes, predictions as to what man of the future will be like are not really difficult. The study of past forms of life over stretches of time running into many millions of years provides convincing evidence that certain trends are fairly early detectable in the evolutionary history of an animal group, and the tendency of the group is to realize these trends in its development. For example, the rabbit-sized horse (*Hyracotherium*) of 60 million years ago, we can now see, exhibited a tendency over this long stretch of time to increase in size and to lose some of its digits while modifying one into a hoof. Similarly, when we study trends among the order of animals to which man belongs, the primates, we find the tendency to increase in body size, the development of highly specialized forelimbs, and the abandonment more or less successfully of the quadrupedal posture for the obliquely quadrupedal posture of the great apes, culminating in the erect posture of man. There are, of course, many other trends that one can observe.

It is on the basis of such trends that one can predict with something resembling a high degree of probability what man in the world of the future will be like, both physically and psychologically.

In making predictions about the future of humanity the error is commonly committed of judging from the anthropocentric viewpoint of the white man. The fact is that the larger number of human beings belong to the nonwhite major groups of mankind. And predictions concerning the future of mankind must take this fact into consideration. All predictions of this kind, indeed, must be based upon the first of our predictions, namely, the high probability that all the varieties of humanity will increasingly come together and intermix so that eventually all human beings will look very much more like one another than they do today. In other words, instead of the large variety of ethnic groups which exist today there will be but a single ethnic group of the single species *Homo sapiens.* This single ethnic group will become a single breeding population. In this way will the early history of humanity be reversed, for in the early and greater part of man's history human populations were separated from one another and were constantly migrating away from one another. Their migratory tendencies were centrifugal, and hence such populations for the greater part of human history were constantly being separated from each other. At the present time, and increasingly in the future, the tendency is for populations to move toward each other. It should not take more than 1,000 years for this tendency to be completely realized in the biological unification of humanity.

The biological unification of humanity. What does that imply? Does it imply the uniformization of humanity? Most certainly it does not. Human beings will continue to be among the most variable of creatures. Their intragroup variability will be increased; their intergroup variability will be decreased. Whatever groupings human beings of the future will develop, they will not be on a biological or morphological basis. In other words, people will not group themselves on the basis of physical characters, because no aggregation of physical characters will be limited to any one group, but virtually every kind of physical character that we now know will be found distributed through all groups of human beings.

White skin color is likely to become somewhat darker, while dark skin colors are likely to become considerably lightened. Nevertheless, some very light and some very dark skin colors are likely to occur. The same is true of hair color. Hair form is also likely to undergo appreciable change. Negroid kinky hair is likely to become a comparative rarity, and while straight hair is likely always to be with us there is almost certainly likely to be an increase in curly hair, owing to extensive admixtures principally with Negroid peoples.

There are some authorities who believe that men of the world of the future will have lost all their hair, that baldness will be the rule. I believe this to be an error. In the first place, baldness is mainly limited to a certain proportion of the white peoples of the earth. In the second place, since the so-called racial differences which now exist between peoples will be eliminated by virtually complete intermixture, this means that baldness is likely to lose out. In other words, on genetic grounds it is possible to say that baldness is likely to be less frequent than it is today. On other grounds it is possible to predict that scientific research will have, long before the distant future arrives, found ways in which to prevent the development of baldness.

The question is often asked: How tall will the men of the future be? There are some who answer: Very tall. But I think this, too, is an error. During the last 50 years the average height of Americans has been constantly increasing. The average American today is some two inches taller than his grandfather. At this rate of increase Americans 500 years hence should be about three feet taller than they are today, which would make them just a little short of nine feet tall. Will any people ever attain such a height? The answer is: No. There are mechanical and physiological reasons which render such a height both inefficient and inadaptive. The body becomes far too heavy for a creature that walks in the erect posture as man does. Human beings sometimes do attain or very nearly attain such a height, but they almost invariably die at an early age from the consequences brought about by their condition—they die of sheer exhaustion.

There seem to be no advantages to a height exceeding, on the average, five feet eight inches, and it would appear very likely that this is the height which will characterize the average man of the future. The recent increases recorded in height are almost certainly due to improvement in nutrition and not to evolutionary changes. The evolutionary trend in man appears to be rather for the bones to become somewhat more gracile, smaller, smoother, and rounder, less coarse and more refined. If anything, body mass will tend to become reduced. This

231]

will involve not only bones but also muscle and fat, and hence average weight will be lower than it now is. One of the consequences of such changes will be a virtually automatic increase in longevity, for the heart and circulatory system, among others, will be called upon to do less work and will therefore last longer. An average duration of life of well over a hundred years is a high probability.

Contrary to the views of most prognosticators in this area, I do not believe that the brain, and consequently the head, will grow larger in size. The notion that the brain will increase in size is due to the mistaken view that the human brain is continuing to increase in size. On the other hand, we have good evidence that the brain, so far as size is concerned, long ago turned the evolutionary corner, and that for the last few score thousand years the brain has not increased in size but has perhaps somewhat increased in complexity. The brains of Neanderthal men were quite as large as ours and in many cases larger. The men of Předmostí in Czechoslovakia of the Late Aurignacian of some 15,000 years ago had brain volumes 1,590 c.c. while modern Europeans have brains with an average volume of 1,400 c.c. Indeed, the total variability in brain size today is rather low, thus indicating a relatively high degree of stabilization in brain size.

The brain can increase in volume without increasing in size, by the deepening of its convolutions, thus increasing its surface area. The notion of a globular head situated on a puny frame is the Sunday-supplement writer's envisagement of a development which will never come about.

Head form is likely to grow rounder, the continuing development of an evolutionary trend. But the face is not likely to grow smaller nor the jaws to shrivel. It is extremely unlikely, in spite of its frequent impaction, that the third molar will be lost in either the upper or the lower jaw, or that the jaws will become smaller. We shall continue to need all the teeth we have— all thirty-two of them.

The little toe, which is often condemned to extinction by the Sunday-supplement writers, will continue to perform the important functions it is called upon to serve as long as man continues to stand, to walk, and to run. Similarly, his body hair will continue to persist because it serves important functions, such as protection against blows, abrasions, and various sensory functions.

Man's senses are not likely to diminish in acuity; his ears are likely to continue to remain attached to his head. In short, while his evolution will continue, he is likely to remain physically in every way much as we know him today.

21. Anthropological reflections on makeup

There is a story of the man who asked his friend, "How do you like my wife?" And the friend replied, "Compared with what?" Quite possibly what the friend had in mind was the face beneath the mask. What is the face really like? Is the mask really more important than the reality? Mankind, it is known, cannot stand too much reality, and since it is man who looks at woman, woman gets the message—she accommodates herself to the image she sees in his eye.

The larger truth, of course, is that not only do men look at women, but women do, too, and not only at other women but at themselves. Together these constitute a combination of forces that are quite irresistible—both for women and men. Men want women to look attractive, and women want to appeal to men and to win the approval of other women as well as to maintain their own self-esteem.

Women being, as one perspicacious philosopher once remarked, a sex so to speak unto themselves, they have always, as a consequence of their superior survival qualities, had to compete for the males' attention, in a market in which those creatures were relatively scarce. It is an interesting fact that in those rare societies in which females are rather more rare than males, as among the Australian aborigines, the Eskimos, and the Todas of southern India, women do little or nothing in the way of making themselves artificially attractive to the males. But such societies are exceptional. In by far the greater number of human societies women resort to all sorts of artificial embellishments. No one, so far as I know, has ever made a study of the motivations that cause women to make themselves more attractive in such nonliterate societies, but we may suspect that they are not very different from those that are operative in more advanced societies.

Judging from the quantities of red ocher that have been found in the graves of Neanderthal man, it may be inferred that decoration of the body with colored pigments of various sorts is of great antiquity—50 thousand or more years. The New Stone Age is almost everywhere associated with beads, bracelets, necklaces, and other articles of feminine decoration, and it may be assumed that facial decoration was not neglected. It is not, however, until the development of urbanism that feminine decoration in attire, ornament, and makeup come into their own. Some of the most elaborate examples of makeup come from some of the earliest urban centers, such as pre-Biblical Jericho, Sumer, predynastic Egypt, and Mohenjo-Daro. During the two millennia of our own era the historic record is clear: women have continued to make the most of themselves in every possible way—perhaps this is what makeup really means.

In 1968 American women spent more than 2 billion dollars for cosmetics, an increase of nearly 10 percent over the preceding year. It may safely be predicted that every following year they will increasingly spend more.

From the viewpoint of an anthropological observer, feminine makeup and the varieties of change it has undergone should be of the greatest interest. Rather surprisingly, however, this is an area of human behavior to which anthropologists have paid very little attention. The present chapter, therefore, is something of a bold venture into an anthropological *terra incognita*. A good anthropologist should monitor the cultures not only of other peoples but of his own. Makeup happens to constitute a more than ordinarily interesting form of human behavior, and no apology need be made for taking a look at it.

What is so striking to me, as an anthropologist, about makeup is how little, if anything, that is new has been invented during last 5,000 years. Anyone looking at the extraordinary variety of beautiful feminine ornaments, as well as the cosmetics discovered in ancient Sumer, which date back to some 3,000 years before the birth of Christ, or at any of the effigies of women of early dynastic Egypt, will be able to judge for himself how very little that is new has appeared in the modern world in feminine makeup. Except for artificial eyelashes, I can think of nothing that is new, not even the Marcel Wave of an earlier generation nor the Sassoon haircut of today, for women in Egypt, Hellenic Greece, and in Rome often artificially curled their hair. But strictly speaking, hairdressing is not a part of makeup, makeup being restricted to the embellishment of the face by the use of such cosmetics as rouge, lipstick, mascara, powder, etc. But, of course, though the manner in which one's hair is dressed may not fall within the definition of makeup, no woman is properly accoutered unless to her makeup there is added the appropriate dressing of the hair. It need hardly be said that there is not a single hairdo that has appeared in modern times that had not been earlier devised somewhere in the world.

Since there is so little that is new in makeup, what becomes of interest are the changes in makeup style. The one new invention in makeup of the modern world, namely, artificial eyelashes (and I should not be surprised to learn that even *that* is not new), is of some anthropological interest. Young children tend to have longer and more curved eyelashes than their elders. It is well known that the preferred type of beauty in the United States is the "baby face." There was, I seem to remember, a song celebrating the type in its title and theme, "Baby Face." The average Hollywood starlet represents a good example of the type. Long curved eyelashes do, indeed, enhance the beauty of a woman, and it is, therefore, not to be wondered at that they have become so popular.

While on the subject of eyelashes a word may be said about eye shading. The use of eye shading is at least as old as Sumer and predynastic Egypt. There is reason to believe that in these ancient societies malachite green, the most popular of eye shades, was first used by both sexes to repel the flies which are still such a pest in the Middle East and which settle in unrelenting numbers upon the eyes. One can readily see how such an originally prophylactic practice became adapted for use as a part of feminine makeup. It is interesting to observe that in recent years malachite green has again returned to favor as a very popular color for eye shading.

The striking eye shading and eye lining used by Elizabeth Taylor in the film *Cleopatra* have served to revive and popularize an eye makeup style that had been extinct for several thousand years. The heavy eye lining possibly presages the advent of even more bold and adventuresome forms of makeup. It is unlikely that American women will ever develop an interest in enlarging their earlobes to pendulosity or that they will seriously consider lengthening their necks by encircling them with escalating metal rings. Nor do I foresee them ever resorting to nose or lip plugs, nor even the knocking out of front teeth by way of beautifying themselves, as women in many other societies do. Such practices, limited mostly to nonliterate peoples, do not conform to our conceptions of beauty. The broad strokes of the paintbrush recently used in eye makeup with its laterally extended lines do suggest that something of a breakthrough may have occurred in women's makeup, and that we may soon be seeing very much more festive forms of makeup.

High-caste women of India have worn precious stones in their nostrils, and some bravura types even among ourselves have already pioneered with irridescent paper diamonds flashing their messages from the upper eyelids. The effect can be quite fetching. Others have already committed themselves to such extravaganzas as multicolored, beaded or laced or brocaded eyebrows, as well as eyelids similarly embellished—the possibilities here seem to be unlimited. Again, however, the basic pattern of such eye ornamentation is not new, as anyone who has seen the wall carvings of Darius at Persepolis will know. But enough of these beaded baubles beckoning at the brim of what we have been traditionally told is the entrance to the soul. It is fitting that the entrance to such a shrine be appropriately ornamented with imagination, with valor, and with heart.

Eyebrow plucking is, of course, a very ancient practice, and its practice is preserved for us in the portraits that remain of ladies of dynastic Egypt and of Rome.

Makeup in common with the decoration of all other visible parts of the body is clearly a manifestation of the universal artistic impulse of human beings to decorate, to render more interesting and attractive anything and everything that the combination of skill and leisure is able to accomplish. Food-gathering and hunting peoples do not regularly practice their artistry upon themselves, except for ritual or ceremonial purposes, and even then, interestingly enough, it is the men who do most of the self-decorating, according to the traditional designs. Everyone in such small populations is too busily engaged in the process of surviving to be able to pay much attention to such self-indulgences as self-adornment. Art, in general, does not flourish in such communities. It is not until the increased leisure made available by the development of agriculture that we begin to see the gradual development of regular self-decorating practices among women. With the invention of urban life, feminine self-decoration began to assume highly sophisticated forms. Over the last 6,000 or more years the vagaries and cycles of fashion in feminine makeup have closely followed the periods of marked social change and upheaval of established values. The rate and amplitude of social change in the present century has, perhaps, exceeded that of any previous century, and it is therefore not surprising to find that makeup (as well as fashion in general) reflects something of the nature of those changes. The emancipation of women in a period of as great social change as we have experienced during the last fifty years has no doubt had not a little to do with the freedom and increasing daring with which women have ventured to experiment with makeup. While some examples of extravagant makeup have essayed an appearance, they have not been generally adopted. Women have realized that just as the best-dressed woman is the most unostentatiously attired, so the woman who has used her makeup with taste and discretion is the woman who has done so most unobtrusively. It is therefore as it should be that the current look in makeup is "natural" or "quiet."

22. *The human frame and furniture*

Perhaps one of the most significant things to be said about the aging process is that by the age of 25 years, the 10 billion cells in the gray matter of the human brain begin to die at the rate of about 50,000 a day or 18.25 million a year, with only 9 billion left by the time the age of 75 is attained. Since the young repudiate and are uninterested in age, it may be that this prodigious depletion in functional gray matter in the older members of the population is the true explanation of the tardy recognition of their status, their qualities, and their needs.

In a society which places so overweening a premium upon youth everyone wants to be young, to live as long as possible, but not to be old. As has been said, youth, alas, is wasted on the young, and the old, unfortunately, are unable to take advantage of that late acquired knowledge.

Growing old is a dubiously regarded privilege to which no one looks forward and upon which everyone looks backward with a bleary eye. It is, therefore, a privilege which is not intelligently anticipated or sympathetically understood and hence is, as it were by default, frequently abused. Age, therefore, for only too many of us turns out to be the period during which we spend most of our time paying the debts accumulated in our less thoughtful years. The proper time to prepare for age is in the years preceding it. All growth is growing older, and as Amiel wrote, "To know how to grow old is the master work of wisdom, and one of the most difficult chapters in the great art of living."

In the present chapter I shall be immediately concerned with one of the arts of living—namely, furniture—in the later years, say from 65 years on.

Up to the year 1861 the average age of death of human beings was about 33 years. Less than 100 years later the expectation of life in most civilized nations of the world had doubled. In the United States in the year 1965 a female child could expect to reach an age of 74.1 years and a male child an age of 67.4 years. While only a short time ago persons of 65 years and over constituted a relatively small proportion of the population, we today have more than 17 million persons aged 65 and over. In less than a half century hence that number will have risen to about 34 million. The members of this age group are living and will increasingly continue to live in an environment very different from that which was possible not much more than a generation ago. In the preautomobile age the extended family— that is, the members of the biological family and their immediate relatives: cousins, uncles, aunts, and grandparents—all lived closely together. In rural areas three or more generations together were often members of the same household, and this was not infrequently the case in urban areas. Both the biological and extended families were reciprocally supportive units. It was expected that children would grow up to support or contribute to the support of their parents in their old age. The situation today is virtually reversed, and parents are today expected to support their children in their old age! Today more than ever before the older person is on his own, and insofar as this change in relations leads to a revised estimate of the useful role that older persons can play in our society, the change is a good one.

In order that an individual play a useful role of any kind, the maintenance of health at an optimum level is desirable. In what follows I shall be concerned with the maintenance of the health of the older person with special reference to the contribution that properly designed furniture can make.

Let me say at once that as an anatomist and physical anthropologist I have for many years been acutely aware not alone of the inadequacies but of the numerous undesirable features of modern man's furniture insofar as his physical health is concerned—and this applies to every age level, not merely to older persons. I not only consider that much of our furniture has always been in many respects detrimental to the health of young people as well as older people, but such furniture designed—if it is designed—without any consideration whatever for the physiological needs of human beings has the effect of accelerating the aging process, of inducing premature aging, by producing damaging stresses and strains upon various systems of the body. A breakdown in one system of the body leads to the premature breakdown and death of an otherwise healthy individual. Too many persons die from the breakdown of a single system in an otherwise thoroughly healthy body.

It is a deplorable fact that in the Western world cardiovascular disease is one of the most frequent causes of death. Among the many factors contributing to that high rate of disease poorly designed furniture has rarely, if at all, been considered. Until the first urban revolution some 12,000 years ago, and to a very large extent up to the present day, the greater part of mankind when it sat, sat or squatted on the ground. Today we sit on devices known as chairs. The *Oxford English Dictionary* defines a chair as "a seat for one person (always implying more or less of comfort and ease); now the common name for the movable four-legged seat with a rest for the back, which constitutes, in many forms of rudeness or elegance, an ordinary article of household furniture, and is also used in gardens or wherever it is usual to sit." The first usage of the word in English occurs in the year 1300. The reference is to the work known as *Cursor Mundi* (line 9954), and the quotation is, "Was never yet king nor kaiser, that ever sat in such chair." This tells us a great deal about the origin of the chair. In the first place the chair is of recent origin. Its first use in the eleventh and twelfth centuries was as a mark of position, almost as a throne, a *cathedra,* from which word our own for chair is actually derived—from the Latin *Cathedra* to the Old French *chaiere,* to the Middle English *chayere,* and so to *chair.* The chair was evolved from the chest by adding a back and two arms and shortening the seat. All the variations that have been played upon that original theme have, in my view, scarcely improved upon the original model.

Let us consider the average chair. It is an atrocity. It is an atrocity because with its flat or rounded back and flat or contoured horizontal or forward-upward sloping seat, it represents the most unmorphologically and unphysiologically designed of man's contributions to his own comfort. In fact, the average chair could not be better designed than it is to produce simultaneous breakdown in several of the body's sustaining systems. Take, for example, the cardiovascular system.

One of the miracles of the physiology of the human body is the manner (still largely a mystery) in which the venous blood from the lower extremities is returned to the heart. Consider what a great distance the blood drained from the toes, legs, knees, and thighs must travel to reach the heart. It is the greatest distance traversed by the venous blood in the whole body. How does this blood, against the force of gravity, ascend in the veins to reach the heart? The answer at this late date is that we do not know. The veins in the lower extremities are equipped with valves to prevent the backflow of blood and to facilitate in the upward movement of the blood. The veins of the lower extremities constitute a system, as it were, of canals and locks, which assist to raise the blood higher and higher. This process is complemented by the milking action of the contracting muscles of the lower extremities. Anything that impedes the ascent of the blood in the lower extremities puts a tremendous back pressure upon the valves in these veins, causing their weakening and ultimate breakdown—with the resulting painful varicosities with which civilized man is only too frequently afflicted. The average chair is most unadmirably designed to produce such impediments to the venous return from the legs. This is achieved principally by so designing the front edge of the chair that it invariably produces an occult pressure on the vessels in the superficially situated popliteal spaces, the spaces behind the knees. The popliteal arteries, veins, and nerves supply the tissues of the leg and foot. Calculate the number of times one sits in chairs during the first thirty or forty years of life, not to mention the later years, and the astonishing thing is that the cardiovascular system does not break down from this cause alone more frequently than it does. The stress and strain is exerted not only upon the veins of the lower extremity, but also upon the heart, for venous return and cardiac output are interdependent functional processes. When venous return is retarded, right atrial pressure falls, causing the heart to pump diminished amounts of blood. Right, that is to say venous, atrial pressure determines the pumping ability of the heart. Chairs tend to diminish that pumping ability.

The inadequate chair produces the tendency to cross the knees when sitting, which again produces undesirable pressure against the popliteal vessels and nerves. In the latter connection it is to be observed that this noxious habit has not infrequently resulted in damage to the peroneal nerves, resulting in the condition know as "foot drop."

How then should a chair be properly designed? Since I cannot make the least claim to be a designer of furniture, it is with the greatest diffidence that I venture to make the following suggestions. It seems to me that furniture designed to support the body or to minister to its comfort should be built with due regard to the requirements both of the structure and functions of that body.

As a beginning, I would make the seat shorter, or tilt its forward half downward with a rounded and desirably soft edge. In conformity with the structure of the human back I would eliminate that abomination, the straight back of the chair, and design one that fitted the curves of accommodation and compensation of the vertebral column.

Most people, and certainly all makers of chairs, apparently consider the vertebral column to resemble a straight vertical rod. This is exactly what the vertebral column is not, and he who neglects this fact of life does so at his own and others' peril.

The human vertebral column is an astonishing piece of structural and functional engineering. It probably takes more abuse than any other part of the body—as we shall see. The vertebral column extends from the base of the skull to the tip of the coccyx. In the child and adult the neck vertebrae together form a curve which is convex in front, whereas the chest vertebrae are concave forward and convex at the back. This curve of accommodation is compensated for by the abdominal (lumbar) vertebrae, which are convex forward and concave at the back. The pelvic or sacral vertebrae are again accommodative, being concave forward and convex at the back. There are, therefore, alternately two curves of compensation and two curves of accommodation. Furniture makers appear to be quite unaware of these elementary facts. The back of the chair, whether low-backed or high-backed, should be designed to fit these vertebral curves, to give the back the support it needs, rather than to act, as it at present does, as an instrument of calculated breakdown with its usually convex or straight form, which puts considerable stress and strain on the lower back. In the older person this is particularly undesirable because of the shrinkage of the intervertebral discs and the tendency, with age, of the neck and lower back curves to disappear (resulting in old-age stoop).

It seems to me very likely that the high frequency of lower-back disorders in Western societies in middle-aged and older persons is a direct consequence of our unbiologically designed furniture.

Perhaps the most atrocious of all seats is the automobile seat, which must, I think, also be regarded as an article of furniture, since modern man spends so much of his life in these vehicles. The automobile seat is a piece of anarchy. It is a wonder to me that no one has yet suggested that the Russians have perpetrated this upon the American public through their secret agents working, of course, through Detroit. It is a thought which I freely offer to the Un-American Activities Committee. I suppose that an industry which is based on the principle of planned obsolescence need concern itself only with appearance rather than with reality. Long-term or short-term health considerations do not come within the purview of its interest. The automobile seat cannot be too strongly condemned, for its convex back and convex seat with the tilt upward and forward put an enormous strain on the human back. Nothing, indeed, could be better designed to assist in the deformation of the human back, which is neither convex nor concave but both. Various articles are sold to compensate for the deficiencies of the automobile seat, and those that I have tried certainly do so to some extent. There is, however, not the slightest reason why the automobile manufacturers couldn't supply a properly designed seat in the first place. But who is the consumer to protest? His business is to consume and to be consumed—or so it would appear.

Not much better than the automobile seat is the living-room sofa or the club lounge chair. These are generally too long in the seat and far too yielding.

The nearest approach to a morphologically satisfactory chair was the rocking chair of an earlier generation. The rocking chair, with its arm rests which enabled the older person to rise from it without too great strain and to rest his forearms in a position which made venous return to the heart easier, has many advantages, especially for older persons. The motions of rocking have not only a relaxing effect but in addition probably also contribute to gastrointestinal tone by counteracting the stasis of the gastrointestinal tract at rest. At the same time the circulation is assisted, and any tendency to the formation of clots, particularly in the lower extremities, is reduced.

Of all the iniquities that man, in the name of comfort, has ever visited upon himself by way of furniture, I do believe the bed is the worst. As John Paul so sagely wrote:

> Of all the foes that man should dread
> The first and worst one is a bed.

For the first thirty years or so of life the human frame can take an awful beating without any overt symptoms of the abuse, but after that period, and especially in connection with the back, the accumulated effects of sleeping on beds such as we inflict upon ourselves begin to express themselves in disorders, particularly of the lower back. Man, for almost the whole of his history—some 2 million years—has slept on the ground. Most of the peoples of the world still do. The bed is a comparatively recent innovation; it is a product of civilization. The principal fault of the modern bed is that it is too soft. Most persons tend to sleep on their sides, although there are some peoples who, like the Japanese, sleep on their backs on boards, with a neck block instead of a pillow. Most Western peoples sleep on their sides.

The modern bed, because it is too soft and yielding, puts a great strain on the vertebral column, causing it to sag laterally, mostly in the lower back. The scoliosis or crookedness so habitually produced undoubtedly sets up a chronic irritation which leads to early pathological changes in the vertebral bones, intervertebral discs, joints, and other associated structures. It is seldom that one sees a vertebral column in civilized men of forty years and over that does not show the evidences of such inflammatory changes or spondylitis. The stresses and strains put upon the lumbosacral promontory and the sacroiliac joints are likewise very considerable. These joints are extremely strong, but after years of abuse even they are capable of being affected.

Another joint which must be deterimentally affected is the shoulder joint, which is subjected to a variety of stresses and strains by those who habitually sleep on their sides. Bursitis I would suppose to be a frequent by-product of this posture in bed.

I do not think that sleeping on alternate sides is the best possible posture for sleeping, particularly for older people. A physiologically more desirable posture would be sleeping on one's right and left front alternately, with legs separated and resting on the homolateral knee and elbow, with the opposite arm and leg extended along the other side. Side-sleeping generally renders two pillows necessary because the elevation of the shoulder removes the head a fair distance from the single pillow. Two pillows are undesirable because they put a strain upon the neck vertebrae as well as upon other structures in the neck.

The best time to begin mitigating the effects of aging is when aging begins: from birth. If we would all sleep on physiologically adequately designed beds from infancy this would, I am convinced, substantially reduce some of the undesirable addenda of aging. What, then, is the physiologically adequately designed bed?

Whatever the material of which it is constructed, the surface of the bed should be firm and resist all inclination to sag. The foot of the bed should be higher by about nine inches than the rest of the bed. The purpose of this is to assist venous return from the feet and legs. Combined with simple flexion and extension exercises of the feet, this would serve greatly to reduce the frequency of superficial varicosities and of deep vein thromboses of the legs, conditions which only too frequently develop in the middle-aged and in older persons. A simple form of cradle designed to keep the bedclothes off the feet and thus render their movement easy should be incorporated in the bed. There should be only one pillow, and the bed should not be higher than twenty-one inches when getting into and resting in it. For the purposes of bedmaking the bed could be elevated by some automatic device.

All davenports, sofas, and other seats should be equally firm.

Tables should be of adjustable height, but at a standard height of between thirty-one and thirty-two inches.

In all furniture sharp and jagged edges should be avoided and rounded ones made standard.

If rugs are used then they should be wall to wall. Scatter rugs and free-edged rugs should be strongly discouraged. One slips on the former and stumbles against and trips on the latter. Falls account for more than half the fatal accidents in the home, and persons over the age of sixty-five are involved in 85 percent of the fatal falls. Being thrown by a loose rug accounts for a good proportion of these accidents.

Floors should, of course, never be polished. The bones of older persons are brittle, and the bones of the pelvic girdle are

specially so. This is why fractures of the pelvis are so frequent
1 older persons.

Handrails and extra illumination on staircases and the elimi-
ation of all tripping hazards should be considered mandatory.
The furniture of the bathroom is yet another colligation re-
uiring consideration. All glass shelves and other projections
1ould be eliminated or rendered less lethal. Projecting handles
nd faucets in the bathtub should be made as little projecting
nd as rounded as possible. The bathtub itself should have a
onskid bottom, and the flat tops of the sides should also be
1ade of a nonskid material. Grab-bars should be available on
oth sides of the tub. The hot-water supply should be so con-
rolled as to turn off automatically after a volume designed to
rovide the necessary heat has been reached. Many older per-
)ns have died from the effect of scalding where such protection
'as not provided.

The horizontal toilet seat is in an unphysiological plane. It
1ould be obliquely oriented, higher in front than behind, in
his way facilitating an approximation to the squatting posi-
ion, which in turn facilitates more efficient elimination.

All unnecessary and potentially hazardous impedimenta
1ould be removed from living quarters. Low tables, for ex-
mple, are a hazard and a frequent cause of stumblings and
alls. So are low chairs. The environment of older persons
1ould be uncluttered, with plenty of free and open space for
ree and open movement. The pilgrim's progress must not be
mpeded by placing any bunions of unnecessary furniture in
.is way. Sinks, shelves, and accessible storage space should be
vailable without the need for excessive bending, reaching or
limbing.

It was Oscar Wilde who remarked that the tragedy about
rowing old was not that we feel old, but that we don't. That,
' think, is a very pleasant thought, if only our furniture could
ontribute to make it so.

23. *Maternal emotions*

Some of the oldest and most persistent of the old wives tales have to do with the emotions of pregnant women an their effects on unborn children. Women have always believe that shock or grief or happiness could be transmitted in som mysterious fashion from mother to child. Beliefs held by scien tists until recent years that the pregnant woman and her chil are two separate entities, divided from each other by an imper meable barrier, simply passed by the large majority of wome who either were entirely ignorant of them or indifferent to them Older women in any family have always made a strong effor to protect the young pregnant woman from unnecessary shock and the young wife, even the modern, educated young woman protects herself by turning her gaze inward when she is preg nant and setting her back to the part of the outside world tha she knows can harm her child. Perhaps she no longer present the endearing picture of the young woman earnestly sittin down to read poetry every day so that her unborn child wil have an appreciation of beautiful thoughts, but frequently sh refrains from reading the front page of the daily newspape She no longer believes, perhaps, that the appearance of a snak lying across the path in the woods will mark her child's ski with a long dark smear, but if she is badly frightened by snake—or an automobile—she is likely to place her hands firml on her protruding belly and then go indoors and lie down. Sh

nows in her bones—or in some other center of knowledge—
hat when her own emotions are deeply stirred, her child must
lso feel something.

Nature, too, conspires with the old wives and the young wives
o protect the unborn child by throwing up an invisible veil
etween the pregnant woman and the world around her. This
eil serves to screen out much of the impact of the happenings
n her immediate neighborhood, so that for the time being
hey appear not to concern her directly, and she may be free
o concentrate on the important things, the changes that are
aking place in her own body.

In addition to this intensely personal view of the connection
etween mother and unborn child, the old wives—and the
middle-aged wives, too—know from close observation of female
elatives, friends and neighbors—in all perhaps no more than
wo dozen cases, but sufficient to convince—that a woman who
has had a difficult pregnancy, who has been ill, who has perhaps lost her father and has grieved deeply, whose husband has
een in danger, whose other children have been ill or par-
icularly troublesome is quite likely to have a difficult child.
Conversely, a serene woman who floats through her pregnancy
eeming not to touch the ground and who is lucky in the accidents of her life will probably have a child who is serene like
his mother. Heredity? Or environment? Or a tangle of the
wo? The old, the middle-aged and the young wives debate this
question endlessly and come to no conclusions.

Scientists, on the other hand, must come to conclusions or
must at least try to make progress toward conclusions. During
ecent years disciplined inquiry into the possible connection
etween the emotions of a pregnant mother and the development of her unborn child has been carried out by a number of
investigators. Progress has been slow and hampered by the
difficulties of separating the various factors which must be
aken into consideration—genetic, nutritional, and economic as
well as emotional—and of collecting data that is dependent in
many cases on the personal recollections of pregnant women.
Pregnant women are no more objective and accurate in their
observations of themselves than are other members of the

human race, and conclusions based on their evidence must be weighed against this fact.

Some valid conclusions have been reached, however. There seems to be no doubt, even in the minds of the most demanding investigators, that a strong emotion in a pregnant woman can produce a strong reaction in her unborn child. Specifically scientists are reasonably certain that in some cases the mother's emotional disturbance can cause a great increase in the physical activity of the fetus and, after birth, a set of symptoms in the infant that is characterized by irritability, excessive crying difficulties with food, vomiting and sometimes diarrhea.

Other investigators have found good evidence, although not enough to constitute proof, to support the claim that when a woman suffers from a profoundly disturbing emotional experience during the first twelve weeks of her pregnancy, the physical development of the child may be affected. This is the period when the child's organs are being formed, and the stress is believed to interfere with this process.

Still further evidence points to the possibility that emotional disturbance of the mother at a later stage of the pregnancy may produce such physical changes in the fetus as the development of a prenatal peptic ulcer. This is far from certain at the present time; it is simply a path marked out for future research to explore.

Whether the effect of an emotionally disturbed mother endures in the physical endowment or temperament or general potentialities of her child beyond early babyhood is a matter that is still virtually unexplored.

It must be clearly understood here that we are discussing *some women* whose emotional disturbances *may* affect their unborn children. By necessity, also, we are concerned exclusively with unpleasant emotions and their subsequent harmful results; these emotions are easier to identify and to measure than the pleasant emotions, and their results, if any, are clearer The danger of reporting studies of this kind is that the reader is almost inescapably left with the impression that all women including herself, are under discussion, and that all pregnant

es, including her own, are doomed. This, of course, is not
ue.

Any woman who has ever been pregnant can recall occasions
iring her pregnancy when she was clearly under severe emo-
>nal strain. In fact, it is a well-established fact that a large
imber of women actively dislike being pregnant and experi-
ice a variety of emotional disorders because of that dislike.
r. W. T. Tompkins and Miss D. G. Wiehl go so far as to say
at their studies have suggested that "in every patient, no
atter how 'normal,' there is some degree of unconscious con-
ct concerning pregnancy." It is this conflict, they say, that is
sponsible for many cases of nausea and vomiting in early
egnancy.

In addition to their unconscious conflicts, the majority of
egnant women have conscious problems which are quite capa-
e of affecting their emotional stability. Relationships with
her people—husbands, parents, other children—all undergo
anges with the onset of pregnancy. Money, which presents a
orny problem to most people at all times, often becomes an
ute worry when another child must be provided for. The
mple details of living—how to accomplish the chores and how
arrange for a little pleasure—become more difficult. All this
n add up to a severely disturbing situation.

If it is true, then, that emotional disturbances in pregnant
omen can cause unfortunate results in their unborn children,
nd if most women are under emotional stress during preg-
ancy, how does it happen that any children at all are born
ealthy and, as we say, normal?

The answer lies, of course, in the ability, possessed by the
arge majority of women, to absorb potentially disturbing
tuations into their lives. Dr. Lyon P. Strean and Dr. Lyndon
. Peer put this idea into scientifically acceptable language by
eferring to a possible "threshold of stress tolerance" below
hich a fetus remains unaffected. This threshold, they point
ut, may vary with different women and also at different times
ith the same woman, depending on her condition and her
tuation.

One of the primary difficulties in studying the connections

between the emotions of a mother and their effect on the fetu
is our ignorance of the emotions themselves. We do not kno
the precise manner in which the emotions originate, nor ha
we even discovered exactly where in the body they arise. I
deed, how the emotions operate at all, or even what they are,
known only in a general and tentative way. Fortunately, th
general knowledge is enough to give us a start toward unde
standing how emotions actually work in the pregnant woma
and the mechanics of their connection with her child.

An emotion as experienced by a human being cannot,
course, pass in that form from a mother to her child. Fear
the snake lying across the path, anxiety for the husband i
danger during wartime, anger at a friend, grief for the death
a father—each of these is a subjective feeling experienced b
one person alone and not to be shared. But this feeling is th
beginning of a lengthy series of physical and chemical change
and reactions that take place throughout the body. It is th
subjective feeling *plus* all the resultant changes in the bod
which are properly called the emotion. In fact, an emotion ma
be defined as a strong feeling or mental state that gives rise t
measurable physical changes. These changes are of two kind
the manufacture of certain chemical substances at the ends
the nerves, and the release of hormones from the endocrin
glands. These are the two agents that bridge the gap betwee
the emotion as originally felt by the mother and the develop
ment of her child.

In considering the emotions, it is necessary to keep in min
several distinctions. It is quite possible that at some time i
the future these distinctions will become so clear as to meri
separate names, and the word "emotion" may become to
general to be of any scientific use. Now, however, we must us
our common sense and distinguish, for example, between con
tinuing and prolonged states of anxiety and depression an
brief experiences of the same feelings. Also, we must recogniz
that some prolonged emotional states can be deeply disturbing
while others can be comparatively superficial. Furthermore, a
emotion need not be prolonged to be profoundly disturbing
panic terror, for example, is nearly always short-lived, bu
clearly it makes up in intensity what it lacks in duration. I

ct, an emotion, to be profoundly disturbing, need have no ecific qualities of its own; it need only give rise to abnormal tivity of the nervous and glandular systems of the body.

In order to understand the connection between a strong feel-g on the part of a mother and an effect felt by a fetus, and in der to appreciate the significance of the experimental work in is field, it is perhaps sensible to review briefly the path rough the body, as far as we know it, from first feeling to ial manifestation of an emotion.

It begins in the gray matter of the brain, in the cerebral rtex. It is here that a feeling is perceived and understood. his perception causes changes, neurochemical in nature, hich in turn set off reflexes, which in their turn pass either rectly into the autonomic nervous system or through the alamus and the hypothalamus where they are translated into pulses leading to both muscles and endocrine glands.

To put this series of changes into a neat set of words is not, course, to understand it. Exactly how these changes and flexes are accomplished is only dimly understood at best. rtunately, it is not necessary to understand each step of the ocess from beginning to end; it is possible—indeed, this is indard practice in all scientific research—to study bits and eces of any process and then to put together those that appear fit, hoping to make a complete picture someday. At the oment, then, we know this much: the impulses set in motion the perception of a feeling are expressed through two chan-ls, the autonomic nervous system and the hypothalamus.

The autonomic nervous system is that part of the total ner->us system which leads to the involuntary muscles and glands. his is in contrast to the central nervous system, which leads to e muscles of the skeletal system and is under conscious con-ol. The autonomic system, as the name implies, is independent all such conscious control; it leads to muscles of the stomach, e intestines, the heart and blood vessels, the bladder, the erus, the iris of the eye, the tear glands, the sweat glands, the gestive glands, the air tubes, the bronchi, and the gastro-testinal and genitourinary tracts.

This is a powerful and pervasive system; when it is function-

ing normally it regulates the activities of all these organs a
systems, and the body as a whole experiences a sensation of we
being. When it is not functioning normally—when, for e
ample, the brain perceives danger and flashes a signal down t
line—chemical substances are liberated from the nerve endin
One of the substances released in this way is *sympathin,* whi
closely resembles adrenalin. This substance may enter direc
into the bloodstream and in this form reach the placenta a
finally find its way into the bloodstream of the fetus.

The hypothalamus marks another path by which impuls
from the cerebral cortex reach out into the mother's body a
from there into her unborn child. The hypothalamus is situat
at the base of the brain and can be considered as the coordin
ing center of the autonomic system. In addition, the hypotha
mus appears to secrete hormones, and there is good eviden
that through these hormones it initiates the activities of t
pituitary gland. It is suspected that this exercises a regulati
effect upon the whole system of ductless glands and there
affects the whole body.

The emotional state of a pregnant woman can affect her chi
through just this mechanism: by causing an abnormal activi
in the endocrine glands and pouring hormones into her bloo
stream, and from there to the fetus. For example, the pituita
gland secretes, among numerous others, a substance known
the adrenocorticotrophic hormone, or ACTH. When this
liberated, it stimulates other glands to action, principally t
adrenal glands, which secrete cortisone. In the pregnant woma
such secretions are known to pass through the placenta to t
fetus.

This, then, is the end product of the original state of fea
anxiety, or grief that the pregnant woman was feeling. It is
this complex and not clearly understood mechanism that t
sight of a snake, a war, a bereavement can affect an unbor
child.

Exactly what the effect is has only recently begun to
systematically studied. Most of the evidence regarding infan
in utero has rested on the two forms of fetal behavior that a

[256

well known, reasonably well understood, and measurable: the movements of the fetus within the womb, and the beating of its heart. The variations that occur from time to time in both movements and heartbeat give us a simple but valuable yardstick. By correlating these two forms of behavior and their variations as closely as possible with the known emotional conditions of the mothers involved, it is possible to arrive at the beginnings of an understanding of the connection between the two. When it is possible to observe these same infants after birth, to study their behavior and their health, and to correlate these facts with what is already known about their prenatal life, we begin to see the train of events as it actually happens, and we can then begin to draw tentative conclusions about cause and effect.

It is also possible to mark out reasonable fields for study and to anticipate the general direction in which the results will take us by investigating newborn infants who exhibit certain clearly defined forms of behavior and correlating this behavior with reports given by their mothers regarding their anxieties and stresses during pregnancy. These investigations are clearly less reliable than those that include study by trained observers of the women during the period of emotional stress, but in the absence of objective observation, personal recollections at least provide signposts along the road.

Much of our knowledge in this field is due to work done from the early 1930s until the 1950s at the Fels Research Institute at Yellow Springs, Ohio, under the direction of Dr. Lester Sontag. We are indebted to Helen Newberry Norman of the Fels Institute for the most usable, if not the first, classification of fetal movements. She identifies three kinds: a slow squirming movement, a small rhythmic movement called hiccoughs, and a sharp kicking movement.

Kicking movements can vary from mild to convulsive. In fact, the connection between a mother's emotional condition and this kind of movement of the fetus was first observed and recorded, and the cause deduced, as long ago as 1867 by Dr. James Whitehead. Both sides of the equation presented powerful forces: the mother had just finished nursing her twenty-month-old child, an only child, through a severe three-week attack of an acute disease. At the end of this period, when it became clear to the mother that the child would live, she collapsed, exhausted. The fetus, in its ninth month, then exhibited a variety of kicking movements so violent and so prolonged as to prompt Dr. Whitehead to label it convulsion. The attack lasted for six hours, growing in severity and finally subsiding, possibly due to chloroform and "nepenthe" given to the mother. Twenty-one days after this episode, the baby was born, healthy and vigorous, and during the first month of its life, which was the extent of Dr. Whitehead's observation, showed no tendency toward convulsions. Dr. Whitehead, well before his time in his understanding of this phenomenon, points out that although severe physical shock, such as falling from a height, may leave a fetus quite unperturbed and unharmed, "it seems to be otherwise when the mental system of the mother becomes unbalanced by violent and sudden shocks of anguish, or by prolonged and severe anxiety, attended with a waste of physical power."

Contemporary observers have begun one aspect of their work by studying pregnant women who could be considered undisturbed and normal, together with the behavior of their unborn children. Recognizing that the emotions act largely through the autonomic nervous system, they measured the physical activity of the fetus in relation to the autonomic activity in each of the undisturbed women. These measurements included the resting heart rate, the respiration rate, and the conductivity of the skin, all functions of the autonomic system. The results of the measurements showed clearly that the women who had the highest autonomic activity—that is, the most rapid heart and respiration rate and the highest conductivity of the skin—also had the most active fetuses. Furthermore, those who showed the greatest degree of variability in their autonomic patterns during their undisturbed states also had the most active fetuses.

Measurements were also made of the autonomic patterns at different periods of pregnancy. In almost every case, there was a significant drop in heart rate, respiration rate and skin conductivity during the last month of pregnancy. It is interesting to note that this drop in maternal autonomic activity occurs at the same time as a marked decrease in fetal activity. These measurements showed clearly, it is believed, that there is a close connection between the mother's autonomic nervous system and the physical movements of the fetus.

In situations where mothers were undergoing emotional stress, Dr. Sontag and his collaborators at Fels Institute observed that the body movements of the fetuses increased by several hundred percent. Even when the mother's disturbance was short-lived, the activity of the fetus lasted for several hours, and where the mother's disturbance lasted for a period of several weeks, the hourly averages of activity of the fetus during the entire period were greatly increased.

It was also discovered that fetuses that had been very active during their last two months *in utero*, whose mothers had suffered from emotional distress or fatigue, tended to be light in weight at birth, even though their length was normal. As Dr. Sontag points out, the hyperactive fetus employs a common method of slimming: exercise without an increase in food consumption. Since he does not use the mineral part of his food for the production of energy, his skeleton grows normally, but he loses weight by burning up in physical activity what would otherwise have gone into the deposit of bodily fat.

These same children, it was discovered by workers at Fels Institute, also tend to be more advanced in their motor development during their first postnatal year than children who have been less active in the womb. This is an interesting finding primarily because it is so reasonable: human beings who use their muscles actively develop them more quickly and to a greater degree of skill than human beings who are physically quiet, whether these human beings are adults or children or fetuses.

The behavior at birth of infants whose mothers have experienced severe emotional stresses during their pregnancies is an important observation in these studies. Dr. Sontag describes such a child in a way that will cause a shock of recognition in many mothers: ". . . from the beginning a hyperactive, irritable, squirming, crying child who cries for his feeding every two or three hours instead of sleeping through his four-hour feeding. Because his irritability involves the control of his gastro-intestinal tract, he empties his bowels at unusually frequent intervals, spits up half his feeding and generally makes a nuisance of himself. He is to all intents and purposes a neurotic infant when he is born—the result of an unsatisfactory fetal environment. . . . In certain instances of severely disturbed maternal emotions which we have observed, for example, one in which the father became violently insane during his wife's pregnancy, the infant's bodily functions were so disturbed that a severe feeding problem resulted. The child was unable to retain food and became markedly emaciated and dehydrated."

An unmarried woman of thirty-five was another typical case described by Dr. Sontag. "She had suddenly learned that the father of her child, to whom she had expected to be married, was already a married man. To add to her distress, her very severe family made life entirely miserable for her." When her child was born, he was among those who were hyperirritable and unable to eat.

In eight cases studied by workers at Fels Institute, where emotional distress was an obvious factor and had existed over a prolonged period of time, seven infants presented moderate or severe feeding difficulties in the form of inability to retain food. In several instances, there was a tendency for frequent stools for several months.

A group of symptoms in infants characterized by restlessness, excessive crying, irritability, vomiting and frequent loose stools was observed by Dr. E. K. Turner in Australia. She noted that this group of symptoms was particularly frequent among illegitimate babies. Furthermore, many of the mothers of these babies admitted to having been under considerable emotional stress during their pregnancies.

These cases are interesting and suggestive, but it is clear from their small number that they cannot possibly be conclusive. In fact, our total knowledge on this subject is small, and the area in which we have no information, or only scattered observations, is enormous. Medical journals and other scientific publications contain numerous reports of individual mothers whose emotional experiences are believed to have affected their unborn children. These reports are interesting, but they do not constitute scientific evidence; they prove nothing.

Other reports, some of them involving relatively larger numbers of women and children, must be accepted with qualifications because of the emergence of factors which confuse the issue. An experiment carried out by Dr. D. H. Stott in Bristol, England, for example, involved a group of 102 retarded children. There was no question about some of the results: of those children whose mothers reported illness or stress during pregnancy, 76 percent were ill themselves of the same illnesses, as against 29 percent of those children whose mothers had no such illness or stress. This is surely a significant difference, but was it due to both illness and emotional stress, or illness alone, or emotional stress alone? Or does illness during pregnancy bring with it a certain amount of emotional disturbance? These questions were not studied and their answers are needed in order to understand the significance of the findings.

When the 102 retarded children were compared with 450 normal children of the same general background, striking differences were noted: illness or stress during pregnancy was reported by mothers of 66 percent of the retarded children, but by only 31 percent of the mothers of normal children, while ill health in the children themselves after birth occurred in 55 percent of the retarded but in only 18 percent of the normal children. Congenital malformations were found in 15 percent of the retarded children but in only 1.5 percent of the normal children. Of the 22 malformations within the combined total of 522 children, 18 were associated with difficulties during pregnancy.

Stott also reports a finding to the effect that emotional and physical shock occurring during the early months of pregnancy are associated with a significantly higher frequency of mongoloid and otherwise mentally retarded children than occur in the group in which such shocks were experienced during the later months of pregnancy. The difficulty here is that mongolism has been associated with a genetic aberration and it is difficult to accept the idea that the mother's emotional disturbance could affect cell division. On the other hand, we have so little knowledge about this that we must defer judgment until future research resolves the doubt.

Still other effects of maternal emotional stress have been suggested, although certainly not proved, by other investigators. Dr. James L. Halliday, in his book, *Psychosocial Medicine,* writes, "The clinical impression (which has not yet been subjected to clinical testing) that patients who develop recurring depressive states in adult life frequently provide a history—if this can be obtained and confirmed—showing that the mother was grievously disturbed emotionally during the intrauterine phase of the patient. . . . Similar biographical findings, though to a less spectacular degree, are not uncommon in duodenal ulcer." It has also been suggested that ulcers are actually produced in fetuses by the emotional stresses of their mothers. In any case, there have been instances of newborn infants with duodenal ulcers, clearly a result of some long-term disturbance in the womb.

Other suggestions, also not yet tested or proved, concern the connection between the prenatal experience and tendencies in adult life toward anxiety and heart conditions.

These associations are extremely difficult to prove, even under the best of conditions, but they are suggestions which are not inherently improbable. In fact, the more we know of these matters, the more probable these connections appear to be.

Several interesting experiments involving animals have been carried out in this field. Professor William R. Thompson, now of the Psychological Laboratory at Wesleyan University, undertook to test the hypothesis that emotional trauma undergone by female rats during pregnancy can affect the emotional characteristics of their offspring. Previous studies had indicated that the injection into the pregnant mother of cortisone and adrenalin produces drastic effects on the fetus, and since strong emotion may release the same substances into the mother's bloodstream, Thompson reasoned that there were grounds for supposing that strong emotion may have an important influence on this aspect of fetal development.

The experiment was accomplished by teaching the rats to

expect a strong shock at the sound of a buzzer and then to avoid the shock by opening a door and running into another compartment of the cage. The next step was to sound the buzzer, disconnect the shock mechanism and lock the door. The assumption was that strong anxiety would be generated in the pregnant rats and that any resultant hormonal changes would be transmitted to the fetus through the placenta.

After the young rats were born, their emotional characteristics were tested twice—at 30 days and again at 130 days of age— and the results were compared with similar tests carried out on the same number of rats who had not been subjected to this prenatal treatment. Dr. Thompson reported that there was no doubt that the experimental animals exhibited considerably more emotionality than the others and that the differences persisted to a great extent into adulthood. He went on to say, however: "While there is no question about the reliability of these differences, there is some ambiguity regarding their cause. Thus, we do not know exactly how the stress used had effects. It is possible that the buzzer was strong enough to act on the fetuses directly rather than indirectly by causing release of hormones in the mother."

Other experiments, carried out independently by Dr. F. C. Fraser, Dr. T. D. Fainstat, Dr. H. Kalter, and Dr. T. H. Ingalls, have demonstrated that when cortisone is injected into pregnant mice during the period when the embryo's jaws and palate are forming—that is, from the ninth to the seventeenth day of gestation—a very high frequency of cleft palate is produced in the offspring. Ingalls and Curley refined this experiment to the point where they proved, by successive doses of hydrocortisone acetate, that the twelfth and thirteenth days of pregnancy in mice are the critical periods in the development of the palate. If an abnormally high amount of cortisone is circulating in the maternal bloodstream at this period, inhibiting the proliferation of some of the cells that are important in the formation of bone, the chance that the offspring will be born with a cleft palate skyrockets.

Inevitably, the suggestion has been made that similar mechanisms are at work in the human mother and her fetus to produce in a certain percentage of cases not only cleft palate in the embryo but also other comparable conditions. In 1956, Dr. Lyon R. Strean and Dr. Lyndon A. Peer reported the result of their investigation of 228 mothers of children with cleft palate or harelip. This necessarily was an investigation begun after the children were born and identified; the mothers were then questioned to try to determine whether any relationship existed between their medical history, particularly during the first trimester of pregnancy, and the incidence of cleft palate and harelip.

The investigators found that severe emotional stress, particularly when coupled with excessive vomiting, appeared to have been the single most important factor associated with cleft palate in the children. Forty percent of the children with cleft palate were firstborn children, and the investigators attributed this high figure to the severe anxiety frequently associated with a first pregnancy, perhaps combined with other situations.

Dr. Strean and Dr. Peer asked the same mothers in a second inquiry to state the kind of disturbances, if any, which they had undergone during the first trimester of pregnancy with their other children who were born without harelip or cleft palate. Eighty-five percent of the mothers replied that they had not suffered from similar disturbances when pregnant with their other children. Only 15 percent of the mothers claimed to have undergone similar stresses during their other pregnancies.

Twenty-five percent of the mothers said that some member of their families had cleft palate or harelip. It is clear from this, the investigators believed, that in these cases a hereditary factor almost certainly played a role. Strean and Peer reported their conclusion then, that "it is possible, and perhaps probable, that two factors operate in the production of this congenital abnormality—genic activity and stress. One operating without the other may be unable to produce cleft palate." In other words, if there is a tendency toward maldevelopment of any part of the body, it will be augmented by any unfavorable environment, particularly if it occurs at a crucial prenatal period.

The effects of war on the emotional lives of pregnant women

constitute an area that has so far received almost no attention from investigators. Dr. Sontag of Fels Institute published a paper during World War II entitled "War and the Fetal-Maternal Relationship," but except for that and one or two studies from concentration camps where many other factors were bearing on the situation in addition to the mothers' emotional disturbances, there have been no studies reported. Dr. Sontag offered the following comments:

> There is evidence that fetal environment is an extremely important factor delineating the original structure, function and behavior patterns of human beings. The alterations in fetal environment most important in war are perhaps in nutrition and in the chemical-physiological changes in the mother's body brought about by maternal emotion, and possibly fatigue. Alterations in these factors may produce infants more susceptible to disease, to rickets and scurvy, to dental decay, and children whose growth progress is slower. It is conceivable that there may be gross alterations in skeletal structure and that alterations in the structure of such organs as the central nervous system may limit the ultimate potentialities of individuals. The chemical-physiological aspect of severely disturbed maternal emotions may be responsible for the birth during wartime of children exhibiting a high incidence of unstable behavior and functional disorders.

This observation opens the door to a series of interesting speculations: is war responsible for unstable behavior? Or are the unstable human beings, grown to adulthood, responsible for war? Or do we find here a spiral of action and reaction that has no exit? Or is this connection an oversimplification of a complex subject?

Dr. Sontag's comments suggest another line of thought, this one based on the melancholy fact that there is nothing that can be done at this time by any single pregnant woman to protect herself and her unborn child from the dangerous effects of many profoundly disturbing emotional experiences. She cannot stop or prevent a war, for example, and if her husband is serving in it, it is inevitable that she will be filled with fears for his safety. She can, by taking heed, avoid tensions and anxieties that arise from alterable circumstances, but she cannot halt the progress of a disease that is taking the life of her father. Emotional disturbances will be with us always; they are part of living, and the fetus must take his chances *in utero* as he will have to continue taking them all the rest of his life.

Dr. Strean and Dr. Peer have conducted an experiment, again with mice with cleft palates, that holds out a little hope in this connection. It is only one experiment, and the significance of it is doubtful. It is suggestive but certainly not conclusive. They used as subjects a group of mice who had been treated with cortisone on the ninth, tenth and eleventh days of pregnancy and could be expected to produce, as many others had done before them, a high incidence of offspring with cleft palates. These mice were fed a diet containing an excess of certain vitamins that have the effect of breaking down the by-products of cortisone. The number of young mice born with cleft palates was appreciably smaller than expected.

Is this conceivably the forerunner of studies that may eventually show us how to control the effects of maternal emotion on the fetus? Is it possible that even before we fully understand the connection between emotion in the mother and the development of her unborn child, we will have worked out techniques to obviate it?

It is abundantly clear that this is a vast territory indeed that must be explored and that the results of the exploration will be of greatest possible significance to all human beings.

24. *"Race" and war*

Almost a hundred years have passed since that fatal morning when a dust-laden Prussian officer cantered into Paris at the head of a small advance party of Uhlans, thus signalizing the capitulation of the French and the unequivocal victory of the Germans in the Franco-Prussian War of 1870. Forty years later this selfsame Prussian officer, now a general, careered into Europe with a book which at once attained universal notoriety. This book was entitled *Germany and the Next War*. Few books have before or since been so fervidly and widely discussed. In this book the author, General Friedrich von Bernhardi, boldly threw down the gauntlet to the world and, virtually with saber in hand, called upon the German people to protest against the "aspirations for peace which seem to dominate our age and threaten to poison the soul of the German people."

It is understandably hard for an iron-headed soldier, after some forty years of comparative inactivity, to recall an event as stirring as the entry at the head of a victorious army into a defeated enemy's capital without feeling that if things were not actually going to the dogs, at least it was high time that something was done to prevent the possibility. And so, in order to convince the German people of the "unnaturalness" of that "inactivity which saps the blood from a nation's sinews," von Bernhardi did something he had never done before: he wrote and published a popular propagandistic book, making the pen,

267]

as it were, temporarily do service for the sword and ink for blood. "War," declared von Bernhardi, "is a biological necessity"; it "is as necessary as the struggle of the elements in Nature; . . . it gives a biologically just decision, since its decisions rest on the very nature of things. . . . The whole idea of arbitration represents a presumptuous encroachment on the natural laws of development," for "what is right is decided by the arbitrament of War." [1] In proof whereof such Darwinian notions as "the struggle for existence," "natural selection," and "survival of the fittest" are invoked with a loud fanfare of trumpets. According to von Bernhardi, it is plainly evident to anyone who makes a study of plant and animal life that "war is a universal law of nature." [2]

Darwin himself regarded the biological influence of modern war as distinctly bad. In *The Descent of Man* he wrote: "In every country in which a large standing army is kept, the finest young men are taken by the conscription or are enlisted. They are thus exposed to early death during war, are often tempted into vice, and are prevented from marrying during the prime of life. On the other hand, the shorter and feeble men, with poor constitutions are left at home and consequently have a much better chance of marrying and propagating their kind."

As Professor S. J. Holmes, the distinguished social biologist, has put it: "One may be a strict orthodox Darwinian and maintain with entire consistency that, under present conditions, war is an evil of the very first magnitude." [3]

Von Bernhardi's declaration and fortification of Germany's will to war—for it had the highest official sanction and approval—was published in 1912. Two years later the greatest holocaust the world had yet known was launched upon its ghastly way by those

> . . . vultures sick for battle
> Those bloodless wolves whose dry throats rattle,
> Those crows perched on the murrained cattle,
> Those vipers tangled into one.
> After Shelley, "To Sidmouth and Castlereagh"

—the confused, inhuman, militaristic von Bernhardis and the other legislators of a victimized Europe.

World War I came to a technical end in 1918, having cost the lives of 18 million men. Of these, 8 million were slaughtered upon the field of battle and 10 million civilians died either directly or indirectly as a result of the war. As for the maimed and wounded combatants, these amounted to a mere 20 million. The cost to the United States of running this fracas amounted to $125,000,000 a day during the first three years and $224,000,000 a day, or $10,000,000 an hour, during 1918, the total cost of the killing amounting to some 400 billion dollars.[4]

During World War II the United States was spending $250,000,000 a day on the war, and by 1945 the total cost had run up to 1,030 billion dollars.[5]

Although most human beings now living, with the exception of some militarists and politicians, can see neither sense, good, nor anything but misery in war, there are many who, like von Bernhardi, continue to aver that war has its biological justification. Among these was my old friend and teacher Sir Arthur Keith (1866–1955), who in many articles beginning in 1915 and in later books [6] maintained that the impulses which lead men to aggressive and defensive wars are "nature's mechanisms for preserving the individual and the tribe or nation" and "make individuals and nations willing to risk life itself to further the means and opportunities of life." In all theories of this kind "race" and "race" prejudice are conceived by their proponents to play a basic and "natural" part.

Sir Arthur Keith's opinions on this subject first received wide attention with the publication of his rectorial address to the students of Aberdeen University in 1931.[7] In the present chapter I propose to take Sir Arthur Keith's views on the nature of war and its relation to "race" prejudice and, treating them as representative of the "race-prejudice-biological-nature-of-war" school, subject them to a brief critical examination.

Keith begins by declaring his firm conviction that "prejudices are inborn; are part of the birthright of every child." These prejudices "have been grafted in our natures for a special purpose—an evolutionary purpose. . . . They are essential parts of the evolutionary machinery which Nature employed throughout eons of time to secure the separation of man into permanent groups and thus to attain production of new and improved

269]

races of Mankind. . . . Nature endowed her tribal teams with this spirit of antagonism for her own purposes. It has come down to us and creeps out from our modern life in many shapes, as national rivalries and jealousies and as racial hatreds. The modern name for this spirit of antagonism is race prejudice. . . . Race prejudice, I believe," continues Keith, "works for the ultimate good of Mankind and must be given a recognized place in all our efforts to obtain natural justice in the world." [8] Here, sadly, we may recall von Bernhardi's "war renders a biologically just decision, since its decisions rest on the very nature of things." It is the same argument, endlessly repeated, in almost the same words.

And now for the passage from Keith which gained such widespread notoriety: "Without competition Mankind can never progress; the price of progress is competition. Nay, race prejudice and, what is the same thing, national antagonism, have to be purchased, not with gold, but with life. Nature throughout the past has demanded that a people who seeks independence as well as peace can obtain these privileges only in one way—by being prepared to sacrifice their blood to secure them. Nature keeps her orchard healthy by pruning; war is her pruning hook. We cannot dispense with her services. This harsh and repugnant forecast of man's future is wrung from me. The future of my dreams is a warless world." [9]

Essentially similar views were expressed by Sir Arthur Keith in his Robert Boyle Lecture *Nationality and Race,* published twelve years earlier, and were repeated by him in 1950.[10] Unlike von Bernhardi, Sir Arthur Keith was a distinguished physical anthropologist and, as all who knew him well know, a man of the noblest and most generous nature who was himself as free of anything resembling "race" prejudice as a man could well be. Nevertheless, in his treatment of the subject of "race" prejudice and war the fact was unfortunately betrayed that he had overstepped the frontiers of his own particular field, a field to which he has made lasting contributions. Charles Singer has well said that "even professional men of science, when they pass beyond the frontiers of their own special studies, usually exhibit no more balanced judgment or unprejudiced outlook than do nonscientific men of comparable social and educational standing." Sir Arthur Keith's views on war and "race" prejudice may be taken as a case in point.

What, we may ask to begin with, is this "Nature," generally, it is to be observed, spelled with a capital N? Keith's Nature is apparently a very intelligent being, working things out purposefully with much premeditation. I use the term "intelligent" here in a generic sense to cover the operations of what is conventionally understood as the intellect; I make no comment on the quality of that putative intelligence, beyond saying that an intellect which can conceive of no better device to improve its breed than by warfare must be a very poor intellect indeed. For surely the biological vitality of a species can be preserved and improved by many immeasurably more effective means than this—means which do not necessitate or require the annihilation of a single individual. But what, in fact, *is* this Nature of von Bernhardi and Keith which, according to them, justifies "race" prejudice and renders war a biological necessity?

Apparently it is an anthropomorphism akin to the *élan vital* of Bergson or the "life force" of Bernard Shaw. In other words, it would appear to be some form of directing Godhead with the capital G in very much the old style, divested here and there of a few sacraments and perfectly clean shaven, but otherwise much the same. Voltaire's gibe that if God had made men after his own image they had returned the compliment is as appropriate a truth today as it ever was. Nature or God today is an anthropologist as well as a mathematical physicist—sometimes an entelechist and often enough merely a set of differential equations, unlimitedly limited and with an infinite number of functions at one and the same time, but if the truth were really known, merely a set of conditioned reflexes in the cosmic movement continuum. In fact, nature may mean anything, according to the whim of the user.[11] Nature, says Aristotle, makes some men slaves and others free. In nature, says Hobbes, "the life of man is solitary, poor, nasty, brutish, and short"; it is a condition of "war of every man against every man," in which "the notions of right and wrong, justice and injustice have no place" and "force and fraud are the two cardinal virtues." "The state all men are naturally in," replies Locke, is "a state of perfect freedom to order their actions . . . as they think fit, within the bounds of the law of nature . . . a state also of equality." "Nature," writes Wordsworth, "to me was all in all, she never did betray the heart that loved her." "Nature," rejoins Tennyson, "red in tooth and claw, shrieks against the creed of man." And as Professor A. F. Pollard has remarked of these antinomies, "Some see red, others see God; it all depends upon the kingdom that is within them." In fact, nature is the name we give to the projection of the totality of our ignorance concerning the forces which are conceived to be involved in, or responsible for, the generation of life and its maintenance. Nature is not a "thing in itself" which operates upon other things. The term denotes, rather, if it denotes anything at all, an artificial construct whose function is to serve as a general stereotype for our ignorance, in addition to serving as a *deus ex machina* to which, in a quandary, we may appeal in order to be comfortably relieved of our perplexities. For most people to say that a thing is "natural" explains it. But does it? What do we mean by "natural"? Prejudices are natural according to Keith and others, prose as Monsieur Jourdain was surprised to learn, warfare according to von Bernhardi, and "the golden lie" according to Plato and some of his modern successors. Nature, it is further added, operates according to definite laws. All, in fact, is determined by law. The movements of the planets are determined by laws as immutable as those which determine the behavior of a dog or a man. But all this is mythical.

The universe, as far as we know, is composed of a system of ever-changing *relations,* in the form, for example, of electro-magnetic fields, gases, stresses, forces, strains, velocities, dimensions, substances, and so forth, truly *ad infinitum.*

Nothing in it is fixed; all is flux.[12] Between certain limits of infinity or finity, that is, in a given space-time continuum, the relations of certain planetary velocities, for example, may remain (relatively) constant. The recurring averages in which these relations manifest themselves may be calculated to a high degree of probability, and when so calculated they may be stated as laws. These laws are always probability laws, and are valid only as long as the relations of the planetary velocities, as well as numerous other factors, remain (relatively) constant. Should any of these relations change, the old laws will have to be modified or entirely new ones will have to be elaborated.

With this in mind we may proceed further, and for the purpose in view let us be deliberately brief and therefore oversimple. A unicellular organism living at the bottom of a stagnant pool and environed by a stable universe of internal and external stimuli will tend to undergo little change as long as the constancy of these stimuli persists; but modify its relations, the form and nature of the stimuli acting upon it, alter its internal and external environments, and if you go on long enough—let us say for a few thousand million years—sufficiently and adequately varying the nature of the environmental stimuli and allowing for the important part played by the inherent tendency of the organism to vary, you will, let us suppose, produce a man. And your man, as an organism, will obviously represent the sum of the effects of the responses to the totality of the environments organically made by his ancestors. Organically, your man will be the product of an innumerable variety of conditions—the changing relations collectively called "heredity" and "environment." So will be, and so indeed is, any plant or any other form of animal life. Thus, all plant and animal life is not *produced* according to definite laws, but in response to a series of arbitrary or *chance* alterations in the relations of the conditions affecting it. Nature is thus not an intelligent, teleologically directed process which acts according to predetermined law but is a composite of *chance* relations which may be arbitrarily observed as unit groups of recurring averages of relations, the behavior of the independent variables, or the quanta [13] of which both are indeterminable and unpredictable, whence the *principle of indeterminacy* or, more accurately, *limited meaningful measurability*. Man, indeed, may owe his present supremacy to just such a series of undetermined chance relations, which may be more briefly described as an accident, the accident referred to having been initiated in the late Pliocene epoch some 3 or 4 million years ago, when according to those who hold this theory, owing to the denudation of the forests, due to causes which can at present only be conjectured, a group of unspecialized anthropoidlike creatures, resembling the extinct ape known to paleontologists as *Kenya-pithecus wickeri*, was abandoned by the trees and was constrained to assume a life upon the ground. This revolutionary change in their environment must be considered an important factor in contributing to the ultimate development of all those physical characteristics which we have learned to recognize as distinctive of man. Those apes who lived in the unaffected regions stayed up in the trees, descending to earth only when, presumably, their weight became too great; they remain apes.

Was there any directive, purposeful, intelligent, natural force at work here? None at all. A gradual series of environmental changes accidentally precipitated may have been responsible for the descent from the trees, or the cause may simply have been the cumulative changes produced by mutation—and all mutation is random. The colossal number of varied forms of life, extinct and living, which are to be found upon this earth today have arisen because of the operation of very similar causes. Every form of life with which we are acquainted owes its peculiar form to the enormous number of changes which have been and are in process of taking place both in the materials of its inherent structure and in the environment peculiar to each— the internal as well as the external environment. These changes are not regulated by law but by chance. The processes of the universe of life are discontinuous and practically infinitely variable. The universe consists of an infinitely changeable and changing series of relations. Action and reaction, stimulus and response take place always *relatively,* never *absolutely.* Nature, in short, in the determined immutable sense of the traditionalists, does not exist save as a procrustean fiction.

The law and order that man sees in nature he introduces there, a fact of which he seems to have grown quite unconscious. Natural systems of classification work so well that, following an unconscious pragmatic principle, they are assumed to be true, or at least representative of the truth, the latter being conveniently defined as correspondence with the reality of whatsoever it may be; in this way the tacit assumption is made that one has but to seek and one will find the law and order that undoubtedly exists in nature. This process is termed "discovery."

Now, while systems of classification are of incalculable value in aiding the process of discovery and understanding, such systems are nonetheless quite artificial and do not in any way reflect a law and order which characterizes the operation of the processes we commonly ascribe to nature itself. Nature is a fiction which uses neither measuring rod nor timetable. It is man alone who uses such instruments in order that he may the more fittingly orient himself in relation to this self-created fiction. The classificatory systems of man are *interpretative devices* and merely represent the attempt—and it is a grand attempt—to unravel the tangled skein of some of the relations of the various forms of life to one another, but no more, "a compromise between the complexity of biological fact and the logic of practical convenience." Of this man loses sight and confuses himself with the belief that the law and order which he has worked out into an arbitrary scheme *is* the law and order according to which nature "works." *"Homo additus Naturae,"* remarked Bacon long ago. Nature, if it consists of anything, represents a discontinuous series of processes, a network of entangled gossamer strands, which man attempts to gather together and spin into a web which he naïvely imagines is the *real thing,* the "real thing" being merely as he sees it, and he sees it in an infinite number of ways, according to the kingdom that is within him. Nature comes in this way to mean anything, and what may mean anything in fact means nothing. It is a personification of purely imagined purposes. Logically, the conception of nature is without the slightest value; psychologically, perhaps, the term may not be without some significance in the sense of Nietzsche's words in *The Joyful Wisdom*: "Laws and laws of nature are the remains of mythological dreaming." Such "laws of nature" can be a menace. If one thing is natural to man it is to be artificial. And the artificial, it has been said, is the highest form of the natural.

Julian Huxley has, I think, adequately disposed of the type

of purposive personification in which Sir Arthur Keith has indulged. He writes:

> The ordinary man, or at least the ordinary poet, philosopher, and theologian, is always asking himself what is the purpose of human life, and is anxious to discover some extraneous purpose to which he and humanity may conform. Some find such a purpose exhibited directly in revealed religion; others think they can uncover it from the facts of nature. One of the commonest methods of this form of natural religion is to point to evolution as manifesting such a purpose. The history of life, it is asserted, manifests guidance on the part of some external power; and the usual deduction is that we can safely trust that same power for further guidance in the future.
>
> I believe this reasoning to be wholly false. The purpose manifested in evolution, whether in adaptation, specialization, or biological progress, is only an apparent purpose. It is just as much a product of blind forces as is the falling of a stone to earth or the ebb and flow of the tides. It is we who have read purpose into evolution, as earlier men projected will and emotion into inorganic phenomena like storm or earthquake. If we wish to work towards a purpose for the future of man, we must formulate that purpose ourselves. Purposes in life are made, not found.[14]

Professor A. P. Pollard has said: "The statement that 'war is natural' has no meaning, and any comment on it must be mainly speculation as to what those who make it imagine they mean when they repeat the words. 'Natural' to whom, when, and under what conditions? 'Let dogs delight to bark and bite, it is their nature to.' Is it the nature, too, of men of science?" [15] About as natural as the alleged "universal law of Nature" which makes the whole of nature "fight" and some scientists "bark and bite." We are told that even trees and flowers "fight." Do they? There is not the slightest evidence that they do. And if they do, what connection has this "fighting" with the warfare practiced by men? Some flowers digest insects; some plants "strangle" others. Does this constitute war between the flowers and the insects concerned? Do the plants that strangle others have to

plead guilty to murder? Are these "warlike" actions of plants
and flowers advance or rearguard actions?

Apropos of plants, Professor Frits Went writes,

> In our minds the struggle for existence is usually associated
> with a ruthless extermination of the less well adapted by those
> better adapted. There is no cold war or even aggression in the
> desert or jungle. Most plants are not equipped with mechanisms
> to combat others. All plants grow up together and share whatever
> light or water or nutrients are available. It is only when the
> supply of one of these factors becomes critical that competition
> starts. But it appears likely that in the jungle, as in the desert,
> survival is taken care of by the control of germination. . . . As a
> general moral we conclude that war as man wages it finds no
> counterpart in nature, and it has no justification on the basis of
> evolution or natural selection.[16]

It would be extremely helpful to know whether it is defensive
or offensive war that is natural. Sir Arthur Keith believed that
both are. The illegitimate use of such terms as "struggle,"
"fighting," "force," and so forth, when applied to plant and
animal life, and the deliberate confusion of these terms with
"war" occur too often and too frequently are allowed to pass
unchallenged.[17] Professor Pollard has amusingly remarked of
this confusion: "The sun and the moon, we suppose, declare
war with great regularity because they get into opposition every
month. Parties in the House of Commons are perpetually at
war because they are opposed. The police wage war because
they are a force; for 'naturally' if we use force against a criminal,
we must needs make war upon other communities. War, indeed, will last for ever, because men will never 'cease to
struggle.' So the League of Nations has obviously failed whenever a stern parent is caught in the act of chastising a peccant
child; and 'fighting' will go on without end because drowning
men will fight for life, doctors will fight disease, and women
will fight for places at drapery sales. And this is war!"[18] The
semantic fallacy could not be pointed more neatly.

Man kills a variety of animals for the purposes of food and
various other uses, but he does so as a husbandman, a domesti-

cator of animals, not as a maker of war upon animals. He breeds animals in order to eat them. Does this constitute war? In any event, is the domestication and slaughtering of these animals natural? It is certainly not natural to man, who commenced the domestication of animals not more than 10,000 years ago. Moreover, it is more unnatural for the vast majority of the animals who are members of the same order of mammals as man, namely, the primates, to attack other animal groups or, except on rare occasions, consume any part of them. The anthropoid apes are vegetarian. The fact is that man possesses the gastrointestinal tract of an herbivore, like the anthropoids. Man's meat eating is undoubtedly an acquired taste forced upon him under conditions of scarcity. But it is neither innate in the psychophysical disposition of man nor necessary that he may live, to kill any animal whatever or plant, for that matter, at least not for men living in the highly civilized centers of the Western world. Man's taste in food is culturally determined, like his taste in tobacco and alcohol. Under primitive conditions of life he is forced to kill animals for food and apparel, just as it was considered "natural" for some nations, not so long ago, to kill prisoners of war in order that the food supply might not unnecessarily be depleted. Animals in the wild state kill digestible numbers and varieties of other animals where they are available for the satisfaction of their hunger, for the very good reason that they have no other means of remaining alive— but man has.

In medieval England it was considered natural and perfectly legal for all claims to real property to be settled and tried by battle. Since those days man has elaborated more peaceful means of settling such disputes, not by blood but by reason, because of an understanding and sympathy made possible by a more enlightened form of culture. For culture, if it means anything, represents the fact of man's ability to elaborate and improve upon the normal processes of the universe, commonly called nature. It is through the agency of culture that man is able to elaborate and improve upon his original endowment, to turn first into second nature. It is not so much that culture is an extension of him as that he is an extension of culture. Indeed, today, by means purely cultural, man is in a position to control and regulate, in almost every possible respect, his own future evolution. He holds the power within himself of total self-extermination or more complete development, and it will be by the weakness or strength of his humanity alone that either the one or the other effect will eventually be brought about. Fundamentally, man is quite an intelligent animal, but he is a victim, alas, of the two-handed engine of his culture which distorts his mind and renders him unintelligent. Outworn traditional teachings have made of Western man a shockingly unintelligent creature who lives under the continuous and unrelieved domination of a chaos of ideas more degrading, more stupid, more idiotic, and more saddening than it may ever be possible to describe. This confused morality has without question been substantially responsible for his present deplorable state, for the reflexes and patterns of thought of every child born into the Western world today have been conditioned according to the prescriptions of these teachings, so that culturally Western man has come to be a function almost entirely of the reigning spirit of confusion and prejudice. And since in his conduct he functions without effort as a victim of confusion and prejudice, he arrives at the belief that it is *natural* to act and think thus. In this way is produced the mentally and spiritually bludgeoned person who gropes his way confusedly through life—and whose number is legion. The frustrations which he has suffered seek an outlet in aggressiveness, and it is in his world alone that force and war still remain a legitimate and defensible means of settling a difference.

With regard to Keith's "race prejudice," that, of course, is an acquired sentiment, a constellation of socially acquired emotions, as Sir Arthur Keith would undoubtedly have known had he made as deep a study of cultural as he had of physical anthropology. Nature, according to him, secures the separation of man into permanent groups by means of the operation of "race" prejudices, which express themselves as national rivalries and jealousies, in order to produce "new and improved races of mankind." This, presumably, is a form of natural selection operating from inherited psychological bases, a form of selection peculiar to man alone, for no other animal, as far as we know, exhibits the slightest symptom of anything akin to what Sir Arthur Keith calls "race prejudice." "Race" prejudices among lower animals, like their "natural" fears and terrors, are *acquired,* not inborn. This is probably true of the psychological barriers which exist between different groups of birds and in various other animals. Experiments on young animals first carried out by Benjamin Kidd many years ago and by numerous investigators since conclusively prove that the "instinctive" fear and terror exhibited in the presence of their allegedly natural enemies by the adult members of the species are emotions which are generally completely absent in the young and that they are acquired only by *learning* from other members of the species or by individual experience.[19] A lamb or any other animal, for example, which has had no long association with members of its own species from whom it could have acquired the fear—or past experience with lions—will exhibit not the slightest fear of a lion when confronted with one. On the other hand, when chickens raised in complete isolation are first brought into association with other chickens they sometimes exhibit both fear and aggressive reactions.[20] A certain amount of social, of cooperative, experience would seem to be necessary if the fears nurtured by isolation or any other factors are to be overcome.

No animal or human being is born with any prejudice or specific fear whatever, either of snakes, mice, or the dark, to mention a few of the most familiar common fears usually considered of "instinctive" origin; all these fears or prejudices are *acquired* by learning and may, and usually do, act very like conditioned reflexes, simulating physical reflexes which are innate, but which in these cases are conditioned to react culturally, not biologically or instinctively.

Upon the theory that "race" prejudice is innate, how are we to account for the well-authenticated fact, familiar to most people of experience, that children of one nation, brought up in the milieu of a "foreign" nation, feel no prejudices whatever, in wartime or in peacetime, against the nation of their adoption but, on the contrary, are generally to be found in the ranks of their adopted land fighting against the motherland of their ancestors, whether it be with ideas or with powder? No more impressive demonstration of this is to be found than in the case of the thousands of Japanese-Americans who in World War II bravely fought on all fronts as American citizens and soldiers against the Axis forces. Japanese-Americans especially distinguished themselves in action against Japanese forces.[21] In fact, the Japanese-American 442d Regimental Combat Team was the most decorated unit in United States history.[22]

A notorious example of transmutation is the case of Houston Stewart Chamberlain, the egregious author of that stupendous miracle of nonsense *The Foundations of the Nineteenth Century,* in which the spectacle is witnessed of an apostate Englishman glorifying the Teutonic spirit, the German brand in particular, at the expense, among others, of his ancestral land and heritage. One may well wonder what happened to Chamberlain's "birthright" of prejudice when as an adult he became a champion of German prejudices. Possibly William James' law of transitoriness of instinct may be invoked here. And what shall we say of Sir Thomas Browne (1605–1682), the author of *Religio Medici,* who wrote: "I am of a constitution so general, that it consorts and sympathiseth with all things; I have no antipathy, or rather idiosyncrasy, in any thing. Those national repugnances do not touch me, nor do I behold with prejudice the French, Italian, Spanish, or Dutch"?

Or of Oliver Goldsmith (1728–1774) who wrote,

> Among all the famous sayings of antiquity, there is none that does greater honor to the author, or affords greater pleasure to the reader, (at least if he be a person of a generous and benevolent heart,) than that of the philosopher, who, being asked what countryman he was, replied that he was a citizen of the world. How few are there to be found in modern times who can say the same, or whose conduct is consistent with such a profession! We are now become so much Englishmen, Frenchmen, Dutchmen, Spaniards, or Germans, that we are no longer citizens of the world; so much the natives of one particular spot, or members of one petty society, that we no longer consider ourselves as the general inhabitants of the globe, or members of that grand society

which comprehends the whole human kind. . . . Let a man's birth be ever so high, his station ever so exalted, or his fortune ever so large, yet, if he is not free from the national and all other prejudices, I should make bold to tell him, that he had a low and vulgar mind, and had no just claim to the character of a gentleman. And, in fact, you will always find, that those are most apt to boast of national merit, who have little or no merit of their own to depend on, than which, to be sure, nothing is more natural: the slender vine twists around the sturdy oak for no other reason in the world, but because it has not strength sufficient to support itself.[23]

Or of that great and universal genius Thomas Young (1773–1829), who, as a young man, wrote:

A man who has formed intimacies and friendships with inhabitants of different parts of the globe will find enough to love and to disapprove among every people; and perhaps one who has acquired the faculty of communicating his thoughts with equal ease and pleasure to the individuals of several nations, will find himself as much at home in the one as in the other. Certainly one who is totally destitute of this attainment can never be admitted to judge with impartiality of the character of any country.[24]

There is every reason to believe that "race" sentiment and antipathies are comparatively recent developments in the societies of Western man.

In America, where white and black populations frequently live side by side, it is an indisputable fact that white children do not learn to consider themselves superior to Negro children until they are told that they are so,[25] a fact which is revealingly illustrated by the words of a white American farmer from the South who, in answer to the query as to what he thought of the Negro, replied, "I ain't got anything against niggers; I was fourteen years old before I know'd I was better than a nigger." Numerous other examples could be cited of the cultural acquisitions of prejudices, demonstrating that all ideas of "race" prejudice are inherited in just the same manner as are our clothes, not innately but culturally. Man as a social being is custom made, and his own ideas are tailored according to the prevailing fashion. The statement so frequently heard that "war is a universal and everlasting law of nature" is at best a shallow judgment, for it seems never to occur to those who make it that the conflicts which they are pleased to term "war" and which are alleged to take place between animals in the wild state are pertinent only in referring to conflicts between animals of widely separated species, genera, orders, and, almost universally, classes. Under certain conditions lions will attack almost anything that moves; so will, to a lesser extent, wolves and hyenas; domestic cats will kill small rodents and birds; monkeys will kill birds and insects; baboons will sometimes kill and eat small monkeys; but in all these examples, selected at random, not a single animal will fight with a member of its *own* species in the sense that it will fight with members of other species, orders, or classes of animals.

Under natural conditions it is not usual for animals of one species to prey upon or to fight with each other, but rather to attack only animals of different breeds. To this rule there are few exceptions. Of course, hungry animals will devour, upon occasion, members of their own species, but this is a form of conduct which is normally resorted to only because of extreme necessity. In serious conflicts between wild or domesticated animals of the same species the fight is rarely between more than two animals, and usually the causes and the motives which have provoked the fight are similar to those which influence men, namely, the will to possess a sexually desirable mate or an object of physical value such as food. Gibbons feed contentedly in the same tree with monkeys such as macaques and langurs but will not tolerate the presence of another gibbon group of the same species or any other. Practically all vertebrates defend themselves against attack by members of other groups of their own species. But this sort of defensive fighting is quite different from war. War is an organized attack of one community upon another community, and as such is never fought by animals other than those of the "human" variety. It is impossible to produce a single instance from the animal kingdom, outside of man, to show that within a single species a form of behavior resembling warfare is waged by one group of its members upon any other group of the same species—as a means of improving the species or what not.

Pliny the Elder (A.D. 23–79) is perhaps the earliest writer to have pointed out that man is the only creature that makes war upon his own kind. "In fine, all other living creatures pass their time worthily among their own species: we see them herd together and stand firm against other kinds of animals—fierce lions do not fight among themselves, the serpent's bite attacks not serpents, even the monsters of the sea are only cruel against different species; whereas to man, I vow, most of his evils come from his fellow man." [26]

It was Leonardo da Vinci who defined man as the creature that persecutes its *own* as well as other living species.

If one thing is certain, it is that it is *not* natural for members either of the same species or of any other to wage "war" upon one another. "One species of animal may destroy another and individuals may kill other individuals, but *group* struggles to the death between members of the same species, such as occur in human warfare, can hardly be found among nonhuman animals." [27] As Dr. L. P. Jacks wrote, while World War I was raging, "there is nothing in the life of the lowest beasts which can be compared for utter senselessness with the mutual rending to pieces of the Nations."

War, let it be said at once, is the most unnatural, the most artificial of all human activities, for it originates in artificial causes, is waged by artificial entities called "states," and is fought from artificial motives, with artificial weapons, for artificial ends. Like our civilization, war is an artificial product of that civilization itself, the civilization that has been achieved by the repeal and the repudiation of those very processes of "Nature" which our von Bernhardis are pleased to regard as an everlasting universal law.[28] Far from being a universal law or even a common occurrence, as Julian Huxley has pointed out, it is a very rare exception.[29]

First among ten pertinent and basic principles subscribed to by more than 2,000 American psychologists is the following: *"War can be avoided: War is not born in men; it is built into men.* No race, nation, or social group is inevitably warlike. The frustrations and conflicting interests which lie at the root of aggressive wars can be reduced and re-directed by social engineering. Men can realize their ambitions within the framework of human cooperation and can direct their aggressions against those natural obstacles that thwart them in the attainment of their goals." [30]

Just as there is good reason to believe that aggressive "race" sentiment and prejudice are comparatively recent developments of civilized man, so, too, there is good reason to believe that warfare is but a recent development resulting from the artificial and perverted activities of men living in highly civilized groups. Among the extinct varieties of men of whom we have any knowledge no evidence of anything resembling warfare has ever been found. Plenty of weapons of a rather simple nature have been discovered in association with the remains of ancient man, but they appear to have been made for use against animals, not against his fellow men. Throughout the Old Stone Age (Paleolithic), a period which occupies 96 percent of man's entire history, all known human groups lived by food-gathering and hunting, as did the Middle Stone Age (Mesolithic) groups who succeeded them. Adam Smith long ago pointed out that a hunting population is always thinly spread over a large area and possesses but little accumulated property. Primitive man was, and in many cases still is, a food-gatherer and a hunter, and no doubt, as in the case among most existing nonliterate peoples, his hunting grounds were marked off by definite boundaries, boundaries separating different communities; "these boundaries were sacred, and as no one would think of violating them they could not form a cause of war."

Havelock Ellis writes:

Savages are on the whole not warlike, although they often try to make out that they are terribly bloodthirsty fellows; it is only with difficulty that they work themselves up to a fighting pitch and even then all sorts of religious beliefs and magical practices restrain warfare and limit its effects. Even among the fiercest peoples of East Africa the bloodshed is usually small. Speke mentions a war that lasted three years; the total losses were three men on each side. In all parts of the world there are people who rarely or never fight; and if, indeed . . . the old notion that primitive people are in chronic warfare of the most ferocious character were really correct, humanity could not have survived. Primitive man had far more formidable enemies than his own species to fight against, and it was in protection against these, and not against his fellows, that the beginnings of cooperation and the foundation of the State were laid.[31]

Verrier Elwin, writing of the Gonds and Baigas of central India, tells a charming story which throws some light on the attitude of nonliterate peoples to war:

An old woman put it very well. "This," she said, "is how God equalizes things. Our sons and daughters die young, of hunger or disease or the attacks of wild beasts. The sons and daughters of the English could grow old in comfort and happiness. But God sends madness upon them, and they destroy each other, and so in the end their great knowledge and their religion is useless and we are all the same."

Some of the tribesmen, always excited by a quarrel, were anxious to help. A party of Baigas came one day with a bundle of bows and arrows which they wanted me to forward to the Govern-men to aid in the war. When I told them that modern battles were no longer fought with these weapons they were much concerned. "But if they use guns people will really get killed," they said.[32]

The late Professor W. J. Perry wrote: "Civilized people are far more ferocious than the majority of 'savages,' and whenever 'savages' are uncommonly ferocious, it is usually possible to detect the influence of civilized men. It is the civilized man who is the savage."[33]

Dr. Ragner Numelin, having made a thoroughgoing study of the subject concludes that:

Warfare as such, *i.e.*, organized warfare, is . . . not customary among primitive peoples. When war occurs it is obviously more of the nature of robbery and plundering raids. The simplest communities do not organize war, and war for expansion is relatively rare in the primitive world. . . . Further, we have found that peaceable relations dominate among the primitive, wandering peoples, the food-gatherers, the fishing and hunting tribes. The rather peaceful character of such peoples is usually confirmed by their traditions and legends which often form a rich ethnological treasure-house. Instead of spending their days in fighting they lead peaceful lives when left undisturbed. They seldom use violence in their personal relations and they do not fight as communities. Savages do not usually live at odds with their neighbors.[34]

War came into being only after men had begun to cultivate the land upon which they were then able to settle permanently. Such an agricultural stage of development, we know, first appeared among men about 12,000 years ago, in upper Neolithic times.[35] The agricultural life results in the accumulation of property, the accumulation of property eventually results in more or less organized industry, industry in wealth, wealth in power, power in expansive ambitions, and the desire to acquire additional property—the source of additional power—necessary to gratify those ambitions, and thus, by no very complicated process, in war. Such conditions, which are peculiar to the industrial civilizations of today, are, of course, highly artificial, as are the prejudices and the "race" sentiment which they serve to generate.

In the modern world undoubtedly the most potent cause of war is economic rivalry, a cultural phenomenon having no biological basis whatever. The desire for foreign concessions and markets, an expanding population, the lust for *Lebensraum* —such things will upon little provocation set nations in opposition and at each other's throats.[36] It is from such economic causes that patriotism, chauvinism, and the widespread fear of aggression, which more than anything else serves to consolidate the group and is responsible for the generation of "race" prejudice and sentiment, are born. As Malinowski has put it, "human beings fight not because they are biologically impelled but because they are culturally induced, by trophies, as in head-hunting, by wealth as in looting, by revenge as in punitive wars, by propaganda as it occurs under modern conditions." [37]

If all this is true, then it is apparent that war arises not as the

result of natural or biological conditions but from purely contrived artificial social conditions created by highly "civilized"
modes of interaction between human groups.

With respect to the "natural antagonisms" with which man
is alleged to be endowed, it may be said at once that these are
pure creations of Sir Arthur Keith's imagination, for certainly
there exists no evidence that man is born with any antagonisms
whatever.[38] The evidence is, on the other hand, quite contrary
to such a suggestion. Sir Charles Sherrington has set out some of
this evidence in his masterly book *Man on His Nature,* while
Professor W. C. Allee has recently given reasons together with
some of the evidence, observational, inductive, and experimental, which indicates that the spirit of altruism, of cooperation, is very much more natural to man than is that of egoism or
antagonism. Professor Allee writes:

> After much consideration it is my mature conclusion, contrary
> to Herbert Spencer, that the cooperative forces are biologically
> the more important and vital. The balance between the coopera-
> tive, altruistic tendencies and those which are disoperative and
> egoistic is relatively close. Under many conditions the cooperative
> forces lose. In the long run, however, the group-centered, more
> altruistic drives are slightly stronger.
>
> If cooperation had not been the stronger force, the more com-
> plicated animals, whether arthropods or vertebrates, could not
> have evolved from the simpler ones, and there would have been
> no men to worry each other with their distressing and biologically
> foolish wars. While I know of no laboratory experiments that
> make a direct test of this problem, I have come to this conclusion
> by studying the implications of many experiments which bear on
> both sides of the problem, and from considering the trends of
> organic evolution in nature. Despite many known appearances to
> the contrary, human altruistic drives are as firmly based on an
> animal ancestry as is man himself. Our tendencies towards good-
> ness, such as they are, are as innate as our tendencies toward
> intelligence; we could do well with more of both.[39]

Prince Petr Kropotkin arrived at similar conclusions at a
time when such ideas were scarcely mentioned; these he set out

in a remarkable book, *Mutual Aid.* "If," wrote Kropotkin, "we resort to an indirect test, and ask Nature: 'Who are the fittest: those who are continually at war with each other, or those who support one another?' we at once see that those animals which acquire habits of mutual aid are undoubtedly the fittest. They have more chances to survive, and they attain, in their respective classes, the highest development of intelligence and bodily organization." More recently J. B. S. Haldane has concluded that "in so far as it makes for the survival of one's descendants and near relations, altruistic behaviour is a kind of Darwinian fitness, and may be expected to spread as the result of natural selection." [40] And this, indeed, is what Darwin believed. "As man advances in civilization," he wrote, "and small tribes are united into larger communities, the simplest reason would tell each individual that he ought to extend his social instincts and sympathies to all members of the same nation, though personally unknown to him. This point being once reached, there is only an artificial barrier to prevent his sympathies extending to the men of all nations and races." [41]

Professor William Patten has devoted a highly original book to the consideration of cooperation as a factor in evolution.[42] Indeed, many distinguished students of evolutionary process have dealt with the evidence pointing to the cardinal importance of the role which cooperation has played in evolution, but their work is only now being rescued from the neglect into which it has fallen.[43]

Professor A. E. Emerson's views on the biological basis of social cooperation are identical with those of Allee. Emerson points out that:

Just as the cell in the body functions for the benefit of the whole organism, so does the individual organism become subordinate to the population. It is in harmony with natural law to have an individual function for the benefit of other contemporary individuals and also for future generations. This principle gives us a scientific basis for ethics.[44]

Professor Emerson goes on to say:

Coöperation is probably not an end in itself, but is rather a means to an end. The all-over directional trend in organic evolution seems to have been toward optimum conditions for existence. What was the uncontrolled external environment of the cell became the balanced internal environment of the multicellular organism. Selection of variations leads toward more efficient division of labor and more integration and coöperation between the parts. Differentiation would be useless without integration, and integration would be useless without differentiation. Natural selection has constantly guided organic evolution in the direction of increasing complexity and increasing coöperation. This trend is easily seen in the study of the evolution of intra-specific populations and reaches its culmination in the social insects and in man.[45]

Certainly aggressiveness exists in nature,[46] but there is also a healthy nonruthless competition and strong basic drives toward social and cooperative behavior. These forces do not operate independently but together, as a whole, and the evidence strongly indicates that of all these drives the principal of co-operation is dominant and biologically the most important. The coexistence of so many different species of animals throughout the world is sufficient testimony to the importance of that principle. It is probable that man owes more to the development of his cooperative drives than to any other in his biological and social evolution.[47] His future lies with their further development, not with their suppression.

In 1939 a group of leading scientists formulated the principle naturally operative in governing human conduct as follows: "The probability of survival of a relationship between individual humans or groups of humans increases with the extent to which that relationship is mutually satisfying." This principle is but a special case of the more general principle that "the probability of survival of individual, or groups of, living things increases with the degree with which they harmoniously adjust themselves to each other and their environment." [48] This, essentially, is the principle of cooperation, of mutual aid, the conscious recognition of which has been the basis of most religious and ethical systems. The biological corroboration of the soundness of that ethical principle must be counted one of the greatest discoveries in the history of mankind. That principle has played a great part in the development of mankind. It must be made to play an even greater role in the future.

Our efforts to obtain natural justice in the world will be rewarded only when we have banished such pathological phenomena as "race" prejudice and the causes which give rise to it from our sick societies. The original conception of natural justice which was held by men down to the nineteenth century was one that was valid for the whole community of mankind. It was in principle an explicit recognition of the intrinsic worth of human personality, implying universal equality and brotherhood. The shift in meaning, in the nineteenth century, from nature as harmony and design to nature as struggle brought about the eclipse of the concept of justice as an ideal of human relations, and the emergence of the idea that what is just is determined by the arbitrament of force, the survival of the fittest.[49]

Without strong drives to cooperation, sociability, and mutual aid, the progress of organic life, the improvement of the organism, and the strengthening of the species becomes utterly incomprehensible. Indeed, Haldane and Huxley suggest that competition between adults of the same species is on the whole a biological evil. The biological effects of such competition, it seems likely, writes Haldane,

> render the species as a whole less successful in coping with its environment. No doubt weaklings are weeded out, but so would they be in competition with the environment. And the special adaptations favoured by interspecific competition divert a certain amount of energy from other functions, just as armaments, subsidies, and tariffs, the organs of international competition, absorb a proportion of the natural wealth which many believe might be better employed.[50]

Not "nature red in tooth and claw" but cooperation is the primary law of natural conduct.

There remains to be examined the statement given expression by Sir Arthur Keith and implied in the writings of many before him that war is nature's "pruning-hook, . . . Nature's method of keeping her orchard healthy." This, of course, is supposed to mean that war acts as a process of natural selection—an idea which on the face of it is absurd; for, as everyone knows, the manner in which modern war acts is to kill off the best members of the group while jealously preserving the worst, such as the mentally and bodily diseased and the generally unfit. And in any case, as World War I fully proved, the nation superior to all others in the processes of waging war, the most ingenious and fertile in the invention and use of the instruments of destruction, may in spite of this lose the war by the selectively irrelevant fact of being overwhelmingly outnumbered. Referring to World War I, Professor Pollard has aptly remarked that

> if the result had depended on scientific invention the Germans would have won. As it was, they neutralized enormous odds in numbers to such an extent that for four years the principal front hardly shifted on an average more than half a dozen miles in either direction. The Allied victory was due not to scientific superiority but to the economic exhaustion of the foe, and to the fact that in Foch's decisive campaign America was pouring more fresh troops into the line of battle in a month than the Germans could raise in a year.[51]

From the standpoint of natural selection it is apparent to all those who lived through it that the Germans, who proved themselves the most intelligent and certainly not the least valorous of all the combatants, should, on the basis of "brains" alone, have won the war of 1914–1918. Instead, they lost it. Something clearly had gone wrong with "natural selection" or, rather, with war as an agency of it. It was, indeed, the confidence in "reeking tube and iron shard" which led the Germans from an even and peaceful development into the disaster of war and humiliation.

As a matter of fact, the whole concept of war as an agency of natural selection in the case of man breaks down when we consider that throughout the historic period there were numerous instances of victories in war gained by peoples who were culturally inferior to the peoples whom they conquered. It must, however, be freely acknowledged that on the whole up to the modern era the peoples victorious in war were generally superior to the people whom they conquered—superior in the strict sense of the *military* superiority of the combatant *individuals*. In former times men actually fought with one another, the superior warrior (who may have been superior simply because he had been better fed) generally killing the inferior in hand-to-hand combat. But in modern warfare the combatants scarcely ever see each other, and when they do it is not military skill or native superiority which decides who shall die, but a shell fired from a battery some miles away or a machine gun hundreds of yards distant, or a bomb dropped from an airplane thousands of feet above them. In actual battle the superior men are the first to go over the top; in dangerous and generally useless raids they are the first to be chosen—and killed. Where, in all this slaughter, is there to be detected any evidence of natural selection? Selection, certainly, in that the superior are selected for death and the inferior are protected against it—in this way does modern warfare act as an agency of unnatural selection, for the worst.[52] Wars of this kind are harmful to mankind. Julian Huxley has stated the point clearly:

> The more total war becomes, both intensively, as diverting more of the energies of the population from construction to destruction, and extensively, as involving more and more of the countries of the globe, the more of a threat does it become to the progress of the human species. As H. G. Wells and many others have urged, it might even turn back the clock of civilization and force the world into another Dark Age. War of this type is an intraspecific struggle from which nobody, neither humanity at large nor any of the groups engaged in the conflict, can really reap any balance of advantage, though of course we may snatch particular advantages out of the results of war.[53]

Man has reached his present supremacy through the inhibitive and integrative powers of his mind, through a unique educability and ability to reject and suppress what he considers to be undesirable, the ability to *control*. Human society depends upon the maintenance of that ability of the mind to control, not so much the brute in man—for there is really nothing that is brutal in him that is not forced upon him—but those elements which under miseducation are capable of making a brute of him. All that is fine, noble, beautiful, and desirable in our civilization has been achieved through the resolute determination of individual minds not so much to conquer and to vanish what is customarily called "Nature," red in tooth and claw, but to enlist the aid of "Nature" in the service of man and to control it effectively. It may be an oversimplification, but it is not far from the truth to say that so much that is ugly, inhuman, and destructive in our civilization is largely due to the activities of those who are anxious to exploit their fellow men to their own advantage and use measures of control only toward that end. To them war is a profitable activity, for it increases their power as well as their fortunes. It is individuals of this order, in all countries and from the earliest historical times, who help to make wars, not nature. Others who assist have the *status quo* to maintain.[54] "The fault, dear Brutus, lies not in our stars, but in ourselves."

Man has too long been deceived by a chaos of ideas for which there is not the slightest basis in fact, ideas which represent, as Spinoza said, the errors of the ages grown hoary with the centuries. The flowers that bloom in the verbal spring of such writers as von Bernhardi and Sir Arthur Keith, not to mention the Hitlers of this world, have nothing whatever to do with either the logical case or the factual reality. Nay, in spite of Kant and others, there is no instinct toward peace in man just as there is none toward war. The early Egyptians, the Cretans, and the people of Mohenjo-Daro in India did not wage war, for the good reason that it was totally unnecessary for them to do so, since socially and economically they were entirely sufficient unto themselves. Aboriginal Australians, however, have on occasion fought with one another, because for economic reasons —such as a dog or a wife—it seemed necessary for them to do so. Men, it seems, fight only when and if they want to; and under primitive conditions that appears to be very seldom indeed. There is nothing within the nature of men, no *primum mobile*, no innate prejudice, save for such prejudices as have been cultivated in them by education, which forces them to do so.[55]

I conclude this chapter with a paragraph from an article published in an obscure student journal not long after World War I.

There looms a day of judgment, a day of judgment pronounced by man upon himself as having committed suicide because he was not fit to live. For we come to a common issue between a common mind to live and common "nature" to kill. If there is Armageddon all will be taken, none will be left, and Fate will be common to victors and vanquished, rich and poor, all the nations, and both the hemispheres. To learn lest we perish is the logic of the League of Nations; learn to destroy is the teaching of "natural" war. Whether mankind survives depends less on its science than on its humanity, upon whether we trust an increasing control over physical forces to men with a decreasing sense of responsibility for their use, and whether we regard as more "natural" the war we think rooted in Nature or the peace we owe to our mind.[56]

REFERENCES

1. It would seem that this idea is at least as old as the sixth century before Christ. We find it clearly stated in a fragment left us by Heracleitus of Ephesus (*circa* 500 B.C.). "We must know," he writes, "that war is common to all and that strife is justice, and that everything comes into being by strife." *Heracleitus*, fragment LXII, trans. by W. H. S. Jones, p. 491.

2. Bernhardi, *Germany and the Next War*, pp. 16–37. Compare with this the following passage written in 1942 by Lord Elton: "War, however we may hate it, is still the supreme agent of the evolutionary process. Blind, brutal and destructive, it remains the final arbiter, the one test mankind has yet contrived of a nation's fitness to survive." *Saint George or the Dragon.*

3. Holmes, *Life and Morals*, p. 198. For a more extended discussion of Darwinism applied to man see Montagu, *Darwin, Competition, and Cooperation.*

4. Bogart, *Direct and Indirect Costs of the Great World War*, pp. 265–68.

5. Fairchild, *The Prodigal Century*, p. 244.

6. Keith, *Essays on Human Evolution*, and *A New Theory of Human Evolution;* for the views of the American warmongers see Hofstadter's

brilliant account in his *Social Darwinism in American Thought, 1860–1915.* See also Nasmyth, *Social Progress and the Darwinian Theory.*

7. Keith, *The Place of Prejudice in Modern Civilization.*

8. In a book published in 1945 its author, echoing Keith, writes: "Whatever may be said against it, in so far as it keeps the race pure, race prejudice is admirable and even necessary." Landry, *The Cult of Equality,* p. 257. The nonsense of such statements is sufficiently refuted by the fact that whenever and whatever ethnic groups meet they have mixed, and by the very consequential fact that no human being alive today is of unmixed origin.

9. Keith, *The Place of Prejudice in Modern Civilization,* p. 50. In *An Autobiography* Keith writes of this address: "I was soon to be aware of the disturbance to which my rectorial address had given rise. My good friend, Dr. Katherine Trail, widow of my venerated mentor of early days, wrote me a most indignant letter accusing me of fanning the embers of war. Other critics laid hold of an unfortunate metaphor I had used—the 'pruning hook of war.' . . . My little booklet met with no demand. And all the time Hitler was demonstrating to the world the truth of my thesis" (pp. 565–66).

10. Keith, *An Autobiography.*

11. "Nature is a word, always very loosely used, to which time has brought increasingly sentimental connotations. The decline of one superstition has encouraged the growth of another. God the Father has been dethroned from many simple hearts only to be replaced by Nature the Mother, an entity of strikingly similar characteristics, mingling benevolence and vindictiveness in quite the old familiar proportions. Nature has consciousness and makes rules and plans, and takes revenge. She is jealous and cannot bear interference. Her workmanship is perfect. Her desire for mastery is always overwhelming, and no one ever gets the upper hand of her for long." Moore, *The Vulgar Heart,* p. 126.

12. Hoyle, *The Nature of the Universe;* Weizsäcker, *The History of Nature.*

13. On quanta and genes see Schrödinger, *What Is Life?*

14. Huxley, *Evolution: The Modern Synthesis,* p. 576.

15. Pollard, "The War of Nature and a Peace of Mind," *Vincula* (University of London Students Journal), 14 December 1925, p. 60.

16. Went, "The Ecology of Desert Plants, *Scientific American,* CXCII (1955), 75.

17. This confusion could not be better illustrated than by Hitler's remark that "war is the most natural, the most every-day matter. War is eternal, war is universal. There is no beginning and there is no peace. Any struggle is war." Rauschning, *The Voice of Destruction,* pp. 7–8.

18. Pollard, "The War of Nature and a Peace of Mind." *Vincula,* 14 December 1925, p. 60.

19. This is not to say that certain *general* fears and aggressive reactions

may not have an innate basis, they may and probably do have; but it is to deny that such reactions are innately determined for any *specific* creature or group.

20. Brückner, "Untersuchungen zur Tiersoziologie, insbesondere zur Auflösung der Familie." *Zeitschrift für Psychologie,* CXXVIII (1933), 1–110.

21. Full accounts of the activities of Japanese-American members of the forces of the United States may be read in the files of the Japanese-American newspaper *Pacific Citizen,* published at Salt Lake City, Utah.

22. *Ibid.,* XXI (October 6, 1945), I; Murphy, *Ambassadors in Arms.*

23. Goldsmith, *On National Prejudices.*

24. Peacock, *Life of Thomas Young,* p. 107.

25. Horowitz, "The Development of Attitudes toward the Negro," *Archives of Psychology,* No. 194 (1936); Radke and Trager, "Children's Perceptions of the Social Roles of Negroes and Whites," *Journal of Psychology,* XXIX (1950), 3–33; Trager and Yarrow, *They Learn What They Live.*

26. Pliny, *Natural History,* Bk. VII, 1.5.

27. Allee, *Cooperation Among Animals,* p. 200. It is even likely that the ants, who are in any event too far removed from man to have any relevance for his behavior, form no exception to this rule. See Maier and Schneirla, *Principles of Animal Psychology,* pp. 164 ff., and Schneirla, " 'Cruel' Ants—and Occam's Razor," *Journal of Comparative Psychology,* XXXIV (1942), 79–83.

28. For an interesting discussion of "animal warfare," in which the author extends the meaning of "warfare" to embrace attacks upon animals of widely separated species, see Wright, *A Study of War,* pp. 42–52, 479–518.

29. Huxley, "War as a Biological Phenomenon," in Huxley, *On Living in a Revolution,* p. 61.

30. Allport, "Human Nature and the Peace," *Psychological Bulletin,* XLII (1945), 376.

31. Ellis, *The Philosophy of Conflict,* pp. 51–52. Ellis was here summarizing the work of Holsti, *The Relation of War to the Origin of the State.* For confirmatory views see Wright's chapter "Primitive Warfare," in *A Study of War,* pp. 53–100, and Hambly, "Primitive Warfare," *Chicago Natural History Museum Bulletin,* XVII (1946), 4–5.

32. Elwin, *The Tribal World of Verrier Elwin,* pp. 122–123.

33. Perry, "Man the Primeval Pacifist," *Vincula,* 14 December 1925, p. 64.

34. Numelin, *The Beginnings of Diplomacy,* p. 104.

35. Childe, *The Dawn of European Civilization; Man Makes Himself;* "War in Prehistoric Societies," *Sociological Review,* XXXIII (1941), 126–38.

36. See Bernhardi, *Germany and the Next War,* for a most illuminating

exemplification of this view. See also Nef, *War and Human Progress;* Bernard, *War and Its Causes.*

37. Malinowski, "War—Past, Present, and Future," in Clarkson and Cochran (eds.), *War as a Social Institution,* pp. 23–24.

38. Bender, "Genesis of Hostility in Children," *American Journal of Psychiatry,* CV (1948), 241–45; Montagu, *On Being Human;* Montagu, *The Direction of Human Development;* Ausubel, *Theory and Problems of Child Development.*

39. Allee, "Where Angels Fear to Tread; a Contribution from General Sociology to Human Ethics," *Science,* XCVII (1943), 521. See also the same author's *Cooperation among Animals* and his *Animal Aggregations.* Along similar lines see Montagu, *On Being Human,* and *Darwin, Competition and Cooperation.*

40. Haldane, *The Causes of Evolution,* p. 130.

41. Darwin, *The Descent of Man,* Chap. IV, pp. 187–88.

42. Patten, *The Grand Strategy of Evolution.*

43. Geddes and Thomson, *Evolution;* Geddes and Thomson, *Sex;* Bernard, *Some Neglected Factors in Evolution;* Reinheimer, *Evolution by Coöperation: a Study in Bio-economics;* Reinheimer, *Symbiosis; a Socio-physiological Study of Evolution;* Berg, *Nomogenesis;* Gibson, *The Morality of Nature;* Delage and Goldsmith, *The Theories of Evolution;* Allee et al., *Principles of Animal Ecology;* and numerous other works. For a discussion of these works see Montagu, *Darwin, Competition and Cooperation;* Montagu, *The Direction of Human Development.*

44. Emerson, "The Biological Basis of Social Cooperation," *Illinois Academy of Science Transactions,* XXXIX (1946), 9–18.

45. *Ibid.,* p. 15.

46. Collias, "Aggressive Behavior among Vertebrate Animals," *Physiological Zoölogy,* XVII (1944), 83–123; Scott, *Aggression.*

47. Allee speaks of "the great drive toward natural altruism that extends throughout the whole animal kingdom." "Biology and International Relations," *New Republic,* CXII (1945), 817; see also Montagu (ed.), *Culture and the Evolution of Man;* Washburn (ed.), *Social Life of Early Man.*

48. Leake, "Ethicogenesis," *Proceedings of the Philosophical Society of Texas,* X (1944), 32–33; also included in Montagu (ed.), *Studies and Essays in the History of Science and Learning.*

49. For an excellent discussion of this subject see Stapleton, *Justice and World Society.* See also Bryson, *Man and Society;* Baker, *The Dignity of Man;* Miller, *The Community of Man; Idem, Progress and Decline.*

50. Haldane, *The Causes of Evolution,* pp 125–26.

51. Pollard, "The War of Nature and a Peace of Mind," *Vincula,* 14 December 1925, p. 61.

52. Kellogg, *Military Selection and Race Deterioration,* p. 178.

53. Huxley, *op. cit.*, p. 66.
54. Rowse, *Appeasement.*
55. For an admirable discussion of "race" relations and war see Andrews, "Racial Influences," in Porritt (ed.), *The Causes of War,* pp. 63–113.
56. Pollard, "The War of Nature and a Peace of Mind," *Vincula* (University of London Students Journal), 14 December 1925, p. 61.